Your Personal

Since 1934 Les Routiers have been rec...
good quality food and accommodation.
friendly welcome – the 1993 *Guide to France* offers a super...
1,700 such establishments – just look out for the distinctive red and blue Les
Routiers symbol!

Contents

Guide Entries

First published in the United Kingdom in 1993
Alan Sutton Publishing Ltd
Phoenix Mill · Far Thrupp · Stroud
Gloucestershire GL5 2BU

First published in the
United States of America in 1993
Alan Sutton Publishing Inc.
83 Washington Street
Dover · NH 03820

ISBN 0 7509 0244 2

First published in Ireland in 1993
Gill & Macmillan Ltd
Goldenbridge · Dublin 8
with associated companies throughout the world

ISBN 0 7171 2097 X

While every care has been taken to ensure that all details given in this book are correct,
the publishers cannot accept any responsibility for inaccuracies or their consequences.
All matters relating to the content of the book should be directed to Les Routiers at the
address below.

Les Routiers inspectors visit each establishment anonymously and settle their bill
before revealing their identity. Complimentary meals and/or accommodation are not
accepted.

LES ROUTIERS: 25 Vanston Place, London SW6 1AZ

Tel: (071) 385 6644 (from Ireland (004471) 385 6644)
Fax: (071) 385 7136 (from Ireland (004471) 385 7136)

Editor: Malcolm Morris
Maps: Martin Latham and Kerry Chambler
Cover illustration: Jeremy Duncan

Typeset by Alan Sutton Publishing Limited.
Printed in Great Britain by
The Bath Press, Bath, Avon.

Foreword

'It is possible to eat your way through France, indulging in riotous gluttony for just a few francs – if you know about Les Relais Routiers.' *Washington Post*

For the traveller in France, the red and blue Les Routiers sign has become as much a part of the scenery as the poplars, châteaux and vineyards. The restaurants and hotels recommended by Les Routiers offer local cuisine, simple accommodation and a warm welcome – all at a price you can afford.

The *Les Routiers Guide* provides a reliable source of reference for all those looking for real French food, an authentic atmosphere and good value. All 'Relais Routiers' are regularly inspected to ensure they provide a warm welcome, serve good quality food, at least one fixed price menu, and observe rules of hygiene in kitchens, bedrooms and bathrooms.

The attractions of France are many – good food, fine wine, hospitable people. Indeed, the French have a unique respect and love of food. Many visitors will find that where to eat dictates their entire holiday plans. With over 1,700 Les Routiers recommended establishments in France, ranging from family restaurants to local brasseries, your *Les Routiers Guide* offers plenty of choice.

By venturing off the motorway you will not only see the beauty of the French countryside, but will also avoid the motorway tolls and most congested routes. Let Les Routiers guide you through the vineyards of Burgundy or the sun-drenched villages of Provence. Taste the world-famous red and white wines and enjoy regional specialities such as *coq au vin* and *salade niçoise*.

As soon as you cross the Channel you will notice the different flavours and styles of cooking. The *Les Routiers Guide* is your assurance of finding a cheerful greeting, homely comfort and traditional food at good value for money. The following pages will explain how to get the best from your guide and make the most of travelling in France.

BON VOYAGE ET BON APPETIT!

What Makes a Relais Routiers

Relais Routiers have been carefully selected since 1934. With the increase in the number of travellers through France, the Relais Routiers establishments have adapted themselves to cater more readily for families and tourists, but the philosophy of Les Routiers remains unchanged – all Relais Routiers are inspected regularly to ensure they provide a warm and friendly welcome, good food and value for money.

Relais Routiers come in all shapes and sizes, from roadside cafés to local bars, pretty country hotels to lively town brasseries – but whatever the style of the establishment, quality and value are served with a generous helping of authentic French cuisine and atmosphere.

The hallmark of the French Relais Routiers is the fixed price menu. To display the red and blue Les Routiers sign, this menu must be available and be displayed on the door of the establishment. The menu will normally be for a three course meal and may or may not include drinks. An à la carte menu may also be offered, but this will be more expensive.

See Why Our Members Prefer Us

J21 BRL

BRITANNIA RESCUE

We Offer You the Choice

Road Rescue – What price peace of mind?
Answer –
Less than you'd think!

For ten years Britannia Rescue has been providing a fast, efficient breakdown and recovery service, originally exclusively for members of the CSMA. But now, this excellent service is offered to buyers of the Les Routiers Guides to Britain and France.

Britain's leading consumer testing magazine in their April 1992 issue, voted Britannia Rescue as their 'Best Buy' with an average callout time of 34 minutes, well ahead of the AA, RAC and National Breakdown.

BRITANNIA RESCUE

What services can you have?

Superstart – a home start-up service from £26.00 per year

An economically priced service, ideal for drivers who use their cars infrequently or for shorter journeys. If your car will not start at home, or if you break down within half a mile of home, our agent will come to your assistance. If the car cannot be started you can be taken to a single destination of your choice (within 10 miles) while your car is transported to a local garage.

Rescue Plus – roadside assistance and local recovery service from £39.50 per year

Designed to offer protection against minor breakdowns away from your home. If your problem can't be solved at the roadside we will transport you, your vehicle and up to five passengers to a nearby garage. We will also reimburse you up to £12 towards the cost of a taxi or other alternative transport.

Standard Cover – roadside assistance and recovery to nearby garage or home or to an onward destination from £52.50 per year or £5.25 per month*

Cover offers protection from every breakdown situation while away from the vicinity of your home, both for your car and for you. We will endeavour to fix any minor problems on the spot as quickly as possible. If, however, this is not possible, our agent will transport you, your vehicle and up to five passengers home or to the destination of your choice.

Comprehensive Cover – roadside assistance, recovery, attendance at home from £68.50 per year or £6.75 per month*

This cover gives you complete peace of mind. We cater for annoying non-start problems such as flat batteries and damp engines to roadside breakdowns and accident recovery. We also include Housecall, covering you at home or within half a mile radius of home. It should be noted that Housecall is not intended as a home maintenance service and we would not expect to attend to recurring faults.

Deluxe Cover – roadside assistance, recovery, attendance at home, free car hire or hotel accommodation from £82.50 per year or £8.25 per month*

As the name suggests, this is the highest level of cover. You and your vehicle are not only catered for both at home and on the road, but if your car cannot be repaired the same day you can choose between a free replacement car (for up to 48 hours), or assistance with overnight hotel accommodation. Please note that car hire is subject to the terms and conditions of Britannia Rescue's car companies, minimum age of drivers must be 23 years.

Personal Cover – £16.00 per year or £1.60 per month*

Whichever Britannia Rescue cover you choose, for just £16 we will extend the cover to include any car you or your spouse may drive.

* Monthly Premiums

Monthly premiums are available on the top three levels of service – Standard, Comprehensive and Deluxe – when paying by Direct Debit.

All Part of Our Service

Legal advice and defence

We offer every member a 24 hour legal advice service. We can also provide representation in magistrates' courts.

Assistance after theft and vandalism

In the case of vehicle immobilization, we will provide roadside repair or transport to a local garage or on to your destination.

Relief driver

Britannia Rescue will arrange a relief driver to assist you in case of illness, injury or severe mental distress.

Tyres and windscreens

We assist on less serious, but often annoying occasions, such as punctures, shattered windscreens, lack of fuel or even locking your keys in the car.

Caravans and trailers

These are covered free of charge (excluding House call).

BRITANNIA RESCUE

Why choose Britannia Rescue?

- Dedicated to providing every member with a fast, caring road rescue service
- 34 minutes average callout time
- Over 3,000 trained personnel on call 24 hours a day 365 days a year
- A BSI registered firm committed to consistent service quality
- Value for money prices with easy payment methods
- Recommended by Britain's leading consumer watchdog as 'Best Buy'

How to apply for Britannia Rescue membership

Turn to pages 401 and 403 for an application form and direct debit mandate. Or if you wish to join immediately by telephone, simply ring FREE on 0800 591563 and quote your credit card number!

Travelling abroad

Available to anyone, whether covered by Britannia Rescue in the UK or not, Britannia Continental is a superb emergency breakdown service, competitively priced, and designed to cover any mishap while travelling abroad. There are two types of cover, one for travel with a vehicle in Europe, and the other for travel anywhere in the world. Personal Insurance includes medical repatriation by air ambulance. For further details and a brochure, ring 0484 514848.

Motoring Peace of Mind in France

Britannia Continental offers you, in France and elsewhere in Europe, the standards of road rescue assistance achieved by Britannia Rescue in the UK. Backed up by a 24-hour emergency helpline, Britannia Continental provides a truly comprehensive breakdown package for car, motor cycle, trailer/caravan and motor caravans.

Real help just when you need it!

When an emergency arises abroad, the first thing you need is help from someone who will understand your problems. Our controllers will give you just that! They've met the problem before and they'll handle it with cool, calm efficiency so that the holiday you have looked forward to need not be spoiled.

Summary of protection provided:

Vehicle Cover

Roadside assistance, towing and emergency repairs	£250
Vehicle repatriation to the UK	vehicle market value
Car hire and continuation of journey	£750
Repatriation of driver and passengers	Unlimited
Alternative driver	Unlimited
Hotel expenses	£150 p.p.
Spare parts delivery	Unlimited
Legal defence and claims recovery following motor accident	£50,000
Advance for bail or Customs Duty	£1,000

BRITANNIA CONTINENTAL

Personal Cover

Medical and incidental expenses	*Unlimited
Hospital benefit	£300
Delayed departure	£120
Cancellation and curtailment	*£3,000
Personal accident	£20,000
Personal effects and baggage	*£1,500
Personal legal liability	£1,000,000
Replacement passport	£100
Hijack, kidnap and detention	£1,000
Missed departure	£500
Personal money and travellers cheques	*£500
Legal expenses	£10,000

*Under these sections the first £25 of each and every claim per person is excluded.

Premiums:

Vehicle Cover

Period	Vehicles up to 6 years old	Vehicles 7 years to under 13 years	Vehicles 13 years and over
3 days	18.00	20.75	25.25
6 days	27.75	32.00	39.00
9 days	32.00	36.75	45.00
14 days	37.75	43.50	53.00
19 days	42.00	48.25	60.00
24 days	46.00	53.00	64.00
31 days	51.00	58.75	71.50
Extra weeks	8.50	9.75	12.50
Caravan/trailer	13.50	15.50	19.00
Annual cover	92.00	106.00	129.00

Personal Cover

Period	Each person 16 years and over	Children aged 4 to 15 years
3 days	8.50	4.25
6 days	12.75	6.50
9 days	15.50	7.75
14 days	17.50	8.75
19 days	21.50	10.75
24 days	23.25	11.75
31 days	27.50	13.75
Extra weeks	6.00	3.00
Annual cover	45.00	38.00

For full details and an application form ring 0484 514848 and ask for the Britannia Continental Department.

Cover can be applied for by telephone by quoting your credit card number.

How to Find a Relais Routiers

---

1. You want to know whether there is a Relais Routiers in a certain locality.

Look for the name of the town in question in the alphabetical index of towns. If the name is not present, there is no Relais Routiers in that town. Each establishment entry gives the name of the department and the number (the French equivalent of the county and postcode) as well as the map reference and the main road reference.

2. You are following an itinerary, and you want to know where to find a Relais Routiers.

Turn to our list of maps of France, opposite, where you will find details of 19 maps covering the whole of the country. The motorways and main roads are shown on these maps and all the places where there are Relais Routiers are marked. Then all you have to do is turn to the alphabetical index of towns which will direct you to the entries for Relais Routiers on your route.

3. You wish to find a hotel.

Although the majority of Relais Routiers are restaurants, many of them also have accommodation. These are denoted in the guide by the hotel symbol, and on the maps by a triangle. However, as the standards in these may vary considerably, we have cited the official classification of Relais Routiers, as approved by the French Tourist Board. The classification is denoted by the number of stars at the top of the entry or see pages 56–60.

4. What is a Casserole Relais?

You will find a 'Casserole' symbol at the top of certain guide entries. This symbol distinguishes those Relais Routiers where particular care is taken to offer above-average meals with perhaps a special menu or specialities of the region. The 'Casserole' is the Les Routiers mark of excellence. A list of all 'Casseroles' can be found on pages 53–5.

List of Maps

Northern France
> 1 Nord, Pas-de-Calais
> 2 Aisne, Oise, Somme

North West France
> 3 Calvados, Eure, Manche, Orne, Seine-Maritime
> 4 Côtes-du-Nord, Finistère, Ille-et-Vilaine, Morbihan
> 5 Loire-Atlantique, Maine-et-Loire, Mayenne, Sarthe, Vendée

The Loire
> 6 Cher, Eure-et-Loir, Indre, Indre-et-Loire, Loir-et-Cher, Loiret
> 7 Charente, Charente-Maritime, Deux-Sèvres, Vienne

South West France
> 8 Dordogne, Gironde, Landes, Lot-et-Garonne, Pyrénées-Atlantiques
> 9 Ariège, Aveyron, Gers, Haute-Garonne, Hautes-Pyrénées, Tarn, Tarn-et-Garonne
> 10 Aude, Gard, Hérault, Lozère, Pyrénées-Orientales

Central
> 11 Corrèze, Creuse, Haute-Vienne
> 12 Allier, Cantal, Haute-Loire, Puy-de-Dôme

South East France
> 13 Alpes-de-Haute-Provence, Alpes Maritimes, Bouches-du-Rhône, Hautes-Alpes,
>   Var, Vaucluse
> 14 Ain, Ardèche, Drôme, Haute-Savoie, Isère, Loire, Rhône, Savoie

North East France
> 15 Côte-d'Or, Nièvre, Saône-et-Loire, Yonne
> 16 Doubs, Haute-Saône, Jura, Territoire-de-Belfort
> 17 Bas-Rhin, Haut-Rhin, Meurthe-et-Moselle, Meuse, Moselle, Vosges
> 18 Ardennes, Aube, Haute-Marne, Marne

Paris and Nearby
> 19 Essonne, Seine-et-Marne, Val-d'Oise, Yvelines

Scale:
> Maps 1–18: 27 miles to 1 inch
> Map 19: 16 miles to 1 inch

Key to Symbols

- food
- food and accommodation
- accommodation
- main town

- city
- motorway
- main road
- county boundary

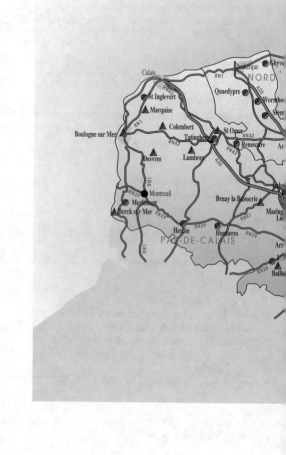

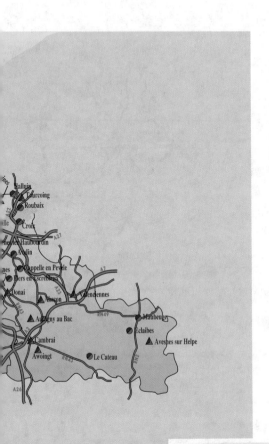

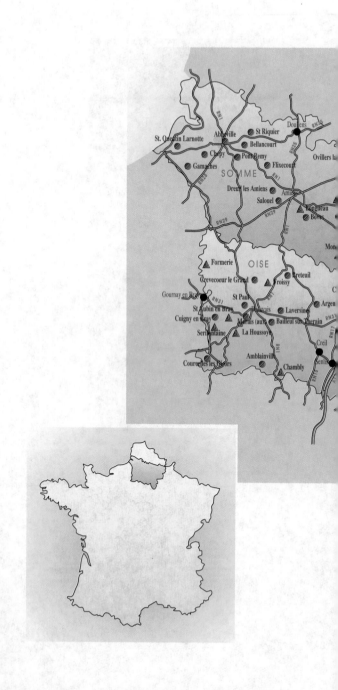

Péronne
onne Asseviller
Devieecourt
Néthees Mons
St Quentin
AISNE
archelepot
iecourt
Flavy le Martel
RN44
Dizy le Gros
Coucy le Chateau
Chauny
Etouvelles
Laon
ayart
gne
RN31
Soissons
Trosly Breuil
RN31
RN2
Villers Cotterets
Fresnes en Tardenois
Marolles Bourneville
A4
Mezy Moulins
RN3
RN3
Hirson
RN99
RN2
RN43

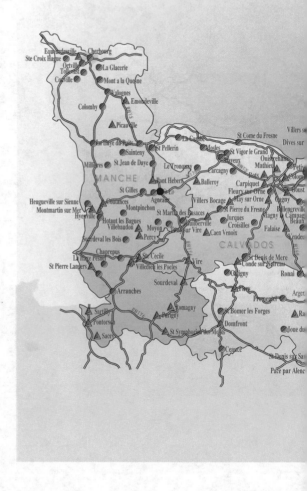

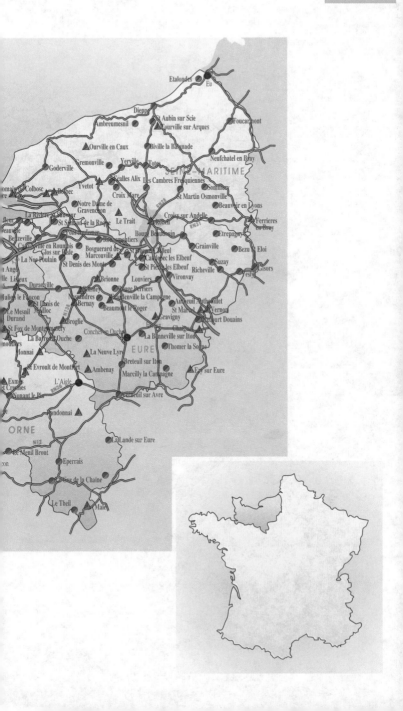

Etalondes
Eu
Dieppe
Ambreumesnil   St Aubin sur Scie
                Ourville sur Arques   Foucarmont
Ourville en Caux   Biville la Baignade
Gremonville   Yerville   Totes   Neufchatel en Bray
Goderville   SEINE-MARITIME
                Ecalles Alix   Les Cambres Froquiennes
Colbosc   Bolbec   Yvetot   Sommery
                Croix Mare   St Martin Osmonville
                Notre Dame de   Beauvoir en Lyons
La Rivière St Sauveur   Gravenchon   Croixy sur Andelle   Ferrieres
Beauvoir   St Samson de la Roque   Le Trait   Rouen   en Bray
Beuzeville   Pont Audemer   Bourg Beaudouin   Etrepagny
Cauverville en Roumois   Bosguerard de   Oissel lleul   Grainville   Bezu St Eloi
Glos sur Risle   Marcouville   Caudebec les Elbeuf   Guzay   Gisors
La Noe Poulain   St Denis des Monts   St Pierre les Elbeuf   Richeville   Fresne
Lisieux   Brionne   Louviers   Vironvay
Duranville   Rouge Perriers
Julien le Faucon   Nassandres   Glenville la Campagne   Aubeuil Authenillet
St Denis de   Bernay   Beaumont le Roger   St Marc   Vernon
Le Mesnil Mailloc   Gravigny   Court Douains
Durand   Broglie   Conche en Ouche   Change
St Foy de Montgommery   La Blanneville sur Iton
La Barre en Ouche   Thomer la Sogne
Monnai   EURE
        La Neuve Lyre   Breteuil sur Iton
St Evroult de Montfort   Ambenay   Marcilly la Campagne   Foix sur Eure
Exmes   L'Aigle
Nonant le Pin   Verneuil sur Avre
        Randonnai
ORNE
        La Lande sur Eure
Le Menil Brout
Eperrais
Gue de la Chaine
Le Theil   Male

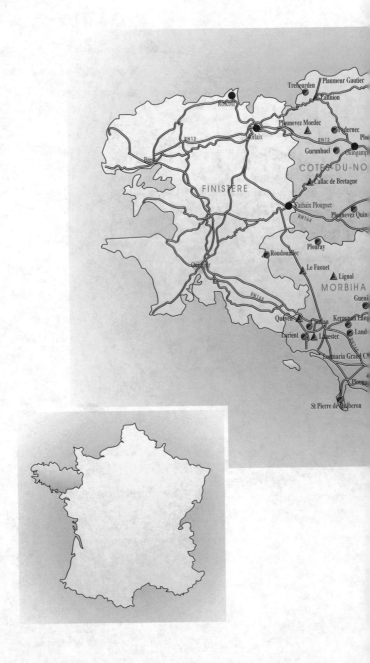

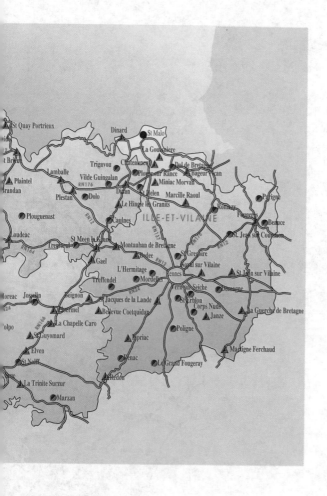

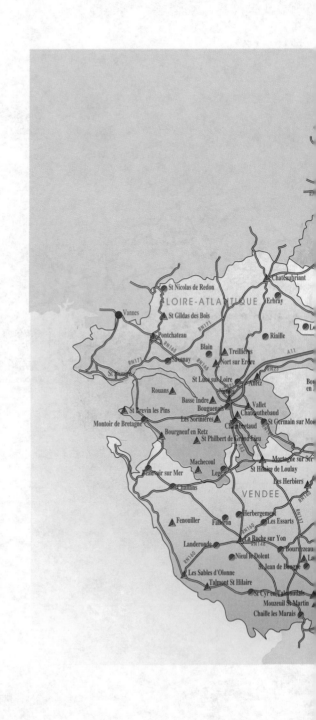

St Nicolas de Redon

LOIRE-ATLANTIQUE   Erbray

Châteaubriant

Vannes

St Gildas des Bois

Pontchateau

Riaille

Le

Blain   Treillières

Savenay   Nort sur Erdre

St Nazaire

St Luce sur Loire

Anetz

Rouans   Nantes

Basse Indre

Bou
en

St Brevin les Pins   Bouguenais   Vallet

Chateauthebaud

St Germain sur Mo

Montoir de Bretagne   Les Sorinières   Chambretaud

Clisson

Bourgneuf en Retz   St Philbert de Grand Lieu

Machecoul   Mortagne sur Sè

St Hilaire de Loulay

Beauvoir sur Mer   Legé   Les Herbiers

Challans   VENDÉE

Herbergement

Fenouiller   Falleron   Les Essarts

Landeronde   La Roche sur Yon   Bournezeau

Nieul le Dolent   La

Les Sables d'Olonne   St Jean de Beugné

Talmont St Hilaire

St Cyr en Talmondais

Mouzeuil St Martin

Chaille les Marais

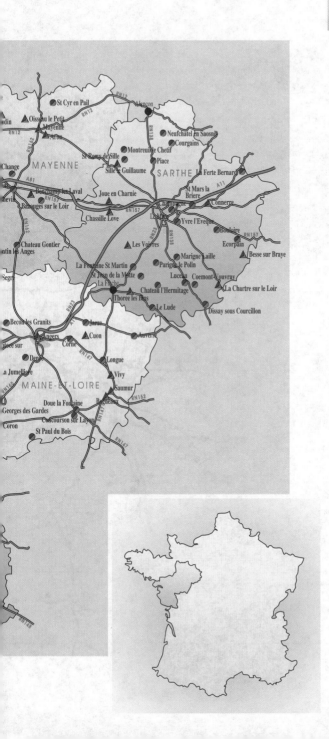

St Cyr en Pail
Oisseau le Petit
Alençon
Mayenne
Aron
RN12
Neufchatel en Saosnis
Courgains
Montreuil le Chetif
St Remy de Sille
Piace
MAYENNE
Change
Sille le Guillaume
SARTHE
La Ferte Bernard
A81
Beauchamp les Laval
Joue en Charnie
St Mars la Briere
RN159
Connerre
Bazouges sur le Loir
RN157
Chassille Love
Le Mans
Yvre l'Eveque
Bouloire
RN157
Les Voutres
Ecorpain
Chateau Gontier
RN138
antin les Anges
Marigne Laille
Besse sur Braye
La Fontaine St Martin
Parigne le Polin
Segre
St Jean de la Motte
Lucean
Coemont Vouvray
La Fleche
La Chartre sur le Loir
Chateau l'Hermitage
Thoree les Pins
Le Lude
Dissay sous Courcillon
Becon les Granits
Jarze
Cuon
Auvers
Angers
Corne
RN147
Denee
Longue
a Jumelliere
Vivy
MAINE-ET-LOIRE
Saumur
Doue la Fontaine
RN152
Georges des Gardes
Concourson sur Layon
Coron
St Paul du Bois
RN147

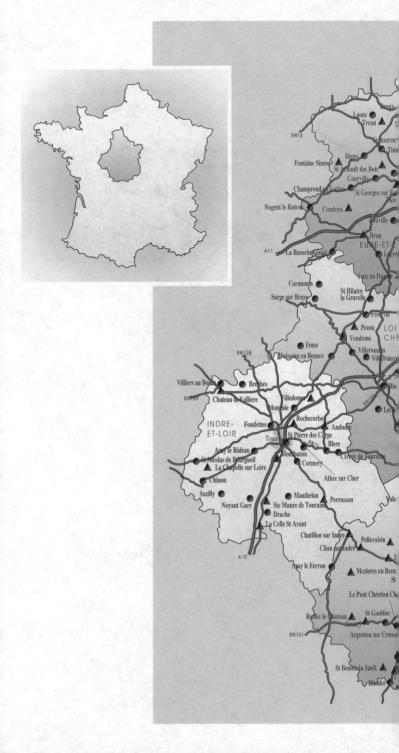

Mœux

Laons
Treon

RN12

Sehazereu
Thi

Fontaine Simon
Digny

St Arnoult des Bois
Courville

Champrond en Gatine
St Georges sur Fu

Nogent le Rotrou
Combres

Thiv

Bouville

Brou
EURE-ET-

La Bazoche Gouet
A11
Lere

Lutz en Dunois

Cormenon
St Hilaire
Sarge sur Braye
la Gravelle

Fretival
Pezou
LOI
Vendome
CH
Fosse
Huisseau en Beauce
Villeroman
Villefranc

RN138

Villiers au Bois
Breches
Bio
Chateau la Valliere
Villedome
RN153
Monnaie
Fondettes
Rochecorbo
Les
INDRE-
Ambose
ET-LOIR
St Pierre des Corps
Tours
Blere
Azay le Rideau
Montbazon
St Nicolas de Bourgueil
Cormery
La Chapelle sur Loire
Civray de Touraine
Chinon
Athee sur Cher
Sazilly
Manthelan
Noyant Gare
Perrusson
Vale
Ste Maure de Touraine
Drache
La Celle St Avant

Chatillon sur Indre
Pellevoisin
Clion sur Indre

Azay le Ferron
Mezieres en Bren
St

Le Pont Chretien Ch

Reffec le Chateau
St Gaultier
Argenton sur Creuse
RN151

St Benoit du Sault
Rhodes

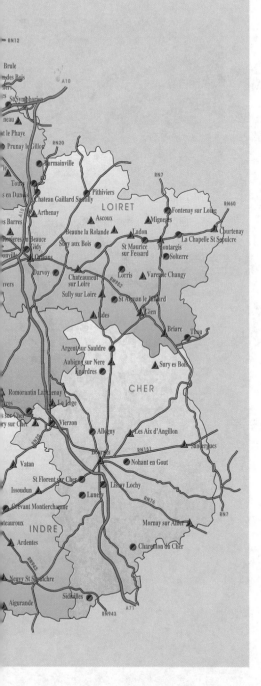

- RN12

Brule
ndes Bois
iers
es   St Symphorien
A10
neau
at le Phaye
Prunay le Gillon
RN20
e   Armainville
Tour
s en Dunois   Chateau Gaillard Santilly   Pithiviers
es Barres   Arthenay   LOIRET
Rossieres en Beauce   Ascoux   Mignères   Fontenay sur Loing
Gidy   Beaune la Rolande   Ladon   RN60
onville   Orleans   Sury aux Bois   La Chapelle St Sepulcre   Courtenay
Darvoy   St Maurice   Montargis
sur Fessard   Solterre
ivers   Chateauneuf   Lorris   Varenne Changy
sur Loire
Sully sur Loire   St Agnan le Mauard
des   Gien
Briare   Thou
Argent sur Sauldre
Aubigny sur Nere   Sury es Bois
Knordres
CHER
Romorantin Lanthenay
res   La Loge
s sur Cher
ry sur Cher   Vierzon   Allogny   Les Aix d'Angillon
Bourges   RN151   Sancergues
Vatan   Nohant en Gout
St Florent sur Cher   Lissay Lochy
Issoudun   Lunery   RN76
Crevant Montierchaume   RN7
teauroux   INDRE   Mornay sur Allier
Ardentes   Charenton du Cher
Neuvy St Sepulchre
Aigurande   Sidailles
RN943   A71

RN7
RN7
A71

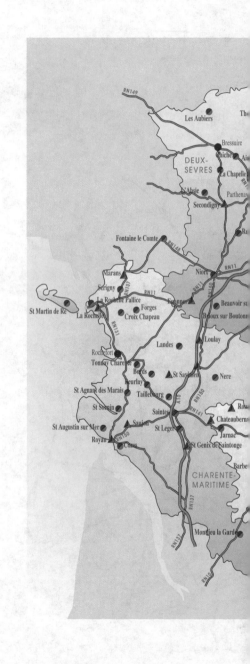

gliers
Verrue ▲

A10

RN10

Lencloitre
Chatellerault

RN147

RN149

erriere

VIENNE

aintre

RN10

Poitiers
RN151
Chauvigny
La Trimouille

RN147
RN151

ombiers
RN11
Vivonne

ouille
RN10
Lussac les Chateaux
RN147
Montmorrilon

Fleure
Chauna le Bourg ▲
Sommieres du Clain ▲
Moulismes ▲

Civray
ais
Charroux ▲
Pressac

Ruffec
Champagne Mouton ▲
Confolens

RN10
RN141
Biagnac

Aussic
ssats par Brie ▲
Roumazieres ▲

RN141

CHARENTE

Angouleme
Chadurie

Montmoreau ▲

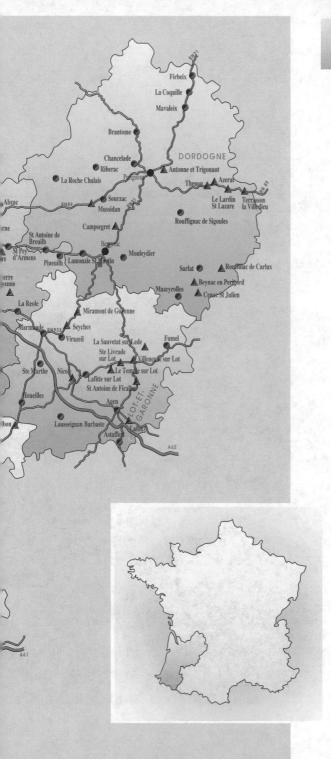

8

Firbeix
La Coquille
Mavaleix

Brantome

Chancelade
Riberac
La Roche Chalais
Périgueux
DORDOGNE
Antonne et Trigonant
Thenon   Azerat

Abzac   RN89   Sourzac
Mussidan
Le Lardin
St Lazare   Terrasson
la Villedieu

Campsegret
Rouffignac de Sigoules

St Antoine de
Breuilh
St Pey
d'Armens   Bergerac   Mouleydier
Pineuilh   Lamonzie St Martin
Sarlat   Rouffillac de Carlux

erre
yenne   Mazeyrolles   Beynac en Perigord
Cenac St Julien

La Reole

Miramont de Guienne

Marmande   RN933   Seyches
Virazeil   La Sauvetat sur Lede   Fumel
Ste Livrade
sur Lot   Villeneuve sur Lot
Ste Marthe   Nicole
Lafitte sur Lot   Le Temple sur Lot
St Antoine de Ficalba
Houeilles   Agen
LOT-ET-
GARONNE
bon   Lausseignan Barbaste   Lafox
Astaffort
A62

A61

Gou

St Germain d

Cal

Cahors Pern.

St Paul de Loubre

TARN-ET-GARC

Montauba

A62

Ligardes

Fleurance

GERS

Marsan Aubiet

Auch

L'Isle Jourdain

Aucamvil
Seilh

Toulo

Riscle

Plaisance du Gers

Castelnau Riviere Basse

RN21

Maubourguet

Masseube

Vic en Bigorre

Boulogne sur Gesse

Carbonne

Les Ba

Tarbes

Trie sur Baise

Mondauezan

Lalobiere

Lannemezan

Villeneuve de Riviere

Beauchalot

Lourdes

RN117

Pierrefitte Nestalas

HAUTES-
PYRENEES

Biars sur Cere
St Cere
Gramat
T
Lacapelle Marival
Figeac
Rignac
Villeneuve d'Aveyron
Villefranche de Rouergue
La Bastide l'Eveque
Rieupeyroux
Baraqueville
Las Farguettes
Carmaux
Albi   Alban
Fontcouverte
Ambres
Realmont
St Paul Cap de Joux
Soual   Castres
Lagarrigue
Cuq Toulza   Valdurenque
Labruguiere
St Felix Lauragais   Albine
Avignonet Lauragais

La Vitarelle
Boisse Penchot
Espalion
Decazeville   Gages   Campagnac
Onet le Chateau   Bertholene
Rodez   Sebazac
Concours
AVEYRON
Lapanouse de Severac
Le Monastier
St Rome de Cernon
L'Hospitalet du Larzac
La Couvertoirade

TARN
Lacaune

Aussillon Mazamet

ARIEGE
us Garrabet
Luzenac

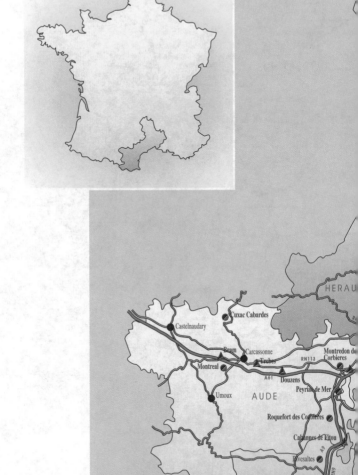

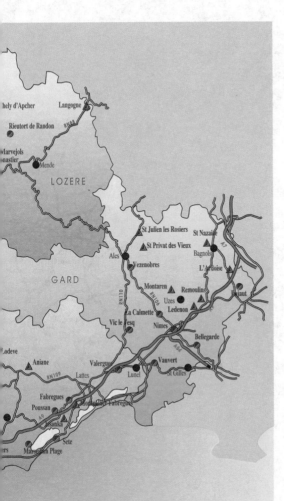

hely d'Apcher Langogne

Rieutort de Randon

RN88

Marvejols
nastier   Mende

LOZERE

St Julien les Rosiers   St Nazaire

St Privat des Vieux

Ales
Vezenobres   Bagnols
GARD   L'Ardoise

RN110   Montaren   Remoulins

RN106   Uzes   Bijaut
La Calmette   Ledenon

Vic le Fesq
Nimes

Bellegarde

Lodeve   Aniane   Valergues   Vauvert
RN109   Lattes   Lunel   St Gilles

Fabregues
Poussan   Montpellier Fabregues
A9   Isanka

ers   Marseillan Plage   Sete

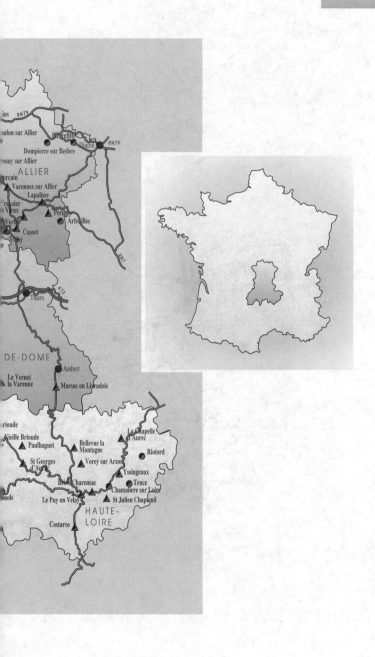

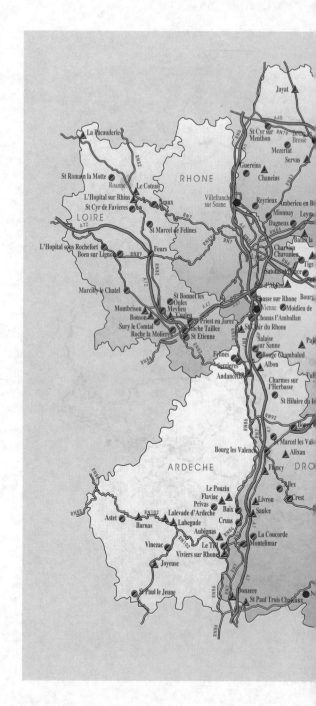

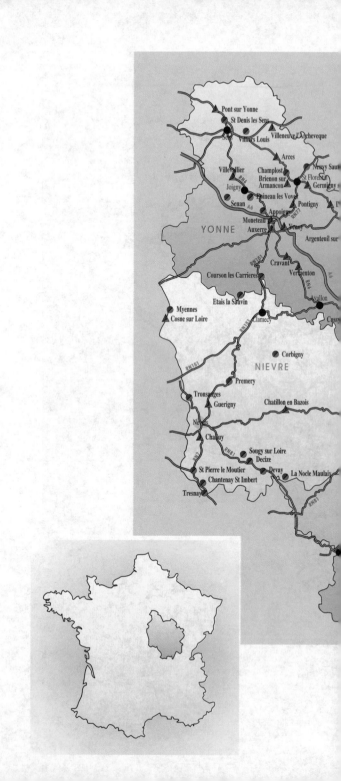

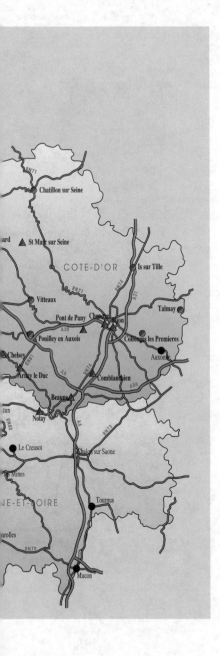

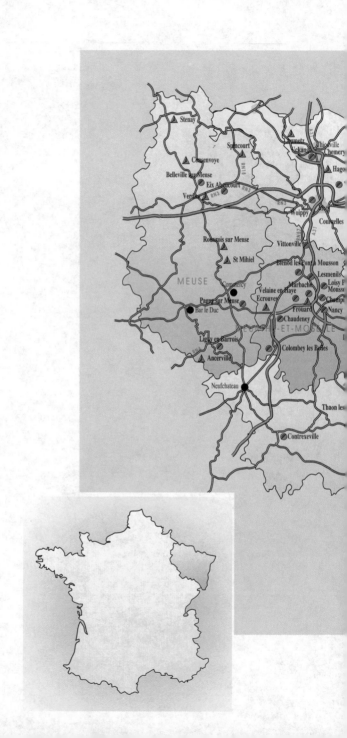

Rocroi

Auvillers les Forges
Tremblois les Rocroi

Novion Porcien

Rethel

Asfeld
Brienne sur Aisne

Witry les Reims

Reims

Prosnes
Beaumont sur Vesle
Su

Pont à Binson   Epernay

Châlons sur Ma

Etoges
Chaintrix

Connantray   Sommesous

Sézanne   RN4   E
Connantre   Cool

Maille le Camp

Maizières la Grande Paroisse

Mesgrigny
Aubeterr

Gumery   Lesmont
Suzanv

Creney près Troyes   Unienville

Fontvannes   Troyes   Lusigny sur
La Rivière de Corps

AUBE

Bouilly

St Phal
Villeneuve au Chemin

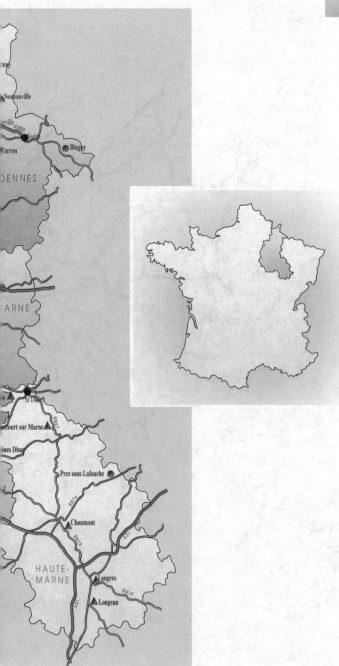

nay

Nouzonville

eville A203

Terron ● Blagny

DENNES

ARNE

St Dizier

court sur Marne ▲

ines Dhuy

Prez sous Lafauche ●

RN74

▲ Chaumont

RN19

A31

HAUTE-
MARNE

▲ Langres

RN19

▲ Longeau

A31

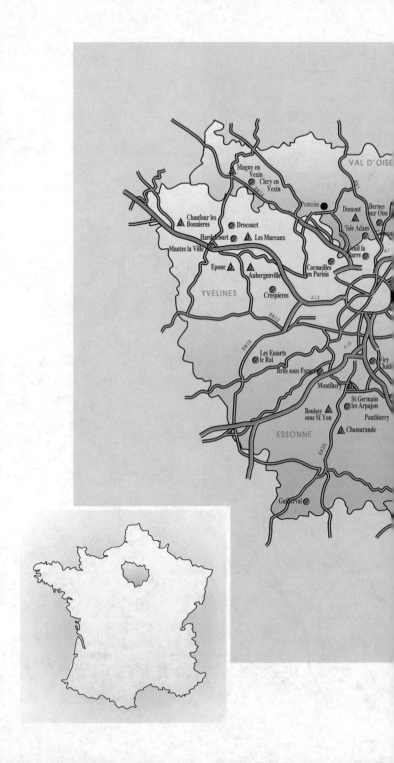

urvilliers

RN3 Meaux ▲ Sammeron

🔵 Claye Souilly

▲

A4

SEINE-ET-MARNE

Pontault Combault
🔵 Ozoir la Ferriere   Voisins Mouroux ▲   La Ferte Gaucher 🔵
                        Sancy les Provins 🔵
RN4
ous Senart   🔵 La Houssage en Brie

RN19 🔵 Voinle Rozay en Brie 🔵
                    🔵 Bannost

                    ▲
                 Provins

🟡 Fontainebleau   Marolles sur Seine
        RN5 Montereau 🔵
   Le Petit Fossard ▲ 🔵
                    🔵 La Brosse
                       Montceaux
apelle   Voulx 🔵
e
Nemours 🔵

afferville

List of Casserole Relais Routiers

TOWN	DEPARTMENT	ESTABLISHMENT
	Paris and Nearby	
PROVINS	Seine-et-Mame 77160	LE RELAIS DE LA CURE D'AIR
VOULX	Seine-et-Mame 77940	LA BRUYERE
	Northern France	
NONE		
	North West France	
BALLEROY	Calvados 14490	LE RELAIS DE LA FORET
BAYEUX	Calvados 14400	LA COLOMBE
BEDEE	Ille-et-Vilaine 35137	HOTEL DU COMMERCE
DINAN	Côtes-du-Nord 22100	LA MARMITE
DINARD	Ille-et-Vilaine 35800	L'EPICURIEN-Hôtel de la Gare
DOL DE BRETAGNE	Ille-et-Vilaine 35120	LE RELAIS DE BELLE LANDE
DOMFRONT	Orne 61700	LE RELAIS SAINT MICHEL
ELVEN	Morbihan 56250	LE RELAIS DE L'ARGOUET
GUERCHE DE BRETAGNE (LA)	Ille-et-Vilaine 35130	LE RELAIS DU PONT D'ANJOU
HAYE DU PUITS (LA)	Manche 50250	RESTAURANT DES AMIS
HAYE PESNEL (LA)	Manche 50320	LE RELAIS – Chez Armelle
HEUGUEVILLE SUR SIENNE	Manche 50200	LE MASCARET
JALLAIS	Maine-et-Loire 49510	LE GALANT VERT – LA CROIX VERTE
LAMBALLE	Côtes-du-Nord 22400	LA TOUR D'ARGENT
LANDEVANT	Morbihan 56690	LE RELAIS DU PELICAN
MONTAUBAN DE BRETAGNE	Ille-et-Vilaine 35360	HOTEL DE FRANCE
MOUZEUIL ST MARTIN	Vendée 85370	CENTRAL ROUTIERS
NONANT LE PIN	Orne 61240	LE RELAIS DES HARAS
PLOUER SUR RANCE	Côtes-du-Nord 22490	LE BON ACCUEIL
PONTCHATEAU	Loire-Atlantique 44160	L'AUBERGE DU CALVAIRE
PONTCHATEAU	Loire-Atlantique 44160	LE RELAIS DE BEAULIEU
REDON	Ille-et-Vilaine 35600	LE RELAIS
RICHEVILLE	Eure 27420	RESTAUROUTE LE BALTO
SAINT GILDAS DES BOIS	Loire-Atlantique 44530	LES ROUTIERS
SAINT MARTIN DES BESACES	Calvados 14350	LA RENAISSANCE
SAINT SYMPHORIEN DES MONTS	Manche 50640	LE RELAIS DU BOIS LEGER
SAINTE LUCE SUR LOIRE	Loire-Atlantique 44980	LA BOUGRIERE
SAUMUR	Maine-et-Loire 49400	HOTEL DE LA GARE
SENE	Morbihan 56860	RELAIS ROUTIERS
VENDEUVRE	Calvados 14170	LE RELAIS DE VENDEUVRE
VIRE	Calvados 14500	HOTEL DE FRANCE
VIVY	Maine-et-Loire 49680	RESTAURANT SAINT PAUL

North East France

AUXERRE	Yonne 89000	LE SAINTE NITASSE
BEAUMONT SUR VESLE	Marne 51360	LA MAISON DU CHAMPAGNE
BOUXWILLER	Bas-Rhin 67330	AU SOLEIL
COSNE SUR LOIRE	Nièvre 58200	LES 3 COULEURS
HYEVRE PAROISSE	Doubs 25110	RELAIS LA CREMAILLERE
MONETEAU	Yonne 89470	AU RENDEZ-VOUS DES PECHEURS
NANCY	Meurthe-et-Moselle 54000	RESTAURANT DU PORT
ORNANS	Doubs 25290	HOTEL LE PROGRES
TOUR DU MEIX (LA)	Jura 39270	AUBERGE DU PONT DE LA PYLE
VENDENHEIM	Bas-Rhin 67550	LE RELAIS DE LA MAISON ROUGE

The Loire

ARGENTON SUR CREUSE	Indre 36200	LE RELAIS
BARBEZIEUX SAINT HILAIRE	Charente 16120	RELAIS DE LA BILLETTE
CHARROUX	Vienne 86250	LA CROIX BLANCHE (RELAIS)
CHARTRES	Eure-et-Loir 28000	RESTAURANT LE PALMIER
CHARTRES	Eure-et-Loir 28000	RELAIS BEAUCERON
CHATEAUNEUF SUR LOIRE	Loiret 45110	HOTEL DE LA PLACE
LOGE (LA)	Loir-et-Cher 41300	RELAIS DE LA LOGE
MAROLLES	Eure-et-Loir 28260	AU RELAIS DE MAROLLES
NEUVY	Loir-et-Cher 41250	LA CHEMINEE
SAINT EUGENE	Charente-Maritime 17520	LES DEUX CHARENTES
SAINT GENIX DE SAINTONGE	Charente-Maritime 17240	LE RELAIS DE SAINTONGE
SECONDIGNY	Deux-Sèvres 79130	LES ROUTIERS
SOLTERRE	Loiret 45700	AUBERGE DE LA ROUTE BLEUE
SUEVRES	Loir-et-Cher 41500	LE RELAIS DE LA PROVIDENCE
SURY AUX BOIS	Loiret 45530	LE RELAIS DU PONT DES BEIGNERS
TRIMOUILLE (LA)	Vienne 86290	L'AUBERGE FLEURIE
VILLEDOMER	Indre-et-Loire 37110	LE RELAIS DES GRANDS VINS DE TOURAINE

Central France

BEAUNE LES MINES	Haute Vienne 87280	LA TERRASSE DE BEAUNE
PONT DE MENAT	Puy-de-Dôme 63580	CHEZ ROGER
SAINT FLOUR	Cantal 15100	HOTEL LE PROGRES
VARENNES SUR ALLIER	Allier 03150	LE RELAIS DES TOURISTES

South West France

BERTHOLENE	Aveyron 12310	HOTEL BANCAREL
BEYNAC EN PERIGORD	Dordogne 24220	HOSTELLERIE MALEVILLE
BRANTOME	Dordogne 24310	LE GERGOVIE
CAMPSEGRET	Dordogne 24140	LE RELAIS DES TAMARIS
CENAC SAINT JULIEN	Dordogne 24250	LA PROMENADE

ESCOURCE	Landes 40210	AU ROUTIER
GRAMAT	Lot 46500	HOTEL DU CENTRE
LANGON	Gironde 33210	RESTAURANT DARLOT
LAUSSEIGNAN BARBASTE	Lot-et-Garonne 47230	LES PALMIERS
MUSSIDAN	Dordogne 24400	LE PERIGORD
ONET LE CHATEAU	Aveyron 12850	LA ROCADE
REMOULINS	Gard 30210	AUBERGE LES PLATANES
ROCHE CHALAIS (LA)	Dordogne 24490	CAFE DU MIDI
ROUFFIGNAC DE SIGOULES	Dordogne 24240	LA TAVERNE ALSACIENNE
SAINT PAUL DE LOUBRESSAC	Lot 46170	RELAIS DE LA MADELEINE
SAINTE MARIE DE GOSSE	Landes 40390	LE RELAIS ROUTIERS
SAINTE TERRE	Gironde 33350	CHEZ REGIS

South East France

CORMORANCHE SUR SAONE	Ain 01290	AUBERGE CHEZ LA MERE MARTINET
CORPS	Isère 38970	RESTAURANT DU TILLEUL
EMBRUN	Hautes-Alpes 05200	LES ROUTIERS
EYGUIANS	Hautes-Alpes 05300	HOTEL DE LA GARE
GUILLESTRE	Hautes-Alpes 05600	HOTEL DE LA GARE
LIGNANE	Bouches-du-Rhône 13540	LE RELAIS DE LIGNANE
MEGEVE	Haute-Savoie 74120	CHALET DES FLEURS
PAJAY	Isère 38260	MA PETITE AUBERGE
PIOLENC	Vaucluse 84420	LE COMMERCE
ROCHETAILLEE	Isère 38520	HOTEL BELLEDONNE
SAINT JEAN DE MAURIENNE	Savoie 73300	BAR RESTAURANT RELAIS ROUTIERS
SAINT RAPHAEL	Var 83700	LE BEL AZUR
THONES	Haute-Savoie 74230	L'HERMITAGE
TOUR DU PIN (LA)	Isère 38110	CHEZ BABETH
VIVIERS SUR RHONE	Ardèche 07220	LE RELAIS DU VIVARAIS

List of Tourist Hotels

STAR RATING	TOWN	DEPARTMENT	ESTABLISHMENT
		Paris and Nearby	
*	CHAMARANDE	Essonne 91730	RELAIS DE MONTFORT
*	MONTLHERY	Essonne 91310	LE SOLOGNE
		Northern France	
*	BAILLEUL	Nord 59270	AUBERGE DU SEAU
*	BAPAUME	Pas-de-Calais 62450	CHEZ BERNADETTE
*	BRUAY LA BUISSIERE	Pas-de-Calais 62700	LA LOUETTE (formerly CHEZ MICHEL)
*	FORMERIE	Oise 60220	CAFE DE LA PAIX
		North West France	
*	BEDEE	Ille-et-Vilaine 35137	HOTEL DU COMMERCE
*	BESSE SUR BRAYE	Sarthe 72310	LES ROUTIERS
**	BRIONNE	Eure 27800	HOTEL DU HAVRE
*	CHATEAUBRIANT	Loire-Atlantique 44110	S.A.R.L. PARIS-OCEAN
*	DOMFRONT	Orne 61700	LE RELAIS SAINT MICHEL
*	ELVEN	Morbihan 56250	LE RELAIS DE L'ARGOUET
*	FOUGERES	Ille-et-Vilaine 35300	AUX AMIS DE LA ROUTE
*	GRAND FOUGERAY (LE)	Ille-et-Vilaine 35390	LE RELAIS DE LA BELLE ETOILE
*	GUERCHE DE BRETAGNE (LA)	Ille-et-Vilaine 35130	LE RELAIS DU PONT D'ANJOU
*	HERBIERS (LES)	Vendée 85500	L'OREE DES BOIS VERTS
**	HERBIERS (LES)	Vendée 85500	CHEZ CAMILLE
**	JALLAIS	Maine-et-Loire 49510	LE GALANT VERT – LA CROIX VERTE
*	JOUE EN CHARNIE	Sarthe 72540	LE CHEVAL BLANC
**	LAMBALLE	Côtes-du-Nord 22400	LA TOUR D'ARGENT
*	LANESTER	Morbihan 56600	LA ROTONDE
*	LOUDEAC	Côtes-du-Nord 22600	LES ROUTIERS
*	MALE	Orne 61260	LA BELLE RENCONTRE
**	MONT SAINT MICHEL (LE)	Manche 50116	HOTEL MOTEL VERT – La Rôtisserie
**	MONTAUBAN DE BRETAGNE	Ille-et-Vilaine 35360	HOTEL DE FRANCE
**	MONTAUBAN DE BRETAGNE	Ille-et-Vilaine 35360	RELAIS DE LA HUCHERAIS
**	MONTMARTIN SUR MER	Manche 50590	HOTELLERIE DU BON VIEUX TEMPS
**	MOREAC	Morbihan 56500	LE RELAIS DU BARDERFF
*	PIPRIAC	Ille-et-Vilaine 35550	HOTEL DE LA TOUR D'AUVERGNE

**	PONTCHATEAU	Loire-Atlantique 44160	L'AUBERGE DU CALVAIRE
*	REDON	Ille-et-Vilaine 35600	LE RELAIS
**	ROCHE SUR YON (LA)	Vendée 85000	HOTEL SULLY
**	ROMAGNY	Manche 50140	AUBERGE DES CLOSEAUX
**	SAINT BERTHEVIN	Mayenne 53940	L'INTERNATIONAL
*	SAINT BRIEUC	Côtes-du-Nord 22000	AU BEAUFEUILLAGE
*	SAINT GUYOMARD	Morbihan 56460	LE RELAIS DES DOLMENS DE LANVAUX
**	SAINT HILAIRE DE LOULAY	Vendée 85600	LE RELAX
*	SAINT MARTIN DES BESACES	Calvados 14350	LA RENAISSANCE
**	SAUMUR	Maine-et-Loire 49400	HOTEL DE LA GARE
*	SENE	Morbihan 56860	RELAIS ROUTIERS
*	VILLERS SUR MER	Calvados 14640	LE NORMAND
**	VIRE	Calvados 14500	HOTEL DE FRANCE
*	VIVY	Maine-et-Loire 49680	RESTAURANT SAINT PAUL

North East France

*	ANCERVILLE	Meuse 55170	LE RELAIS
*	ARCES	Yonne 89320	RELAIS DE LA FORET D'OTHE
**	ARCHES	Vosges 88380	LA TRUITE RENOMMEE
*	AUXERRE	Yonne 89000	LE SAINTE NITASSE
**	BEAUMONT SUR VESLE	Mame 51360	LA MAISON DU CHAMPAGNE
***	BEAUNE	Côte-d'Or 21200	RELAIS DE BEAUNE
*	BOUILLY	Aube 10320	AU RELAIS MONTAIGU
**	BOUXWILLER	Bas-Rhin 67330	AU SOLEIL
*	CHENOVE	Côte-d'Or 21300	AU BON COIN
*	COSNE SUR LOIRE	Nièvre 58200	LES 3 COULEURS
*	FUMAY	Ardennes 08170	HOTEL LION
***	HYEVRE PAROISSE	Doubs 25110	RELAIS LA CREMAILLERE
*	KOGENHEIM	Bas-Rhin 67230	A L'ETOILE
**	MONTBENOIT	Doubs 25650	HOTEL RESTAURANT DES VOYAGEURS
**	NOLAY	Côte-d'Or 21340	HOTEL DU CHEVREUIL
*	ORNANS	Doubs 25290	HOTEL LE PROGRES
*	PLOMBIERES LES BAINS	Vosges 88370	LE RELAIS STRASBOURGEOIS
*	RONCHAMP	Haute-Saône 70250	LE RELAIS DE LA POMME D'OR
**	SAINT PIERREMONT	Vosges 88700	LE RELAIS VOSGIEN
*	SAINTE MARGUERITE	Vosges 88100	LE RELAIS DES AMIS
**	VENOY	Yonne 89290	L'ARCHE DE VENOY 1
**	VENOY	Yonne 89290	L'ARCHE DE VENOY 2

The Loire

**	AIGURANDE	Indre 36140	LE RELAIS DE LA MARCHE

**	ARTHENAY	Loiret 45410	LE RELAIS D'ARTHENAY
*	CHAMPAGNE MOUTON	Charente 16350	HOTEL PLAISANCE
**	CHARTRES	Eure-et-Loir 28000	RELAIS BEAUCERON
**	CHATEAU LA VALLIERE	Indre-et-Loire 37330	LE GRAND CERF
*	CHATEAUROUX	Indre 36000	LE RALLYE
*	CHAUNAY LE BOURG	Vienne 86510	LE COMMERCE
*	LOGE (LA)	Loir-et-Cher 41300	RELAIS DE LA LOGE
*	MOULISMES	Vienne 86500	LA TABLE OUVERTE
*	ROCHELLE (LA)	Charente-Maritime 17000	LA COTE VERTE
*	ROMORANTIN LANTHENAY	Loir-et-Cher 41200	LES AUBIERS
*	SAINT GENIX DE SAINTONGE	Charente-Maritime 17240	LE RELAIS DE SAINTONGE
*	SAINTE MAURE DE TOURAINE	Indre-et-Loire 37800	L'ETOILE DU SUD
*	SAUJON	Charente-Maritime 17600	HOTEL DE LA GARE
*	YMONVILLE	Eure-et-Loir 28150	A L'ETOILE

Central France

*	CLERMONT FERRAND	Puy-de-Dôme 63000	AUVERGNE PYRENEES– Les Routiers
*	CREUZIER LE VIEUX	Allier 03300	CHEZ LA MERE RIBOULIN
**	EYMOUTIERS	Haute-Vienne 87120	LE SAINT PSALMET
*	FRAISSE HAUT	Cantal 15300	HOTEL DES CIMES
*	LAPALISSE	Allier 03120	LE CHAPON DORE
*	MAURIAC	Cantal 15200	LES ROUTIERS
*	PERIGNY	Allier 03120	LE RELAIS DE PERIGNY
**	SAINT FLOUR	Cantal 15100	HOTEL LE PROGRES
*	SAINT JULIEN CHAPTEUIL	Haute-Loire 43260	AUBERGE DU MEYCAL
*	SAUVIAT SURVIGE	Haute-Vienne 87400	HOTEL DE LA POSTE
**	VIEILLE BRIOUDE	Haute-Loire 43100	LES GLYCINES

South West France

*	AIRE SUR L'ADOUR	Landes 40800	LES ROUTIERS – Chez Pierrette
*	AMBRES	Tarn 81500	AUBERGE DES POMMIERS
**	AMOU	Landes 40330	AU FEU DE BOIS
*	ANIANE	Hérault 34150	LA CLAMOUSE
*	BANYULS DELS ASPRES	Pyréneés-Orientales 66300	HOSTAL DE CATALUNYA
**	BARAQUEVILLE	Aveyron 12160	LE PALOUS
*	BERTHOLENE	Aveyron 12310	HOTEL BANCAREL
**	BEYNAC EN PERIGORD	Dordogne 24220	HOSTELLERIE MALEVILLE
**	BEZIERS	Hérault 34440	LA GRILLADE
*	CAMPSEGRET	Dordogne 24140	LE RELAIS DES TAMARIS
*	CARBONNE	Haute-Garonne 31390	CHEZ ROGER
**	CUQ TOULZA	Tarn 81470	LE RELAIS CHEZ ALAIN
*	DENGUIN	Pyrénées-Atlantiques 64230	RELAIS PYRENEES MONTAGNE OCEAN

*	ESPALION	Aveyron 12500	RELAIS DES QUATRE ESPALION ROUTES
*	GAGES	Aveyron 12630	LE RELAIS DE LA PLAINE
*	GAN	Pyrénées-Atlantiques 64290	HOTEL MODERNE
**	GRAMAT	Lot 46500	HOTEL DU CENTRE
**	HOSPITALET DU LARZAC (L')	Aveyron 12230	RELAIS ESPACE
**	ISSANKA	Hérault 34540	LE GARRIGOU
*	LAFOX	Lot-et-Garonne 47270	LE RELAIS TOULOUSAIN
*	LALOUBERE	Hautes-Pyrénées 65310	HOTEL DES PYRENEES
*	LANGOGNE	Lozère 48300	HOTEL DU LUXEMBOURG
*	LIBOURNE	Gironde 33500	LE MOULIN BLANC
**	MIRAMONT DE GUYENNE	Lot-et-Garonne 47800	LE RELAIS DE GUYENNE
*	MONASTIER (LE)	Lozère 48100	LES AJUSTONS
*	MONDAVEZAN	Haute-Garonne 31220	LA FERMIERE
**	MONTPELLIER FABREGUES	Hérault 34690	L'ARCHE DE FABREGUES
**	NARBONNE	Aude 11100	LA CAILLE QUI CHANTE
*	ONET LE CHATEAU	Aveyron 12850	LA ROCADE
*	PAU	Pyrénées-Atlantiques 64000	HOTEL DU BOIS LOUIS
*	PAUILLAC	Gironde 33250	LE YACHTING
**	REMOULINS	Gard 30210	AUBERGE LES PLATANES
*	RIEUPEYROUX	Aveyron 12240	CHEZ PASCAL
*	RISCLE	Gers 32400	RELAIS DE L'AUBERGE
**	ROUFFILLAC DE CARLUX	Dordogne 24370	AUX POISSONS FRAIS
*	SAINT CIERS SUR GIRONDE	Gironde 33820	RELAIS DU CHATEAU
*	SAINT LON LES MINES	Landes 40300	HOTEL DU FRONTON
*	SAINT NAZAIRE	Gard 30200	LES TERAILLES
*	SAINT PAUL DE LOUBRESSAC	Lot 46170	RELAIS DE LA MADELEINE
*	SAINTE LIVRADE SUR LOT	Lot-et-Garonne 47110	AU BON ACCUEIL
*	SAINTE MARIE DE GOSSE	Landes 40390	LE RELAIS ROUTIERS
*	SAUVETERRE DE GUYENNE	Gironde 33540	HOTEL DE GUYENNE
*	TARBES	Hautes-Pyrénées 65000	LE VICTOR HUGO
*	VITARELLE (LA)	Aveyron 12210	LE RELAIS DE LA VITARELLE

South East France

**	AIGUEBELLE	Savoie 73220	HOTEL DE LA POSTE
**	ALIXAN	Drôme 26300	HOTEL ALPES PROVENCE
*	BONSON	Loire 42160	RESTAURANT DES SPORTS
*	CHORGES	Hautes-Alpes 05230	HOTEL DES ALPES
*	CLUSES	Haute-Savoie 74300	LE RESTOPORT DU MONT BLANC
**	CORMORANCHE SUR SAONE	Ain 01290	AUBERGE CHEZ LA MERE MARTINET
**	CORPS	Isère 38970	RESTAURANT DU TILLEUL
*	DONZERE	Drôme 26290	LE BOLO
*	EMBRUN	Hautes-Alpes 05200	LES ROUTIERS

*	EYGUIANS	Hautes-Alpes 05300	HOTEL DE LA GARE
*	FREJUS	Var 83600	LES TROIS CHENES
*	GUILLESTRE	Hautes-Alpes 05600	HOTEL DE LA GARE
**	ISLE D'ABEAU	Isère 38080	L'ARCHE DE L'ISLE D'ABEAU
*	JAYAT	Ain 01340	LE RELAIS DE JAYAT
*	JOYEUSE	Ardèche 07260	LES CEVENNES
*	LALEVADE D'ARDECHE	Ardèche 07380	L'ESCHALLIER
**	MEGEVE	Haute-Savoie 74120	CHALET DES FLEURS
*	MONTFAVET	Vaucluse 84140	RELAIS DE BONPAS
**	MONTFAVET	Vaucluse 84140	RELAIS D'AVIGNON
*	ORGON	Bouches-du-Rhône 13660	RELAIS DES FUMADES
*	ROCHETAILLEE	Isère 38520	HOTEL BELLEDONNE
**	ROGNAC	Bouches-du-Rhône 13340	CADET ROUSSEL
*	SAINT FIRMIN	Hautes-Alpes 05800	LE RELAIS DE LA TRINITE
*	SAINT RAPHAEL	Var 83700	LE BEL AZUR
*	SEYNOD	Haute-Savoie 74600	RELAIS SAINTE CATHERINE
*	THONES	Haute-Savoie 74230	L'HERMITAGE
*	VEYRINS THUELLIN	Isère 38630	L'ASTRAL
*	VIVIERS SUR RHONE	Ardèche 07220	LE RELAIS DU VIVARAIS

Symbols Used in this Guide

⊗   RESTAURANT

♀   BAR, CAFE, SNACKS

⌂   HOTEL – establishment with 4 or more rooms, bed and breakfast available.

🍲   CASSEROLE – the Les Routiers mark of excellence awarded annually to those Relais Routiers where particular care is taken to offer above average meals.

☆   OFFICIAL CLASSIFICATION OF THE FRENCH TOURIST BOARD – the number of stars (1–4) indicates the degree of comfort.

NB. All place-names given in the guide indicate a Relais Routiers – but not its category. Do make sure you check the symbols so that on arrival at a Relais, you do not find a bar only, when what you require is a hotel.

When in France . . .

1. Take your guide with you into restaurants and hotels – it will let the owners know that you have chosen their establishment by using the guide, and that you expect a high standard of food and service.

2. There are two types of meals available – 'repas complet' and 'casse-croûte.' 'Repas complet' is a full meal and is served at set meal times. 'Casse-croûte', a snack meal, can be served at any time and usually consists of something simple, such as an omelette, a sandwich or a plate of cold meats.

3. Following a change in the laws in 1987, service charge must be included in the price of a meal. Tips are rarely expected and are usually given by rounding up the bill.

4. The price quoted for accommodation will be for the room and not per person but a small supplement will be charged if more than two people are sharing a room. This is usually minimal and a great help for families travelling on a budget. The price of the room is usually shown on a card on the back of the door, along with the price of breakfast.

5. French 'Hôtels de Tourisme' are officially classed on a star system. The stars provide a rating of 1–4 and 'luxe', and are usually displayed on a plaque by the main entrance. There are also many unclassified hotels where the standards are equally acceptable.

6. It is normal practice to view the room being offered before deciding to accept it. By doing so, you will be able to check on the level of cleanliness and comfort. However, should you wish to make an advance booking we strongly advise you to make your selection from the approved Relais Routiers 'Tourist Hotels'.

7. If you have booked a hotel room try to arrive before 6.00 p.m. unless you have advised the hotel of your time of arrival. If you have been delayed, do try to contact the hotel. If you do not have a reservation the chances of finding a room are greatly improved if you arrive before 6.00 p.m.

8. Many small hotels will lock their doors quite early at night. If you wish to go out, remember to advise the proprietors who will probably make arrangements for you.

9. Many French people take their holiday between 14 July and 15 August and you may find some hotels and restaurants closed during this period. It is advisable to book accommodation well in advance if you wish to travel at this time.

A L'Hotel . . .

Dear Sir

Your hotel has been recommended to me by Les Routiers. I would be grateful if you would reserve me a single/double room with/without bathroom/shower on the . . . . . . for one night/from . . . . . . to . . . . . .

Please could you confirm this and let me know if a deposit is required.

Thanking you in advance.

Yours sincerely

Monsieur,

Votre hôtel m'a été recommandé par Les Routiers. Je vous prie de vouloir bien me retenir une chambre à un lit/pour deux personnes avec/sans salle de bain/douche pour la nuit . . . . . . /du . . . . . . jusqu'au . . . . . .

Soyez assez aimable de nous confirmer cette location et de nous dire s'il vous faut une caution.

Avec nos remerciements anticipés.

Veuillez agréer, Monsieur, nos sentiments les plus distingués.

single room	– une chambre à un lit
double room	– une chambre pour deux personnes avec un grand lit
twin room	– une chambre avec deux lits
bathroom	– salle de bain
shower	– douche
breakfast	– le petit déjeuner
half board	– demi-pension
full board	– pension complète
Je voudrais retenir/réserver . . .	– I'd like to book/reserve . . .
Combien coûte/vaut la chambre?	– How much does the room cost?

Au Restaurant . . .

Choosing a restaurant and deciding what to eat can be one of the most enjoyable parts of your stay in France. One of the delights of eating in Relais Routiers lies in the discovery of authentic French cuisine and atmosphere. Providing the season is right, you can experiment with regional dishes and taste the true flavours of France. Here are a few useful points.

1. Note the difference between the 'set menu' and à la carte. The set menu is a complete three or four course meal and may or may not include drinks. Many restaurants will offer more than one set menu and the lunch-time menus will often cost less than those of the evening. Please note that you are not entitled to a reduction of the cost of the set menu if you do not eat all courses. Every Relais Routiers must state if drinks are included in the menu price. In these cases a 25 cl glass of wine will be about 6 Frs. The à la carte menu offers a full choice of dishes. The price of each dish is marked separately. A meal selected from the à la carte menu is always more expensive, even if it comprises the same dishes as the set menu.

2. Soft drinks are much more expensive in France than in Britain or Ireland. 'Sirops', which are mixed with water like a cordial, are a cheaper alternative to coke and lemonade.

3. Prices in cafés must be clearly displayed. Drinks are more expensive if you sit at a table as opposed to standing at the bar.

4. Tap water must be provided free by law. If you are unwilling to drink the tap water ask for 'l'eau minéral' but you will be charged for this.

5. 'Vin compris' on a menu means that a pichet (jug) of ordinary or house wine is included in the price. 'Boisson compris' means that 'a drink' is included. As this could be a pichet (jug) of wine, a beer, or a bottle of mineral water do check what is available.

BON APPETIT!

En Route

Traffic rules in France are very similar to those in Britain and Ireland, with the obvious exception that in France you drive on the right. When leaving a restaurant after a relaxing lunch, setting off from your hotel early in the morning, or after using a one-way street, beware! Many experienced British and Irish drivers in France will have tales to tell about the times they have happily set off on the left-hand side of the road. Here are a few extra points.

1. Speed Limits – Dry Roads

50 km (approx. 30 miles per hour) – Built-up areas/towns
90 km (approx. 56 miles per hour) – Main roads
110 km (approx. 68 miles per hour) – Dual carriageways/non-toll motorways
130 km (approx. 80 miles per hour) – Toll motorways

Wet Roads

50 km – Built-up areas/towns
80 km – Main roads
100 km – Dual carriageways/non-toll motorways
110 km – Toll motorways

New drivers must not exceed 90 km in the first year after passing their test. A minimum speed limit of 80 km (50 mph) applies on the outside lane of motorways, on level ground, with good visibility, during dry daylight hours.

2. Motorways

France has over 3,000 miles of motorways, and tolls (péages) are charged on most of these. Usually a ticket is issued and a toll paid when you leave the motorway or at intermediate points during the motorway journey. Some motorway stretches have automatic collection points where you throw the change into a basket. If you do not have the correct change, use the marked separate lane. Travellers cheques are NOT accepted but Visa card can be used as an alternative. Toll charges vary according to route.

To escape the motorway tolls and the most congested roads follow the 'Green Arrow' routes (Itinéraires Bis). There should be less traffic and the routes are designed to provide the holiday-maker with a more attractive journey.

Free emergency telephones are available every 2 km on motorways; parking and resting areas every 10 km; 24-hour services can be found at regular intervals of about 40 km.

3. Insurance

Fully comprehensive cover is advisable. A green card will give you a better coverage than the minimum otherwise applicable in France. Europ Assistance do special schemes for motorists and passengers and discounts can be obtained through membership of Les Routiers' Club Bon Viveur (see page 70 for details of how to join).

4. Petrol – **L'ESSENCE**

NB **Pétrole** translates as crude oil or paraffin.

Super	– **de super**	ordinary	– **d'ordinaire**
lead-free	– **sans plomb**	diesel	– **gazole**

Diesel is considerably cheaper in France and unleaded petrol is widely available.

5. Speeding and drink-driving

Breath test limits are as for the UK (80 mg), but LOWER than the Republic of Ireland (100 mg). Tests are random. On-the-spot fines may be 2,000 to 3,000 Frs.

For speeding the minimum fine is 1,300 Frs. For not wearing a seat-belt a fine of between 450 and 1,100 Frs can be imposed.

The use of car telephones is prohibited, and you should affix a note to the unit indicating the prohibition.

You must carry the original vehicle registration document, a full valid national driving licence and current insurance certificate (plus a letter of authority from the owner if the vehicle is not registered in your name).

During August the southbound motorways are very busy with French families heading to the coast for their summer holiday but most of the time French roads are relatively empty. Equip yourself with a good map and driving in France can be an enjoyable part of your holiday.

6. Points to remember (to avoid hefty on-the-spot fines or worse)

1) Minimum driving age in France is 18 not 17.

2) No driving on a provisional licence.

3) Driver and front passenger must wear seat-belts (rear passengers also if belts are fitted).

4) Under 10s must travel in back.

5) Stop signs mean STOP. Come to a complete halt.

6) Don't stop on open roads unless the car is driven OFF the road.

7) Beware – heavy penalties can be imposed for overtaking on a solid single white line.

8) Red warning triangle must be carried, unless car has hazard flashers. Warning triangles are COMPULSORY when towing a caravan or trailer.

9) Beams must be altered for right-hand drive using beam deflectors. Yellow tinted headlights are no longer compulsory. Sidelights are only permitted when stationary. Take a full kit of spare bulbs – you may be fined if driving with faulty lights.

Useful Information for Travellers

BRITISH EMBASSY
Ambassade de Grande-Bretagne
16 rue d'Anjou, 75008 Paris, France
Tel: 42.66.38.10 (prefix 010-331 if dialling from the UK)

IRISH EMBASSY
12 avenue Foch, 75116 Paris, France
Tel: 45.00.20.87 (prefix 0033 if dialling from the Republic of Ireland)

OFFICE DE TOURISME DE PARIS
127 Champs–Elysées, 75008 Paris, France
Tel: 47.23.61.72

INFORMATION OF ALL KEY EVENTS 1993
Maison de la France
8 avenue de l'Opéra, 75001 Paris, France
Tel: 42.96.10.23

FRENCH GOVERNMENT TOURIST OFFICE
178 Piccadilly, London W1V 0AL
Tel: 071–493 3480

35 Lower Abbey Street, Dublin 1
Tel: 01–7034046

FRENCH NATIONAL PARKS
Parc National des Cévennes
BP 4, 48400 Florac
Tel: 66.44.01.75

Parc National des Ecrins
7 rue du Colonel-Roux, 05000 Gap
Tel: 92.51.40.71

Parc National Mercantour
23 rue d'Italie, 06000 Nice
Tel: 93.87.86.10

Parc National de Port-Cross
50 avenue Gambetta, 83400 Hyères
Tel: 94.65.32.98

Parc National des Pyrénées Occidentales
BP 300, 65000 Tarbes
Tel: 62.93.30.60

Parc National de la Vanoise
135 rue du Docteur Julliand,
BP 705, 73007 Chambéry, Cedex
Tel: 79.62.30.54

Club Bon Viveur

Have you heard of Club Bon Viveur, the club which offers superb benefits for *Les Routiers Guide* users who enjoy good food, wine and travel?

Just look at the full benefit package to which you are entitled!

* Special concessions at up to 1,000 Les Routiers restaurants and hotels throughout Britain on production of your Club Bon Viveur membership card.
* £2 off additional copies of either the *Les Routiers Guide* to Britain or France (no charge for p&p).
* Discounts off motoring services and insurance with Britannia Continental.
* 10 per cent discount off all holidays in the Paris and France brochures booked through Jet Tours and the French Travel Service.
* Newsletters including promotional offers, e.g. special motoring kits for travellers.

New ideas to improve club benefits and to make the club more useful are always welcome, so if you have any thoughts of your own, please let us know.

To join Club Bon Viveur, simply complete the application form on the following page and return it to us with the annual subscription fee of £60.

Application Form

If you use the guide regularly then it would certainly be in your interest to join Club Bon Viveur and receive the exciting benefits on offer.

Remember what they are:

* Discounts at up to 1,000 Les Routiers restaurants and hotels in Britain.
* £2 off additional copies of both Les Routiers Guides.
* Discounts off motoring services and insurance with Britannia Continental.
* Discounts off holidays in the Paris and France brochures booked through Jet Tours and the French Travel Service.
* Newsletters including promotional offers.

We are always pleased to hear your comments on any restaurants and hotels you have visited. On the reverse of this page there is opportunity to give your opinion.

To join Club Bon Viveur simply complete the form below and return it to us with the annual subscription fee of £60.

Name ....

Address ....

....

I enclose a cheque for £—— (payable to Les Routiers Ltd)
OR
Please debit my Access/Visa card for the amount of £——

Card Number .... Expiry Date ....

Return to: Club Bon Viveur, 25 Vanston Place, London SW6 1AZ.
Please allow 28 days for delivery.

Your Opinion

Do you have a favourite pub, restaurant or hotel which you would like to recommend to us, which is not already Les Routiers recommended? If you feel it is worthy of nomination, please let us know on the form below so that, with the establishment's consent, we may arrange for an inspector to call.

Alternatively, if you are dissatisfied with an establishment, we would like to hear your comments.

With your help we can maintain Les Routiers standards, and all correspondence will be treated in the strictest of confidence.

Name of establishment:

Address/Location:

Type of establishment (please circle):

   Restaurant/Public House   Wine Bar/Bistro   Hotel   B&B

Nomination OR Complaint (please circle)

Comments:

Glossary

The following list is not intended as a substitute for a phrase book or French dictionary, but as a quick and easy reference guide in a restaurant or hotel, or while travelling.

GREETINGS/GENERAL CONVERSATION

Good Morning	Bonjour
Goodbye	Au Revoir
Please	S'il vous plaît
Thank you	Merci
Do you speak English?	Parlez-vous anglais?
I don't understand.	Je ne comprends pas.
Sorry/Excuse me.	Je vous prie de m'excuser.
Yes, No	Oui, Non
I come from England	Je viens d'Angleterre
Scotland	d'Ecosse
Wales	du Pays de Galles
Ireland	d'Irelande
United States	des Etats-Unis

A L'HOTEL

Can you recommend a good hotel?	Pouvez-vous m'indiquer un bon hôtel?
Do you have a room available?	Avez-vous une chambre libre?
I would like to reserve a twin room with bathroom.	Je voudrais réserver une chambre à deux lits avec salle de bains.
At what time is dinner?	A quelle heure servez-vous le dîner?
A table for four please?	Je voudrais une table pour quatre personnes?
Can I have the menu please?	Voulez-vous me donner le menu?
Where are the toilets?	Où sont les toilettes?
Could you prepare my bill please?	Pouvez-vous me préparer la note?
How much do I owe you?	Combien vous dois-je?

WHERE IS . . . . . ?

Where is the police station?	Où se trouve la gendarmerie?
Where is . . . Road/Street?	Où se trouve la rue . . . . . ?
Where is the British Embassy?	L'ambassade de Grande Bretagne?
How do I get to the bank?	Comment aller à la banque?
How do I get to the Post Office?	Comment aller à la poste?
Where can I find a post-box?	Comment puis-je trouver une boîte aux lettres?

ACCIDENT/ILLNESS

I have had an accident.	J'ai en un accident.
There are people injured.	Il y a des blessés.
Call an ambulance.	Appelez une ambulance.
Where can I find a doctor?	Où puis-je trouver un docteur?
Where is the nearest chemist?	Où est la pharmacie la plus proche?
I am ill. I have a temperature.	Je suis malade. J'ai de la fièvre.
Do you have any asprin?	Avez-vous des aspirines?

GETTING TO A GARAGE

How far is the nearest garage?	A quelle distance se trouve le garage le plus proche?
Is it far?	Est-ce loin?
Do I go straight on?	Faut-il aller tout droit?
Turn around/Do a U-turn?	Faire demi-tour?
Do I have to turn left/right?	Dois-je tourner à gauche/à droite?
At which crossroads must I turn?	A quel croisement dois-je tourner?
At which traffic lights do I turn?	Je tourne à quel feu?
Fill her up, please.	Le plein, s'il vous plaît.

IN CASE OF BREAKDOWN

I have broken down.	Je suis en panne.
I have a flat tyre.	J'ai un pneu crevé.
It's overheating.	Cela surchauffe.
The battery needs recharging.	Les batteries ont besoin d'être rechargées.
The . . . does not work.	Le/la . . . ne marche pas.
The . . . is broken.	Le/la . . . est cassé(e).
Will it take long?	Ce sera vite fait?
axle	essieu
battery	batterie
brake	frein
carburettor	carburateur
choke	starter
clutch	embrayage
distributor	allumeur
engine	moteur
exhaust-pipe	tuyau d'échappement
fan belt	courroie
fuel tank	réservoir de carburant
gear box	boîte de vitesses
headlight	phare
horn	avertisseur
ignition	allumage
indicator	(feu) clignotant
oil	huile

radiator	radiateur
silencer	silencieux
spark-plug	bougie
steering	direction
steering wheel	volant
suspension	suspension
tyre	pneu
wheel	roue
windscreen	pare-brise
windscreen-wiper	essuie-glace

UNDERSTANDING THE MENU

Les Viandes	**Meat**
boeuf	beef
charolais	best cut
chateaubriand	double fillet steak
contrefilet	siloin
entrecôte	rib steak
faux filet	sirloin steak
filet	fillet
agneau	lamb
porc	pork
jambon	ham
jambon cru	raw smoked ham
veau	veal
foie	liver
foie gras	goose liver
ris	sweetbreads
rognons	kidneys
tripes	tripe

Volaille/Gibier	**Poultry/Game**
caille	quail
canard	duck
dindon	turkey
faisan	pheasant
lièvre	hare
oie	goose
perdreau	partridge
pintade	guineafowl
poulet	chicken

Les Poisons/Coquillages	**Fish/Shellfish**
calmar	squid
coquille St Jacques	scallop

crabe	crab
crevette	prawn
daurade	sea bream
ecrevisse	crayfish
flétan	halibut
fruits de mer	seafood
homard	lobster
huître	oyster
limande	lemon sole
lotte de mer	monkfish
maquereau	mackerel
morue	salt cod
moule	mussel
plie	plaice
raie	skate
saumon	salmon
seiche	cuttlefish
sole	sole
St Pierre	John Dory
thon	tuna
truite	trout

Les Fruits/Les Legumes
Les Herbes/Epices

Fruit/Vegetables
Herbs/Spices

ail	garlic
ananas	pineapple
aneth	dill
abricot	apricot
artichaut	artichoke
asperge	asparagus
avocat	avocado
banane	banana
basilic	basil
cassis	blackcurrant
cérise	cherry
champignon	mushroom
chou	cabbage
choufleur	cauliflower
ciboulette	chive
citron	lemon
citron vert	lime
concombre	cucumber
coriandre	coriander
cornichon	gherkin
courgette	courgette

cresson	watercress
echalotte	shallot
endive	chicory
epinards	spinach
estragon	tarragon
fenouil	fennel
fève	broad bean
fraise	strawberry
framboise	raspberry
gingembre	ginger
groseille	gooseberry
haricot vert	french bean
laitue	lettuce
menthe	mint
mûre	blackberry
muscade	nutmeg
myrtille	blueberry
oignon	onion
oseille	sorrel
pamplemousse	grapefruit
pêche	peach
persil	parsley
petit pois	pea
poire	pear
poireau	leek
poivre	pepper
poivron	green, red, yellow pepper
pomme	apple
pomme de terre	potato
prune	plum
pruneau	prune
radis	radish
raisin	grape
romarin	rosemary
safran	saffron
thym	thyme
tomate	tomato
truffe	truffle

PLACES OF INTEREST

abeille	bee
barrage	dam
beffroi	belfry
blindé	tank
bord	bank (of a river)

77

carrière	quarry
cascade	waterfall
cave	cellar
corderie	rope-making factory
corniche	coast/cliff road
cristallerie	glass works
croisière	cruise
dégustation	tasting
dentelle	lace
dolmen	megalithic tomb
église	church
environs	surroundings
étang	pond
fabrique	factory
faïencerie	earthenware factory
falaise	cliff
fouilles	excavations
fourrure	fur
gouffre	abyss, gulf
grotte	cave
guerre	war
haras	stud farm
hôtel de ville	town hall
marais	marsh
métier	trade, craft
mine d'argent	silver mine
moulin à vent	windmill
pêche	fishing
pierre sculptée	sculpted stone
plage du débarquement	landing beach
plage	beach
pont	bridge
poupée	doll
rapace	bird of prey
sabotier	clog maker
singe	monkey
souffleur de verre	glass blower
tapisserie	tapestry
usine	factory
vieille ville	old town

Paris and Nearby

AUBERGENVILLE, Yvelines 78410, Map 19

⊗ 🍷 🏠 🍽

L'AMI RENE, RN 13 and 190

Languages: Spanish, Portuguese
Menu: 55 to 80 Frs
Accommodation: 145 to 190 Frs
Restaurant.

Hotel: 7 rooms, showers.
Other points: bar, car parking.
Address: 21 rue Gaston Jouillerat.
M. BAYER, tel 30.95.70.07.

AUFFERVILLE, Seine-et-Marne 77570, Map 19

⊗ 🍷

AUBERGE DE LA DILIGENCE, RD 403 between Orléans and Beaumont

Places of interest: Fontainebleau (23km),
Château-Landon (11km), Nemours (9km):
musée de la préhistoire, forêt de Poligny.
Menu: 55 to 75 Frs
Accommodation: 120 Frs
Restaurant: lunch 11–3pm, dinner 6–9pm.
Specialities: couscous, paëlla.

Hotel: 2 rooms: single 1, double 1. Showers,
baths.
Other points: bar, credit cards accepted,
children welcome, garden terrace, pets allowed,
car parking, traditional decor.
Address: 9 Route Nationale.
M. BERNARD VINCENT, tel 64.28.75.91.

BANNOST, Seine-et-Marne 77970, Map 19

⊗ 🍷

LE RELAIS DE LA GARE, RN 4

Restaurant: closed Saturdays, Sundays and in
August.
Other points: bar.

Address: La Gare RN 4.
M. GEORGES FONTAIN, tel 64.01.02.07.

BERNES SUR OISE, Val-d'Oise 95340, Map 19

⊗ 🍷

LE BEL AIR

Menu: 54 Frs including wine
Restaurant: lunch 12–2pm, dinner 8–9pm.
Closed Sundays.
Other points: bar, credit cards accepted,

children welcome, car parking.
Address: 1 rue de Creil.
M. HUBERT ANSEVIN, tel 34.70.04.00.

BOISSY SOUS ST YON, Essonne 91790, Map 19

⊗ 🍷 🏠

LE RELAIS DE TORFOU, RN 20

Places of interest: Arpajon (3km): Saint
Sulpice (église du XIe siècle).
Languages: English, German, Spanish
Menu: 51 Frs
Accommodation: 70 to 80 Frs
Restaurant: lunch 12–3pm, dinner 7–10.30pm.
Closed Saturday afternoons and Sundays.

Hotel: 4 rooms.
Other points: bar, credit cards accepted,
children welcome, à la carte menu, pets
allowed, car parking.
Address: 52 avenue de Paris.
M. MOHAMED TOUFAHI, tel 64.91.30.50.

BRIIS SOUS FORGES, Essonne 91640, Map 19

⊗ 🍷

CAFETERIA DE LIMOURS, A 10

Menu: 55 to 80 Frs
Restaurant: open 24 hours.
Speciality: grillades.
Other points: credit cards accepted, children welcome, self-service, garden terrace, pets allowed, car parking.
Address: Near Limours Janvry.
Tel 64.90.77.18.

BROSSE MONTCEAUX (LA), Seine-et-Marne 77940, Map 19 ⊗♈

LE PETIT PERICHOIS, RN 6 between Fontainebleau and Sens

Places of interest: Vallée de l'Orvanne: château de la Brie, musée de la faïencerie, Montereau.
Language: English
Menu: 56 to 140 Frs
Restaurant: lunch 11–3pm, dinner 7–11pm.
Other points: bar, credit cards accepted, children welcome, à la carte menu, garden terrace, pets allowed, car parking.
Address: Route Nationale 6.
M. AIME VOLLEREAU, tel 60.96.25.75.

CHAMARANDE, Essonne 91730, Map 19 ⊗♈🏠☆

RELAIS DE MONTFORT, RN 20 between Arpajon and Etampes

Language: English
Menu: 46 Frs including wine
Accommodation: 70 to 180 Frs
Restaurant: lunch 12–3pm, dinner 7.30–11pm. Closed Saturday afternoons, Sundays, August and 1 week at Christmas.
Hotel: 32 rooms: single 12, double 20. Showers, private WCs.
Other points: bar, credit cards accepted, car parking.
Address: Route Nationale 20.
M. DANIEL COTTIN, tel 60.82.20.80.

CHAPELLE LA REINE (LA), Seine-et-Marne 77760, Map 19 ⊗♈🏠

LA SALAMANDRE, RN 152 between Fontainebleau and Orléans

Menu: 56 Frs
Accommodation: 150 to 180 Frs
Restaurant: lunch 11.30–2.30pm, dinner 7–9pm. Closed Sundays and 15 days in August.
Hotel: 6 rooms.
Other points: bar, car parking.
Address: 5 rue du Docteur Battesti.
MME MICHELINE BOURLIER, tel 64.24.30.03.

CHAUFOUR LES BONNIERES, Yvelines 78270, Map 19 ⊗♈🏠

AU BON ACCUEIL, RN 13 between Paris and Deauville

Place of interest: Giverny.
Menu: 60 to 165 Frs
Accommodation: 110 to 200 Frs
Restaurant: lunch 11.30–2.30pm, dinner 7.55–10pm. Closed Saturdays and 15 July to 15 August.
Hotel: 15 rooms: single 10, double 5. Showers, private WCs.
Other points: bar, credit cards accepted, children welcome, à la carte menu, pets allowed, car parking, traditional decor.
Address: Route Nationale 13.
M. GERARD MAGNE, tel 34.76.11.29.

CHELLES, Seine-et-Marne 77500, Map 19 ⊗♈🏠

RELAIS DE LA PETITE VITESSE, RN 34

Restaurant: closed Sundays.
Hotel: 7 rooms.
Other points: bar.
Address: 32 avenue du Marais.
M. MICHEL CHEA, tel 64.21.09.47.

CLAYE SOUILLY, Seine-et-Marne 77410, Map 19 ⊗�️

LE RELAIS DE LA ROSEE, CD 212

Places of interest: Euro Disney, la mer de sable.
Menu: 57 Frs including wine
Restaurant: closed Saturdays and Sundays.
Other points: bar, credit cards accepted, garden terrace, pets allowed, car parking, traditional decor.
Address: Chemin Départemental 212.
M. CLAUDE BLOM, tel 60.26.17.74.

CLERY EN VEXIN, Val-d'Oise 95420, Map 19 ⊗�️

AUBERGE DE CLERY EN VEXIN

Restaurant: closed Saturdays and Sundays.
Other points: bar, car parking.
Address: 4 Route Nationale 14.
M. JEAN-GUY DEGOUL, tel 34.67.44.15.

CORMEILLES EN PARISIS, Val-d'Oise 95240, Map 19 ⊗�️

LE BON ACCUEIL, RN 192

Menu: 49,50 Frs
Restaurant: lunch 11.30–4pm, dinner 7.30–9pm. Closed Saturdays and Sundays.
Other points: bar, à la carte menu, traditional decor.
Address: 76 boulevard du Maréchal Joffre.
M. GRANDAY and MME RICHARD, tel 39.78.83.24.

CRESPIERES, Yvelines 78121, Map 19 ⊗�️

AUBERGE DES ROUTIERS, RN 307

Menu: 60 to 80 Frs
Restaurant: lunch 11.30–2.30pm, dinner 7–9pm. Closed Saturdays.
Speciality: gibiers.
Other points: bar, children welcome, à la carte menu, garden terrace, pets allowed, car parking.
Address: Route Nationale 307.
MME MAGDELEINE GLATIGNY, tel 30.54.44.28.

DEUIL LA BARRE, Val-d'Oise 95170, Map 19 ⊗�️

AU COQ HARDI, RN 328 near Saint-Denis Taverny

Menu: 50 to 60 Frs including wine and coffee
Restaurant: lunch 11.30-3pm. Closed Saturdays, Sundays and in August.
Other points: bar.
Address: 62 bis avenue de la Division Leclerc.
M. GERARD LANTINIER, tel 39.64.16.81.

DOMONT, Val-d'Oise 95330, Map 19 ⊗�️🏠

LA VIEILLE AUBERGE, RN 1 between Paris and Beauvais

Language: Spanish
Menu: 52 Frs
Accommodation: 115 to 160 Frs
Restaurant: lunch 11–3pm. Closed Saturdays, Sundays and in August.
Specialities: couscous, paëlla.
Hotel: 6 rooms, showers.
Other points: bar, pets allowed, car parking, traditional decor.
Address: 7 Route Nationale 1.
M. ROGER BADAIRE, tel 39.91.01.66.

DROCOURT, Yvelines 78440, Map 19 ⊗�️

AU RELAIS DU NORD, RN 183 between Mantes la Jolie and Magny en Vexin

Places of interest: Château de la Roche Guyon (8km), jardin de Claude Monet à Giverny (20km), collège de Mantes la Jolie (9km).
Menu: 55 Frs
Restaurant: lunch 12–2pm. Closed Saturdays and Sundays out of season.

Other points: bar, credit cards accepted, children welcome, à la carte menu, pets allowed, car parking, traditional decor.
Address: 15 rue Nationale
M. DANIEL TIROUARD, tel 34.76.71.23.

EPONE, Yvelines 78680, Map 19

REST'AU VERT, RN 13 between Mantes la Jolie and Versailles

Places of interest: Versailles, Paris.
Language: Italian
Menu: 57 Frs
Accommodation: 120 Frs
Restaurant: lunch 11.30–3.30pm, dinner 7.30–10pm. Closed Saturdays and Sundays.
Hotel: 14 rooms: single 5, double 9. Showers,

private WC, TV, phone.
Other points: bar, credit cards accepted, garden terrace, pets allowed, car parking, traditional decor.
Address: Route de Gargenville.
M. ASSUNTA ARTIER, tel 30.95.60.20.

ESSARTS LE ROI (LES), Yvelines 78690, Map 19

A LA GRACE DE DIEU, RN 10 between Paris and Chartres

Places of interest: Château de Rambouillet, château de Versailles, la vallée de Chevreuses.
Menu: 50 to 55 Frs
Restaurant: lunch 11.30–3pm, dinner 6.30–10.30 pm. Closed Saturdays, Sundays and

in August.
Other points: bar, credit cards accepted, children welcome, pets allowed, car parking.
Address: Route Nationale 10.
M. DANIEL BIGOT, tel 30.41.60.04.

ESSARTS LE ROI (LES), Yvelines 78690, Map 19

LE RELAIS DE L'ARCOAT, RN 10 between Rambouillet and Paris

Language: English
Menu: 52 Frs
Restaurant: lunch 12–3pm, dinner 7–10pm. Closed Saturday nights, Sundays, public

holidays and 3 weeks in July.
Other points: bar.
Address: 39 Route Nationale 10.
HOTELS ARCOAT, tel 30.41.60.53.

FERTE GAUCHER (LA), Seine-et-Marne 77320, Map 19

LE CONTRE-TEMPS, RN 34 near Sézanne

Language: English
Menu: 60 to 120 Frs
Restaurant: lunch 12–2.30pm, dinner 7.30–10pm. Closed Sundays.
Other points: bar, credit cards accepted, à la

carte menu, garden terrace, pets allowed, car parking, traditional decor.
Address: 4 avenue de la Gare.
M. HERVE LANGLE, tel 64.04.01.90.

GOUSSAINVILLE, Val-d'Oise 95190, Map 19

AUX SPORTS
Restaurant: closed Saturdays.
Other points: bar.

Address: 22 avenue Albert Sarrault.
M. MARCEL DUFROS, tel 39.88.10.84.

GUILLERVAL, Essonne 91690, Map 19 ⊗ ♉

RELAIS DE MONDESIR, RN 20

Places of interest: Tous planchet, château de Chaloux sur Mars.
Languages: Spanish, Portuguese
Menu: 50 to 60 Frs
Restaurant: closed Sundays.
Speciality: chilli con carne.

Other points: bar, credit cards accepted, children welcome, à la carte menu, pets allowed, car parking, traditional decor.
Address: Hameau de Mondésir.
M. JEAN PICQ, tel 64.95.60.76.

HARDRICOURT, Yvelines 78250, Map 19 ⊗ ♉

A LA DEVINETTE, RN 190

Places of interest: Meulan-Mantes, forêt et château de Saint Germain en Laye.
Menu: 56 Frs
Restaurant: closed Saturdays, Sundays and in August.

Specialities: couscous, paëlla.
Other points: bar, credit cards accepted, pets allowed, car parking, traditional decor.
Address: 30 boulevard Michelet.
MME JEANINE AOUES, tel 34.74.06.32

HOUSSAYE EN BRIE (LA), Seine-et-Marne 77610, Map 19 ⊗ ♉

AUBERGE DU COUCOU, RN 36

Language: English
Restaurant.
Other points: bar.

Address: La Haute-Gonière.
M. CHRISTIAN BROUST, tel 64.07.40.75

ISLE ADAM (L'), Val-d'Oise 95290, Map 19 ⊗ ♉

AU RALLYE, RN 322

Restaurant: closed Saturday nights, Sunday nights and in August.
Other points: bar.

Address: 71 rue de Pontoise.
MME PAULETTE COMBES, tel 34.69.08.24.

MAGNY EN VEXIN, Val-d'Oise 95420, Map 19 ⊗ ♉ 🏠

HOTEL DE LA GARE

Accommodation: 150 to 160 Frs
Restaurant: closed Sundays, 23 December to 1 January.
Speciality: couscous.
Hotel: 10 rooms: single 5, double 5. Showers.

Other points: bar, credit cards accepted, à la carte menu, pets allowed, car parking.
Address: 65 rue de Beauvais.
MME FABIENNE DEGOUL ALVES, tel 34.67.20.70.

MANTES LA VILLE, Yvelines 78200, Map 19 ⊗ ♉

LA DEMIE LUNE

Places of interest: Collège de Mantes la Jolie, château d'Anet (20km), zoo de Thoiry (30km).
Menu: 49 Frs
Restaurant: lunch 11.30–3pm, dinner 7.30–9pm. Closed Sundays.

Other points: bar, children welcome, pets allowed, car parking
Address: 51 boulevard Roger Salengro.
MME NICOLE PETITPAS, tel 34.77.03.66.

MANTES LA VILLE, Yvelines 78200, Map 19 ⊗ ♈

LE HOUDAN BAR, RN 13, 150m from railway station

Places of interest: Collège de Mantes la Jolie (2km), château d'Anet (20km), zoo de Thoiry (30km).
Language: English.
Restaurant.

Speciality: couscous.
Other points: bar, children welcome, pets allowed, car parking, traditional decor.
Address: 43 route de Houdan.
M. HOCINE OUHAB, tel 34.77.06.11.

MAROLLES SUR SEINE, Seine-et-Marne 77130, Map 19 ⊗ ♈

AU RENDEZ-VOUS DES PECHEURS ET DES CHASSEURS

Restaurant: closed Sundays.
Other points: bar.

Address: 70 Grande Rue.
MME BODIC, tel 64.31.32.20.

MITRY MORY, Seine-et-Marne 77290, Map 19 ⊗ ♈

RELAIS DE MITRY

Menu: 49 Frs
Restaurant: lunch 11.30–3pm, closed 15 July to 15 August.
Other points: bar, pets allowed, car parking.

Address: 3 rue Paul Vaillant Couturier.
MME JOSIANE THYPONNET, tel 64.27.11.61.

MONTEREAU, Seine-et-Marne 77130, Map 19 ⊗ ♈

LES ROUTIERS, RN 105

Restaurant: closed Sundays and in July.
Other points: bar.

Address: Route Nationale 105.
MME PICARD, tel 64.32.44.93.

MONTLHERY, Essonne 91310, Map 19 ⊗ ♈ 🏠 ☆

LE SOLOGNE, RN 20, Orléans

Places of interest: tour de Montlhéry, parc animalier de Saint Vrain, vallée de Chevreuses, circuit de compétitions automobiles.
Menu: 48 Frs
Accommodation: 120 to 180 Frs
Restaurant: lunch 11.30–2pm, dinner 7–9pm. Closed Sundays and early August.

Hotel: 7 rooms: single 5, double 2. Showers.
Other points: bar, credit cards accepted, phone, pets allowed, car parking, traditional decor.
Address: 65 route d'Orléans.
M. JACQUES CHERON, tel 69.01.00.98.

MUREAUX (LES), Yvelines 78130, Map 19 ⊗ ♈ 🏠

LE RELAIS ICI ON COUPE SOIF, RD 14

Restaurant: closed Sundays and in August.
Hotel: 7 rooms.
Other points: bar.

Address: 102 avenue du Maréchal Foch.
MME SUZANNE COMPAGNON, tel 34.74.05.04.

NEMOURS, Seine-et-Marne 77140, Map 19 ⊗

RELAIS DE NEMOURS, A 6, over the autoroute, in both directions

Restaurant.
Other points: credit cards accepted, children welcome, à la carte menu, self-service, garden terrace, pets allowed, car parking.

Address: Aire de Service de Darvault.
Tel 64.28.11.97.

OZOIR LA FERRIERE, Seine-et-Marne 77330, Map 19 ⊗ �ं

LA TERRASSE

Restaurant: closed Sundays and in August.
Other points: bar.
Address: 17 avenue du Général de Gaulle.

M. JEAN-FRANCOIS AUDEBERT,
tel 60.28.20.36.

PETIT FOSSARD (LE), Seine-et-Marne 77130, Map 19 ⊗ � ⌂

LE RELAIS DU PETIT FOSSARD, RN 6

Restaurant: lunch 11.30–3pm, dinner 5–11pm.
Closed Saturday afternoons and Sundays.
Hotel: 8 rooms, showers.

Other points: bar, credit cards accepted, à la carte menu, car parking.
M. JEAN GUILLARD, tel 64.32.03.28.

PONTAULT COMBAULT, Seine-et-Marne 77340, Map 19 ⊗ �

LE RELAIS DU PAVE, RN 4 between Paris and Nancy

Restaurant: lunch 12–2pm, dinner 7–10pm.
Closed Sundays and in August.
Other points: bar, à la carte menu.

Address: 9 Route de Paris.
M. JOS DA SILVA, tel 60.28.00.21.

PONTHIERRY, Seine-et-Marne 77310, Map 19 ⊗ �

AUX TROIS MARCHES, RN 7

Menu: 52 Frs including wine
Restaurant: lunch 12–2pm, dinner 8–9pm.
Closed Sundays and in August.

Other points: bar, car parking, traditional decor.
Address: 7 rue de la Saussaie.
MME ODETTE POTHIER, tel 60.65.77.67.

PROVINS, Seine-et-Marne 77160, Map 19 ⊗ � ⌂ ⌷

LE RELAIS DE LA CURE D'AIR, RN 19

Restaurant: closed Fridays and second 2 weeks of July.
Hotel: 8 rooms.

Other points: bar.
Address: 54 avenue du Général de Gaulle.
M. AMROUN, tel 64.00.03.21.

QUINCY SOUS SENART, Essonne 91480, Map 19 ⊗ � ⌂

A LA BONNE TABLE, RN 6

Places of interest: Forêt de Sénart, Fontainebleau, vallée de Seine.
Menu: 48 to 75 Frs
Accommodation: 90 to 120 Frs
Restaurant: lunch 11.30–2.30pm, dinner 7.45–9.30pm. Closed Sundays and in February.
Specialities: alsacienne and normande.

Hotel: 5 rooms, showers, baths.
Other points: bar, credit cards accepted, children welcome, à la carte menu, garden terrace, pets allowed, car parking.
Address: 3 bis avenue Henri Chasles.
M. PIERRE WALTER, tel 69.00.93.81.

SAINT GERMAIN LES ARPAJON, Essonne 91180, Map 19 ⊗�

A L'AS DE TREFLE, RN 20, Orléans

Places of interest: Halles du XIIIe siècle Arpajon, Saint Sulpice de Favire (église).
Language: English
Menu: 58 Frs
Restaurant: lunch 11.45–2.15pm, dinner 7–8.45pm. Closed Sunday afternoons.

Other points: bar, credit cards accepted, self-service, pets allowed, car parking, traditional decor.
Address: 7–11 RN 20, La Petite Folie.
M. GUY BERGOUGNOUX, tel 64.90.02.24.

SAMMERON, Seine-et-Marne 77260, Map 19 ⊗♟

LES CIGOGNES, RN 3

Language: Portuguese
Menu: 60 to 70 Frs
Accommodation: 95 to 130 Frs
Restaurant: lunch 12–3pm, dinner 7–9pm. Closed Sundays and in August.

Hotel: 5 rooms: single 2, double 3. Showers.
Other points: bar, credit cards accepted, children welcome, à la carte menu, car parking.
Address: 2 rue de Metz.
MME GLORIA BENTO, tel 60.22.79.40.

SANCY LES PROVINS, Seine-et-Marne 77320, Map 19 ⊗♟

LE RELAIS DE SANCY, RN 4

Menu: 55 Frs
Restaurant: closed Saturday afternoons and Sundays.
Other points: bar, credit cards accepted, car parking.

Address: Route Nationale 4.
M. PHILIPPE SAVAGE, tel 64.01.92.07.

SURVILLIERS, Val-d'Oise 95470, Map 19 ⊗

RELAIS ILE DE FRANCE, A 1, access via footbridge in both directions

Languages: German, English
Restaurant.
Other points: credit cards accepted, children welcome, self-service, garden terrace, pets

allowed, car parking.
Address: Aire de Service de Vemars.
Tel 34.68.39.20.

SURVILLIERS, Val-d'Oise 95470, Map 19 ⊗♟

LE COQ CHANTANT, RN 17

Places of interest: Château de Chantilly, parc Astérix, Ermenonville, Marne la Vallée.
Menu: 49,50 and 80 Frs
Restaurant: lunch 12–2.45pm, dinner 7.15–10.15pm. Closed Friday nights, Saturday nights, Sundays and mid-July to mid-August.

Other points: bar, credit cards accepted, pets allowed, car parking, traditional decor.
Address: Route Nationale 17.
MME EDITH RESSLEN, tel 34.68.24.65.

VIRY CHATILLON, Essonne 91170, Map 19 ⊗♟

LES ROUTIERS, RN 7 and RD 91 exit Viry Chatillon or Grigny

Restaurant: lunch 11.30–2pm, dinner 7–9pm. Closed Saturdays, Sundays, public holidays and August.

Other points: bar.
Address: 100 route de Fleury.
M. FERNAND GADREAU, tel 69.05.28.46.

VOINSLES ROZAY EN BRIE, Seine-et-Marne 77540, Map 19 ⊗♀

RELAIS DE VOINSLES, RN 4

Restaurant: closed Saturdays and Sundays
Other points: bar.

MARTINE AND PATRICE KLEIN-RENAUDIN, tel 64.07.75.20.

VOISINS MOUROUX, Seine-et-Marne 77120, Map 19 ⊗♀⌂

LE RELAIS DU SOMMET

Restaurant: closed Saturdays, Sundays and in August.
Hotel: 7 rooms.

Other points: bar, garden terrace, pets allowed.
Address: 968 rue du Général de Gaulle.
M. JACQUES SANTERRE, tel 64.03.05.47.

VOULX, Seine-et-Marne 77940, Map 19 ⊗♀🍽

LA BRUYERE, RD 219 between Montereau and Montargis

Menu: 90 to 125 Frs
Restaurant: closed Sunday nights, 16 to 28 February and 16 to 31 August.
Specialities: huîtres, escargots, tête de veau, grillades.

Other points: bar, children welcome, à la carte menu.
Address: 72 Grande Rue.
M. ALBAN BALDRAN, tel 64.31.92.41.

Northern France

ABBEVILLE, Somme 80100, Map 2   ⊗♀

AU CHEVAL NOIR, RN 25

Restaurant: closed Friday afternoons to
Saturday afternoons, and last week of August.
Other points: bar.

Address: Route Nationale 25, Petit Miannay.
M. BERNARD LAFARGUE-FORTIER,
tel 22.24.20.17.

ABBEVILLE, Somme 80100, Map 2   ⊗♀

AUBERGE FLEURIE, RN 1 between Abbeville and Dunkerque

Places of interest: Musées et églises
d'Abbeville (15km).
Menu: 54 Frs
Restaurant: lunch 11.30–3pm, dinner 7–11pm.
Closed Saturdays and Sundays.

Other points: bar, credit cards accepted,
children welcome, pets allowed, car parking,
traditional decor.
Address: 294 Côte de la Justice.
M. MICHEL RUBIN, tel 22.24.88.80.

ABBEVILLE, Somme 80132, Map 2   ⊗♀

CHEZ GILBERT, RN 1 between Boulogne and Calais

Place of interest: Abbeville.
Menu: 50 to 80 Frs
Restaurant: lunch 12–2pm, dinner 7.30–9.30
pm. Closed Saturdays.
Other points: bar, credit cards accepted, pets

allowed, car parking.
Address: 5 Route Nationale, Buigny Saint
Maclou.
M. MARC CARON, tel 22.24.20.47.

ABSCON, Nord 59215, Map 1   ⊗♀⌂

LE MOULIN D'OR, RN 45 between Douai and Denain

Place of interest: Musée de la mine (10km).
Menu: 60 to 90 Frs
Restaurant: closed August.
Hotel: 16 rooms: single 10, double 6.

Other points: bar, car parking, traditional
decor.
Address: 17 place de Gaulle.
MME MONIQUE BAUDUIN, tel 27.36.30.33.

AMBLAINVILLE, Oise 60110, Map 2   ⊗♀

CHEZ MARIE-ODILE, RN 327

Restaurant: closed Sundays.
Other points: bar.
Address: 40 Rue Nationale.

MME MARIE-ODILE PRUNIER,
tel 44.52.03.10.

ARBRET (L'), Pas-de-Calais 62158, Map 1   ⊗♀

LE RELAIS DE LA GARE, RN 25

Place of interest: Château de Grand
Rullecourt.
Restaurant: closed Saturdays and Sundays.

Other points: bar.
Address: 44 Route Nationale.
M. MAURICE VICART, tel 21.48.24.33.

ARGENLIEU, Oise 60130, Map 2   ⊗♀

LE RELAIS D'ARGENLIEU, RN 16

Place of interest: Amiens.
Menu: 53 to 75 Frs
Restaurant: lunch 12–2pm, dinner 7.30–9pm.
Closed Saturday nights, Sundays and 1 week
from 15 August.

Other points: bar, credit cards accepted, pets
allowed, car parking.
Address: 45 rue Thierry d'Argenlieu.
M. ALAIN MEYER, tel 44.51.72.18.

ARMENTIERES, Nord 59280, Map 1

AUBERGE DE LA LYS, RN 42 between Lille and Dunkerque

Menu: 40 to 60 Frs
Restaurant: lunch 12–2.30pm, dinner 7–9pm.
Closed Sundays.
Other points: bar, credit cards accepted,
children welcome, à la carte menu, pets

allowed, car parking, traditional decor.
Address: 110 rue des Résistants.
MME JACQUELINE LEFLON,
tel 20.77.21.83

ARMENTIERES, Nord 59280, Map 1

LA TERRASSE, RN 42 opposite customs

Place of interest: Base du Près du Hem.
Menu: 37 Frs
Restaurant: lunch 11.30–3.30pm, dinner
6–11pm.

Other points: bar, garden terrace, pets
allowed, car parking.
Address: 112 rue des Résistants.
MME JOCELYNE DUBAR, tel 20.35.44.80.

ARRAS, Pas-de-Calais 62000, Map 1

RELAIS DE L'ARTOIS, A 1, access via footbridge, in both directions

Language: English
Restaurant.
Other points: credit cards accepted, children
welcome, self-service, lounge area, garden

terrace, pets allowed, car parking.
Address: Aire de service de Wancourt.
Tel 21.55.97.83.

ARRAS, Pas-de-Calais 62000, Map 1

LE POINT DU JOUR, RN 25

Places of interest: Les places d'Arras, beffroi,
souterrains, musée (300m).
Language: English
Menu: 50 to 100 Frs
Restaurant: closed Sundays.

Other points: bar, credit cards accepted,
children welcome, à la carte menu, pets
allowed, car parking.
Address: 13 avenue Michonneau.
MME SYLVIE KELLE, tel 21.59.96.42.

AUBIGNY AU BAC, Nord 59265, Map 1

LE BERTRESIEN, RN 17 and 43 between Douai and Cambrai

Language: English
Menu: 60 to 162 Frs
Accommodation: 95 to 150 Frs
Restaurant: lunch 11.30–2.30pm, dinner
6.30–10pm.
Hotel: 6 rooms: single 3, double 3. Showers.

Other points: bar, credit cards accepted,
children welcome, à la carte menu, lounge area,
garden terrace, pets allowed, car parking.
Address: 21 Route Nationale.
M. DIDIER WATTELET, tel 27.80.96.40.

AVELIN, Nord 59710, Map 1 ⊗ ♀

A L'EMBUSCADE, RD 949, Seclin exit towards Valenciennes

Menu: 35 to 70 Frs
Restaurant: lunch 11.30–3pm, dinner 7–9pm.
Closed Saturday afternoons and Sundays.
Other points: bar, credit cards accepted,
children welcome, à la carte menu, pets
allowed, car parking, traditional decor.
Address: 14 route de Seclin.
MME GENEVIEVE LEMOINE,
tel 20.32.90.33.

AVESNES SUR HELPE, Nord 59440, Map 1 ⊗ ♀ 🏠

CAFE MARGUERITTE – Au Routiers, RN 2 between Maubeuge and Paris

Menu: 48 to 55 Frs
Accommodation: 60 Frs
Restaurant: lunch 12–2pm. Closed first 2
weeks of August.
Hotel: 6 single rooms.
Other points: bar, pets allowed, car parking,
traditional decor.
Address: 20 avenue de la Gare.
MME MARGUERITTE SORRIAUX,
tel 20.61.17.88.

AWOINGT, Nord 59400, Map 1 ⊗ ♀ 🏠

AUX CHANTS DES OISEAUX, RN 39

Restaurant: closed Saturdays, Sundays and in
August.
Hotel: 12 rooms.
Other points: bar.
Address: 3 Route du Cateau.
M. JEAN-PIERRE PLOUQUET,
tel 27.78.77.05

BAILLEUL, Nord 59270, Map 1 ⊗ ♀

CHEZ ANDRE, RD 933

Restaurant.
Other points: bar.
Address: Route Nationale 4671 for Lille.
M. ANDRE NOORENBERGHE
tel 28.49.29.14

BAILLEUL, Nord 59270, Map 1 ⊗ ♀ 🏠 ☆

AUBERGE DU SEAU, CD 933, autoroute to Lille exit 9, Dunkerque exit 12

Places of interest: Mont des Flandres, le Mont
Noir.
Accommodation: 125 to 200 Frs
Restaurant: lunch 12–2.30pm, dinner 7–10pm.
Specialities: côte à l'os, couscous de poissons,
steak de veau de la mer.
Hotel: 14 rooms: single 3, double 11. Showers,
baths, private WCs, TV, phone.
Other points: bar, credit cards accepted,
children welcome, à la carte menu, garden
terrace, pets allowed, car parking, traditional
decor.
Address: Chemin Départemental 933, Le Seau.
M. JOEL DEQUIDT, tel 20.48.62.00.

BAILLEUL SUR THERAIN, Oise 60930, Map 2 ⊗ ♀

A L'ALOUETTE

Restaurant: closed October.
Other points: bar.
Address: 3 rue de Villers.
MME MICHELINE DUCLOS, tel 44.07.67.25.

BAILLEULVAL, Pas-de-Calais 62123, Map 1   ⊗♈⌂

RELAIS BAC DU SUD, RN 25 between Arras and Doulens

Places of interest: Les grottes de Naourc, Mont
Saint Eloi (30km), Arras (13km), Notre Dame
de Lorette, Vimy.
Languages: English, Dutch
Menu: 55 Frs
Accommodation: 120 to 170 Frs
Restaurant: lunch 12–3pm, dinner 7–10pm.

Closed Sundays and 1 week between Christmas
and New Year.
Hotel: 6 double rooms.
Other points: bar, credit cards accepted,
children welcome, pets allowed, car parking.
Address: Route Nationale 25.
M. YVES SANSON, tel 21.58.79.12.

BAPAUME, Pas-de-Calais 62450, Map 1   ⊗♈⌂☆

CHEZ BERNADETTE, RN 17 between Cambrai and Amiens

Places of interest: Les places d'Arras,
nombreux monuments.
Menu: 53 Frs
Accommodation: 100 to 200 Frs
Restaurant: lunch 12–2.30pm, dinner
8–9.30pm. Closed Saturdays and Sundays.
Hotel: 9 rooms: single 3, double 6. Showers,
baths, private WCs, phone.

Other points: bar, credit cards accepted, self-
service, pets allowed, car parking, traditional
decor.
Address: 45 faubourg de Pronne.
MME BERNADETTE MOLLE,
tel 21.07.12.78

BELLANCOURT, Somme 80132, Map 2   ⊗♈

LE RELAIS DU CORMORAN, RN 1 between Amiens and Abbeville

Places of interest: Le beffroi d'Abbeville, parc
ornithologique, la baie d'Authie, cathédrale
Saint Wulfran.
Menu: 53 to 90 Frs
Restaurant: lunch 11.30–2.30pm, dinner
6.30–10pm. Closed Saturdays, Sunday
mornings (out of season) and 15 days at
Christmas.

Speciality: poissons.
Other points: bar, credit cards accepted,
children welcome, à la carte menu, garden
terrace, pets allowed, car parking, traditional
decor.
Address: 2 Route Nationale 1.
MME ELIANE CAUHAP, tel 22.24.35.13.

BERCK SUR MER, Pas-de-Calais 62600, Map 1   ⊗♈⌂

RELAIS D'ARTOIS

Restaurant.
Hotel: 14 double rooms.
Other points: bar, car parking.

Address: 20 rue Alfred Lambert.
M. RAOUL POSTEL, tel 21.09.29.35

BOULOGNE SUR MER, Pas-de-Calais 62200, Map 1   ⊗♈⌂

LE RELAIS DES 2 GARAGES, RN 1

Language: English
Menu: 55 Frs
Accommodation: 76 to 116 Frs
Restaurant: closed Saturday afternoons and
Sundays.
Hotel: 14 rooms: single 5, double 9.

Other points: bar, credit cards accepted,
children welcome, à la carte menu, pets
allowed.
Address: 54 avenue John Kennedy.
MME CATHERINE LACHER, tel 21.91.12.96.

BOVES, Somme 80440, Map 2 ⊗

LA GRENOUILLERE, RN 334 via expressway to Amiens-Roye

Places of interest: La cathédrale d'Amiens, beffroi.
Language: English
Menu: 55 to 68 Frs
Restaurant: lunch 11–3pm. Closed Sundays (except group dinners) and in August.

Speciality: couscous.
Other points: credit cards accepted, children welcome, garden terrace, pets allowed, car parking, traditional decor.
Address: Route Nationale 334
M. BOUHOU OUANNOUNE, tel 22.09.31.26.

BRETEUIL, Oise 60120, Map 2 ⊗♀

L'AUBERGE DU MARAIS, RN 16 to Clermont

Places of interest: Sites gallo-romains, Vendeuil Caply (3km).
Menu: 47,50 to 65 Frs including wine
Restaurant: lunch 12–3pm, dinner 7–11pm. Closed Sunday nights.
Speciality: ficelle Picarde.
Other points: bar, credit cards accepted,

children welcome, à la carte menu, garden terrace, pets allowed, car parking, traditional decor.
Address: 38 rue de Paris.
JOSIANE AND JEAN-PAUL CLEMENT, tel 44.80.12.21

BRUAY LA BUISSIERE, Pas-de-Calais 62700, Map 1 ⊗♀⌂☆

LA LOUETTE (formerly CHEZ MICHEL)

Places of interest: Base d'Olhain, châteaux, collines de l'Artois.
Languages: German, English
Menu: 60 Frs
Accommodation: 85 to 140 Frs
Restaurant: lunch 11–3pm, dinner 7–9.30pm. Closed Sunday afternoons.
Speciality: fondue bourguignonne.
Hotel: 15 rooms: single 5, double 10. Showers,

baths, private WCs, TV, phone.
Other points: bar, credit cards accepted, children welcome, à la carte menu, lounge area, pets allowed, car parking, traditional decor.
Address: 114 rue Raoul Briquet, Place de la Gare.
SERGE AND DANY DOMART, tel 21.53.42.07.

CAMBRAI, Nord 59400, Map 1 ⊗♀

LA GARGOTE, A 2 and A 23 along canal

Places of interest: Rue des Vignes, archéologie, abbaye de Vaucelle.
Menu: 60 Frs
Restaurant: lunch 12–3pm, dinner 7–11pm. Closed Sundays (except groups) and in August.

Specialities: andouillettes de Cambrai, clafoutis maison.
Other points: bar, garden terrace, pets allowed, car parking.
Address: 136 boulevard Jean Bart.
M. JEAN BEDU, tel 27.81.07.18

CAMBRAI, Nord 59400, Map 1 ⊗♀⌂

CHEZ ROGER, RN 17

Menu: 58 Frs
Accommodation: 65 to 95 Frs
Restaurant: lunch 12–3.30pm, dinner 7.30–

10.30 pm. Closed Saturdays, Sundays and in August.
Hotel: 6 rooms: single 4, double 2. Showers, private WCs.

Other points: bar, credit cards accepted, pets allowed, car parking, traditional decor.

Address: 10 rue des Docks.
M. ROGER LEPRINCE, tel 27.83.26.05.

CAMBRAI, Nord 59400, Map 1 ⊗

AU RELAIS, RN 39 to Charleville

Menu: 45 Frs
Restaurant: lunch 12–2pm, dinner 7–8pm. Closed Sundays and in August.
Hotel: 4 rooms.

Other points: credit cards accepted, pets allowed, traditional decor.
Address: 1084 avenue du Cateau.
M. ROGER GUISGAND, tel 27.81.35.82.

CAPPELLE EN PEVELE, Nord 59242, Map 1 ⊗🍽

LAS VEGAS, RN 393

Restaurant: closed Sundays.
Other points: bar.
Address: 13 rue de l'Obeau.

MME ELIANE DUQUESNOY,
tel 20.61.83.10.

CATEAU (LE), Nord 59360, Map 1 ⊗🍽

HOTELS L'ESCALE, between Charleville Mézières and Cambrai

Menu: 40 to 55 Frs
Restaurant: closed Sundays.
Speciality: flamiches.
Other points: bar, car parking.

Address: 65 route de Bazuel.
MME ELISABETH MASSON,
tel 27.84.25.50.

CHAMBLY, Oise 60230, Map 2 ⊗🍽🏠

LE RELAIS DE CHAMBLY, RN 1 between Paris and Beauvais via Beaumont sur Oise

Places of interest: Chantilly (20km), Senlis (28km), L'Ile Adam (10km), abbaye de Royaumont (35km), abbaye de Maubuisson, Beauvais, musée de l'Archéologie de Guiry en Vexin, musée de l'outil.
Menu: 65 Frs including wine and coffee
Accommodation: 130 Frs to 280 Frs
Restaurant: lunch 12–3.30pm, dinner 7–8.30pm. Closed Saturdays, Sundays and 20 December to 20 January.

Specialities: bourguignon, coq au vin, boeuf-mode.
Hotel: 15 single rooms. Baths, private WCs, TV.
Other points: bar, children welcome, lounge area, garden terrace, pets allowed, car parking.
Address: 660 avenue Aristide Briand.
MME FRANCOISE VIOLETTE,
tel 34.70.50.37.

CHAULNES, Somme 80320, Map 2 ⊗🍽

L'ESCALE DES ROUTIERS, RN 17 exit Roye or Péronne

Places of interest: ville et château de Péronne.
Menu: 55 to 65 Frs
Restaurant: lunch 11.30–2.30pm, dinner 7–10pm. Closed Saturdays, Sundays and in August.

Other points: bar, credit cards accepted, pets allowed, car parking, traditional decor.
Address: Route Nationale 17, Fresnes.
M. JEAN-CLAUDE GUERQUIN,
tel 22.85.28.50.

CHAUNY, Aisne 02300, Map 2 ⊗🍽🏠

LE CASAMANCE, RN 83 between Noyon and Soissons

Places of interest: Châteaux de Coucy et de Blérancourt, fôret de Saint Gobain, cathédrale de Laon.
Language: English
Menu: 50 to 70 Frs
Accommodation: 85 to 140 Frs
Restaurant: lunch 12–2pm, dinner 7–9pm. Closed Sundays.

Hotel: 6 rooms: single 4, double 2. Showers, private WCs, TV.
Other points: bar, credit cards accepted, children welcome, à la carte menu, garden terrace, pets allowed, car parking.
Address: 92 rue de la Chaussée.
M. GILLES CLAISSE, tel 23.52.16.33.

CHAUNY, Aisne 02300, Map 2   ⊗ ☍

LE VAN GOGH

Language: English
Menu: 55 to 120 Frs
Restaurant: lunch 11.45–2pm, dinner 7–8.30pm.
Speciality: boeuf bourguignon.
Other points: bar, credit cards accepted,

children welcome, pets allowed, traditional decor.
Address: 37 rue A. Ternynck.
MME CHRISTINE HAUDIQUET, tel 23.39.40.32.

CHEPY, Somme 80210, Map 2   ⊗ ☍

RELAIS SANS BOIRE, RD 29 between Le Tréport and Oisemont

Places of interest: Château de Rambures, la mer.
Menu: 55 to 120 Frs
Restaurant: lunch 11.30–2.30pm, dinner 7–10pm. Closed Tuesday evenings and in August.
Speciality: ficelle picard.

Other points: bar, credit cards accepted, children welcome, à la carte menu, self-service, garden terrace, pets allowed, car parking, traditional decor.
Address: 40 route de Oisemont, La Croix de Pierre.
M. JACKY SUEUR, tel 22.26.26.67.

COLEMBERT, Pas-de-Calais 62142, Map 1   ⊗ ☍ 🏠

CAFE DU COMMERCE

Menu: 56 Frs
Accommodation: from 130 Frs
Restaurant: closed Saturday afternoons and Sundays (out of season).

Hotel: 9 rooms.
Other points: bar, car parking.
MME MARIE PIERRE, tel 21.33.31.11.

COMINES, Nord 59560, Map 1   ⊗ ☍ 🏠

RESTAURANT DE LA GARE, Lille

Place of interest: Le Mont Noir.
Languages: German, English, Spanish, Italian
Menu: 38 to 95 Frs
Accommodation: 132 Frs
Restaurant: lunch 12–3pm, dinner 6–12pm. Closed Sunday nights.
Speciality: couscous.

Hotel: 10 rooms: single 4, double 6. Showers, baths.
Other points: bar, children welcome, à la carte menu, garden terrace, pets allowed, car parking, traditional decor.
Address: 81–3 avenue du Général Leclerc.
MME YVETTE DESITER, tel 20.39.45.78.

COMPIEGNE, Oise 60200, Map 2   ⊗ ☍

BAR DE LA MARINE

Restaurant: closed Saturdays and Sundays.
Other points: bar.

Address: 17 rue de l'Estacade.
M. AIME LOGGHE, tel 44.40.26.37.

COUCY LE CHATEAU, Aisne 02380, Map 2 ⊗♈⌂

LE LION ROUGE, RD 1 between Soissons and Saint Quentin

Places of interest: Les ruines du château de
Coucy, château de Blérancourt.
Languages: German, English
Menu: 52 to 174 Frs
Accommodation: 86 to 92 Frs
Restaurant: lunch 12–3pm, dinner 7–9.30pm.
Specialities: Magret picards, grillades,
papillottes de poissons, cassoulet.

Hotel: 13 rooms: single 3, double 10.
Other points: bar, credit cards accepted,
children welcome, à la carte menu, lounge area,
garden terrace, pets allowed, car parking,
traditional decor.
Address: 62 avenue Altenkessel.
M. PATRICK CLAVET, tel 23.52.70.13.

COURCELLES-LES-GISORS, Oise 60240, Map 2 ⊗♈

AUBERGE DU CARREFOUR, RD 981

Places of interest: Musée de Claude Monet
(25km), château de Boury (5km), château
féodal de Gisors (3km).
Menu: 44 Frs
Restaurant: closed from Saturday night to
Sunday night, 1 to 15 September.

Other points: bar, credit cards accepted, pets
allowed, car parking, traditional decor.
Address: Route Départementale 981.
M. DANIEL HILLION, tel 32.55.03.16.

CREVECOEUR LE GRAND, Oise 60360, Map 2 ⊗♈

LE RELAX, RN 30 and RD 93

Restaurant: closed Sundays.
Other points: bar.

Address: 12 rue de Breteuil.
M. MICHEL DUBOIS, tel 44.46.87.65.

CROIX, Nord 59170, Map 1 ⊗♈

LE RELAIS DE L'HOTEL DE VILLE, RD 14

Restaurant: closed Monday afternoons and
July.
Other points: bar.

Address: 211 rue Jean Jaurs.
MME LUCETTE STRELEKI, tel 20.70.50.92.

CUIGY EN BRAY, Oise 60850, Map 2 ⊗♈

RELAIS DE SAINT LEU, RN 31 between Gournay en Bray and Beauvais

Places of interest: Abbaye de Saint Germer le
Fly, Gerbevoy.
Menu: 48 Frs
Restaurant: lunch 11–2.30pm, dinner 7–9pm.
Closed Saturday afternoons, Sundays, public
holidays and in August.

Other points: bar, children welcome, pets
allowed, car parking.
Address: 20 rue de Saint Leu.
M. JACQUES DELARUELLE,
tel 44.82.53.17.

CUVILLY, Oise 60490, Map 2 ⊗♈⌂

LA CAMPAGNARDE, RN 17 between Paris and Lille

Places of interest: Compiègne, la vallée de la Somme.
Language: English
Menu: 47 to 60 Frs
Accommodation: 90 to 150 Frs
Restaurant: lunch 11–3pm, dinner 7–10.30pm. Closed Sundays.

Hotel: 9 double rooms. Showers, baths, private WCs.
Other points: bar, credit cards accepted, children welcome, pets allowed, car parking.
Address: 5 route des Flandres.
DANIEL AND ANNE-MARYSE HILLION NICOL, tel 44.85.00.30.

DESVRES, Pas-de-Calais 62240, Map 1 ⊗ 🍸 🏠

LE RELAIS DE LA BELLE CROIX, RN 342 between Boulogne sur Mer and Longfoss

Places of interest: Vallée de la course Nausica, musée de la faïence, musée de la mer.
Language: English
Menu: 45 to 70 Frs
Accommodation: 60 Frs per person
Restaurant: closed Sundays.

Hotel: 5 rooms: single 2, double 3. Showers.
Other points: bar, children welcome, à la carte menu, garden terrace, pets allowed, car parking.
Address: 1 rue du Bidet.
M. JEAN-CLAUDE GRUMELART, tel 21.91.65.81

DEULEMONT, Nord 59890, Map 1 ⊗ 🍸

LA BOULE D'OR

Restaurant: closed Wednesdays.
Other points: bar.

Address: 16 rue du Maréchal Foch, Le Bel Arbre.
M. GUY CATTEAU, tel 20.39.24.28.

DIZY LE GROS, Aisne 02340, Map 2 ⊗ 🍸

LES ROUTIERS, RD 366

Menu: 50 Frs including wine
Restaurant: lunch 11–2pm. Closed Sundays, second 2 weeks in August and 1 week for Christmas.
Hotel: 3 double rooms.

Other points: bar, credit cards accepted, pets allowed, car parking.
Address: route de Reims.
M. CLAUDE GANTIER, tel 23.21.23.15.

DOUAI, Nord 59500, Map 1 ⊗ 🍸

LA PLAMANDRIERE

Menu: 55 Frs
Restaurant: lunch 11.30–3pm. Closed Saturdays.
Other points: bar, credit cards accepted, lounge area, pets allowed, traditional decor.

Address: 3869 route de Tournai.
MME JACQUELINE PLAISANT, tel 27.98.55.28.

DOUAI, Nord 59500, Map 1 ⊗ 🍸 🏠

A L'EPI D'OR, RN 17 and 34

Restaurant: closed Saturdays after 3pm and Sundays.
Hotel: 7 single rooms.

Other points: bar.
Address: 38 faubourg d'Aras, Lambres.
M. MICHEL BARJOU, tel 27.87.04.56.

DOUAI, Nord 59500, Map 1 ⊗ 🍸 🏠

LE RELAIS, RN 17 and 34

Restaurant.
Hotel: 8 rooms.
Other points: bar.

Address: 370 rue d'Aniche.
MME JEANNINE DEYRECK, tel 27.88.12.06.

DREUIL LES AMIENS, Somme 80730, Map 2   ⊗

CHEZ JEAN-MARIE ET CHRISTIANE, RN 235

Places of interest: Picquigny, la Capitale
Picarde (1km).
Menu: 52 Frs
Restaurant: lunch 11.45–2pm, dinner
7.30–9pm. Closed Sundays and in August.

Other points: pets allowed, car parking,
traditional decor.
Address: 285 avenue Pasteur.
M. JEAN-MARIE DUMEIGE, tel 22.54.10.72.

ECLAIBES, Nord 59330, Map 1   ⊗ ♀

LE ROBINSON, RN 2

Restaurant.
Other points: bar.

Address: Route Nationale 2.
M. EL HADI MANSEUR, tel 27.57.81.26.

ESTREES DENIECOURT, Somme 80200, Map 2   ⊗ ♀ ⌂

AUBERGE DE LA MAIRIE, RN 336 exit A 1 Péronne, right towards Amiens

Menu: 55 to 65 Frs
Accommodation: 100 to 225 Frs
Restaurant: dinner 7–11pm. Closed Saturdays,
Sundays and in August.
Hotel: 7 rooms: single 5, double 2. Showers,
private WCs.

Other points: bar, à la carte menu, lounge
area, garden terrace, pets allowed, car parking.
MME CLAUDETTE DEMUYNCK
DEHENRY, tel 22.85.20.16.

ESTREES MONS, Somme 80200, Map 2   ⊗ ♀

A LA POMME D'API, RN 29 between Amiens and Saint Quentin

Menu: 55 Frs
Restaurant: lunch 11.30–2.30pm, dinner
7–9.30pm. Closed Sundays and in August.
Other points: bar, children welcome, lounge

area, garden terrace, pets allowed, car parking,
traditional decor.
Address: 28 Route Nationale.
M. ALBERT GRAS, tel 22.85.60.04.

ETOUVELLES, Aisne 02000, Map 2   ⊗ ♀

CHEZ JEANNOT, RN 2 between Laon and Soissons

Places of interest: Cathédrale de Laon, la ville
et ses remparts, grottes du Dragon, abbaye de
Voclaire.
Menu: 58 to 120 Frs
Restaurant: lunch 12–2.30pm, dinner
7.30–9.30pm. Closed Saturday nights, Sundays
(except reservations) and in August.

Other points: bar, credit cards accepted,
children welcome, à la carte menu, pets
allowed, car parking.
Address: 30 rue de Paris.
M. JEAN-MARIE SERRE, tel 23.20.63.26.

FLAVY LE MARTEL, Aisne 02520, Map 2   ⊗ ♀

LE RELAIS DES ROUTIERS

Restaurant: closed Saturdays.
Other points: bar.

Address: 17 rue André Brulé.
M. JEAN-PAUL BRIERE, tel 23.52.51.31.

FLERS EN ESCREBIEUX, Nord 59128, Map 1 ⊗♟

AU BON CASSE CROUTE, RN 43

Restaurant: closed Saturdays and Sundays.
Other points: bar, car parking.

Address: 59 Route Nationale 43.
M. RAYMOND DUFOUR, tel 27.86.69.41

FLIXECOURT, Somme 80420, Map 2 ⊗♟

LES FLONFLONS DU BAL, RN 1 between Amiens and Abbeville

Places of interest: Camp gaulois 'Samara' (5km), grottes préhistoriques à Naours (20km), ferme de Drugy (prison de Jeanne d'Arc) (15km), cathédrale d'Amiens (20km).
Language: English
Menu: 45 to 100 Frs
Restaurant.

Specialities: canard aux navets, viandes grillées, couscous.
Other points: bar, credit cards accepted, children welcome, à la carte menu, garden terrace, pets allowed, car parking, traditional decor.
Address: 16 rue Georges Clémenceau.
M. JEAN-MARC ROHAUT, tel 22.51.36.34.

FORMERIE, Oise 60220, Map 2 ⊗♟🏠☆

CAFE DE LA PAIX

Menu: 48 Frs
Accommodation: 50 Frs
Restaurant: lunch 12–3pm, dinner 7–9pm.
Specialities: couscous royal, boeuf carottes.
Hotel: 5 double rooms. Showers, baths.

Other points: bar, credit cards accepted, children welcome, self-service, pets allowed.
Address: 8 rue Dornat.
MME FRANCOISE MERLIN, tel 44.46.17.08.

FRESNES EN TARDENOIS, Aisne 02130, Map 2 ⊗

RELAIS DU TARDENOIS, A 4 via footbridge, in both directions

Languages: German, English
Restaurant.
Other points: credit cards accepted, children welcome, self-service, lounge area, garden

terrace, pets allowed, car parking.
Address: Aire de Service du Tardenois.
Tel 23.70.23.16.

FROISSY, Oise 60480, Map 2 ⊗♟🏠

LE BEAUVAIS BRETEUIL, RN 1 between Froissy and Beauvais

Places of interest: Cathédrale de Beauvais, musée, place Jeanne Hachette, parc Saint Paul.
Menu: 50 to 92 Frs
Accommodation: 100 to 150 Frs
Restaurant: lunch 12–3pm, dinner 7–10pm. Closed Sundays, 3 weeks in August and 15 days for Christmas.

Hotel: 5 rooms: single 3, double 2.
Other points: bar, credit cards accepted, children welcome, à la carte menu, pets allowed, car parking, traditional decor.
Address: 5 rue du Bois Saint Martin.
M. RAYMOND JULEN, tel 44.79.13.09.

GAMACHES, Somme 80220, Map 2   ⊗ ♀

LES ROUTIERS

Places of interest: Château de Rambure (15km), château d'Eu (12km).
Menu: 48 to 80 Frs
Restaurant: lunch 12–2.30pm, dinner 7–9pm. Closed Sunday afternoons.

Other points: bar, credit cards accepted, children welcome, à la carte menu, pets allowed, car parking, traditional decor.
Address: 20 place du Général Leclerc.
M. CLAUDE REFFAY, tel 22.26.16.33.

GAVRELLE, Pas-de-Calais 62580, Map 1   ⊗ ♀

RELAIS DE LA CHAUMIERE, RN 50, A 1 exit Fresnes-les-Montaubant

Place of interest: Monument de guerre.
Language: English
Menu: 45 Frs
Restaurant.
Other points: bar, credit cards accepted, à la

carte menu, pets allowed, car parking, traditional decor.
Address: 21 Route Nationale.
M. FRANCK COURCELLE, tel 21.58.16.99.

GHYVELDE, Nord 59254, Map 1   ⊗ ♀

LE SAINT SEBASTIEN, RN 947 on right before Belgian border

Places of interest: Bergues, Dunkerque, Belgique, monts de Flandres.
Language: Dutch
Menu: 45 to 180 Frs
Restaurant: lunch 11–4pm. Closed Tuesdays and in August.

Specialities: flamandes, poissons.
Other points: bar, children welcome, à la carte menu, pets allowed, car parking.
Address: 161 rue Nationale.
MME EDITH MARIE-RUBBEN, tel 28.26.61.95.

HALLENNES LEZ HAUBOURDIN, Nord 59320, Map 1   ⊗

AUX AMIS DE LA ROUTE, RN 41 exit La Bass

Menu: 60 Frs
Restaurant: lunch 11–3.30pm, dinner 7–10pm. Closed Saturdays, Sundays and in August.
Other points: children welcome.

Address: 329 rue du Général de Gaulle.
M. DOMINIQUE DELECLUSE, tel 20.07.14.24

HALLUIN, Nord 59250, Map 1   ⊗ ♀

AU ROUTIER, RD 945 in industrial zone of Col Bras

Languages: Dutch, Polish, Serbo-Croat
Menu: 61,20 Frs
Restaurant: lunch 11.30–2pm, dinner 7–9pm. Closed Saturday afternoons, Sundays and in August.

Speciality: couscous (Fridays).
Other points: bar, credit cards accepted, pets allowed, car parking, traditional decor.
Address: 196 rue de la Lys.
M. RICHARD KOZIOR, tel 20.23.88.20.

HARNES, Pas-de-Calais 62440, Map 1   ⊗ ♀

CHEZ FREDINE

Menu: 60 to 120 Frs
Restaurant.
Other points: bar, car parking.

Address: 17 route de Lille.
MME FREDINE TURNER, tel 21.42.30.90.

HESDIN, Pas-de-Calais 62140, Map 1 ⊗♀

CHEZ GEORGETTE, RD 928 between Dunkerque and Rouen

Places of interest: Vallée de l'Authie, jardins et abbaye de Valoise.
Menu: 50 to 85 Frs
Restaurant: lunch 11–3pm, dinner 7–9pm. Closed 10 to 25 September.

Other points: bar, credit cards accepted, children welcome, pets allowed, car parking, traditional decor.
Address: route du Val d'Authie, Labroye.
M. PAUL FLICOURT, tel 21.86.83.10.

HIRSON, Aisne 02500, Map 2 ⊗♀

JUPITER, RN 43, exit Hirson towards Paris or Lille

Places of interest: Abbaye, forêt, cascades, fontaine.
Languages: English, Italian
Menu: 53 Frs
Restaurant: lunch 11.30–5pm, dinner 5–10pm. Closed Sundays and in August.
Specialities: lasagne, pizza, spaghetti

bolognaise.
Other points: bar, credit cards accepted, children welcome, à la carte menu, pets allowed, car parking.
Address: 151 avenue Joffre.
M. GUILIO CORSINI, tel 23.58.14.03.

HOUSSOYE (LA), Oise 60390, Map 2 ⊗♀

LE CHEVAL BLANC, RN 181

Places of interest: Beauvais, Gisors.
Language: English
Menu: 60 Frs
Accommodation: 100 Frs
Restaurant: lunch 11.30–2.30pm, dinner 7–9.30pm. Closed Saturdays, Sunday nights.
Speciality: filet de daurade à la provençale.

Hotel: 3 single rooms.
Other points: bar, credit cards accepted, pets allowed, car parking, traditional decor.
Address: 5 route de Gisors.
MME LILIANE HEYTHUYZEN, tel 44.81.40.40.

HUMIERES, Pas-de-Calais 62130, Map 1 ⊗♀

LES ROUTIERS, RN 39

Menu: 50 Frs including coffee
Restaurant: lunch 12–2.30pm, dinner 7–9pm. Closed Sundays.
Other points: bar, credit cards accepted,

garden terrace, pets allowed, car parking.
Address: Route Nationale 39.
MME BERTHE TERNISIEN, tel 21.41.85.77

LABOURSE, Pas-de-Calais 62113, Map 1 ⊗♀

LA PARISIENNE

Language: English
Menu: 50 Frs
Restaurant: closed Sundays.

Other points: bar, car parking.
Address: 8 route de Lens.
MME RENEE GEORGES, tel 21.64.07.70.

LAVERSINES, Oise 60510, Map 2 ⊗♀

LE RELAIS ROUTIER, RN 31 between Reims and Rouen

Places of interest: Cathédrale de Beauvais, fabrique d'angora.
Menu: 70 to 90 Frs
Restaurant: lunch 11.30–2.30pm, dinner 7.30–9.30pm. Closed Saturdays, Sundays, second 2 weeks of August and 1 week at Christmas.

Speciality: paëlla (by arrangement).
Other points: bar, credit cards accepted, pets allowed, car parking, traditional decor.
Address: 90 rue Saint Germain.
M. MARCEAU FORESTIER, tel 44.07.75.80.

LEVIGNEN, Oise 60800, Map 2   ⊗☂️

RELAIS DE LA II, RN 2 between Paris and Soissons

Menu: 53 to 70 Frs
Restaurant: lunch 11.30–3pm, dinner 7–10.30pm.
Other points: bar, credit cards accepted, à la

carte menu, pets allowed, car parking.
Address: Route Nationale 2.
M. JACQUES CARRIER, tel 44.94.21.01.

LIEVIN, Pas-de-Calais 62800, Map 1   ⊗☂️

LE ZOLA, A 26

Places of interest: Notre Dame de Lorette, mémorial canadien.
Menu: 55 Frs
Restaurant: lunch 12–3pm, dinner 7–10pm. Closed Sundays and in August.
Specialities: tripes à l'ancienne, moules.

Other points: bar, credit cards accepted, children welcome, à la carte menu, traditional decor.
Address: 215 rue Emile Zola.
M. ANDRE CLEMENT, tel 21.29.29.72.

LONGUEAU, Somme 80330, Map 2   ⊗☂️🏠

LE RELAIS DE L'HOTEL DE VILLE, RN 35

Languages: English, Arabic
Restaurant: closed Sundays.
Hotel: 10 rooms.

Other points: bar.
Address: 105 avenue Henri Barbusse.
M. KONIDER BELLAREDJ, tel 22.46.16.14.

LORGIES, Pas-de-Calais 62840, Map 1   ⊗☂️

AUBERGE DE LA BOMBE

Language: English
Menu: 55 Frs
Restaurant: lunch 11.30–3pm, dinner 6.30–10pm. Closed between Christmas and New Year's day.

Other points: bar, car parking.
Address: 1 route d'Estaires.
M. ROGER DELAMARE, tel 21.02.83.43.

LUMBRES, Pas-de-Calais 62380, Map 1   ⊗☂️🏠

HOTEL MODERNE, opposite the station

Restaurant: closed Sundays and August.
Hotel: 6 double rooms.
Other points: bar.

Address: 18 rue François Cousin.
M. PIERRE FICHAUX, tel 21.39.62.87

MARAIS (AUX), Oise 60000, Map 2   ⊗☂️

AU GRAND R, RN 981 between Mantes and Gisors

Places of interest: Le Vexin, Beauvais.
Menu: 54 Frs
Restaurant: closed Sundays and in August.
Other points: bar, credit cards accepted, children welcome, car parking, traditional decor.
Address: 12 route de Gisors.
M. MARCEL BOUTOILLE, tel 44.48.18.66.

MARCHELEPOT, Somme 80200, Map 2 ⊗♈

RESTAURANT DU PARC, RN 17 between Roye and Péronne

Menu: 55 Frs
Restaurant: closed Saturdays and Sundays.
Other points: bar, credit cards accepted, children welcome, pets allowed, car parking, traditional decor.
Address: Route Nationale 17.
EMILE AND ANGELIQUE JOVANOVIC, tel 22.83.90.85.

MAROLLES BOURNEVILLE, Oise 60890, Map 2 ⊗♈

LES ROUTIERS, RD 936

Menu: 60 to 75 Frs
Restaurant.
Other points: bar, pets allowed, traditional decor.
Address: 7 rue de Meaux.
MME HUGUETTE PICARD-MATHIAS, tel 23.96.72.11.

MARQUISE, Pas-de-Calais 62250, Map 1 ⊗♈🏠

A LA DESCENTE DES VOYAGEURS, between Marquise and Guînes

Places of interest: Forteresse de Mimoueques, carrières, musée de l'aviation.
Menu: 58 to 120 Frs
Accommodation: 100 Frs (demi-pension 150 Frs, pension 180 Frs)
Restaurant: lunch 12–2pm, dinner 7–8.30pm.
Hotel: 4 rooms: single 3, double 1.
Other points: bar.
Address: 17 rue du 8 mai.
MME NELLY BRISBOUT, tel 21.92.85.55.

MAUBEUGE, Nord 59600, Map 1 ⊗♈

LE BERLIOZ, RN 2

Menu: 55 Frs
Restaurant: closed Sunday afternoons.
Other points: bar, car parking.
Address: 27 avenue de la Gare.
M. PHILIPPE CAPPELIEZ, tel 27.64.68.79.

MAZINGARBE, Pas-de-Calais 62670, Map 1 ⊗♈

AU RELAIS DES ROUTIERS, RN 43 between Lens and Béthune

Places of interest: Lorette, Vimy.
Languages: German, Polish
Menu: 55 Frs
Restaurant: lunch 12–2.30pm. Closed Sundays and in August.
Specialities: lapin aux pruneaux, choucroute.
Other points: bar, children welcome, lounge area, car parking.
Address: 85 Route Nationale 43.
MME GENEVIEVE MARCINKOWSKI, tel 21.72.00.09.

MERLIMONT, Pas-de-Calais 62155, Map 1 ⊗♈

LE CURACAO

Places of interest: Berch sur Mer, Montreuil sur Mer, Le Touquet, vallée de la Course.
Language: English
Menu: 53 to 130 Frs
Restaurant: lunch 11–3pm, dinner 7–11pm. Closed Mondays.

Specialities: couscous, paëlla.
Other points: bar, credit cards accepted, children welcome, à la carte menu, garden terrace, pets allowed, car parking.
Address: 611 rue Auguste Biblocq.
M. ALAIN LANTOINE, tel 21.09.45.45.

MEZY MOULINS, Aisne 02650, Map 2 ⊗ ♀

RESTAURANT DU CHEVAL NOIR, RN 3 between Dormans and Château-Thierry.

Menu: 55 to 90 Frs
Restaurant: lunch 12–2.30pm, dinner 7–10.30 pm. Closed Sundays and in September.
Other points: bar, children welcome, à la carte

menu, garden terrace, pets allowed, car parking, traditional decor.
Address: 25 avenue de Champagne.
MME MARTINE CARON, tel 23.71.91.30.

MONTDIDIER, Somme 80500, Map 2 ⊗ ♀ ⌂

LE RELAIS DU MOUTON D'OR, RN 30 and 35

Restaurant: lunch 12–2pm, dinner 7–9pm. Closed Sundays and in August.
Hotel: 5 double rooms.
Other points: bar, credit cards accepted, pets allowed, car parking.

Address: 10 boulevard Debeney.
M. CHRISTIAN PARMENTIER,
tel 22.78.03.43.

NOYON, Oise 60400, Map 2 ⊗ ♀

LE VESUVE

Menu: 55 to 90 Frs
Restaurant: closed Saturday afternoons and Sundays.
Other points: bar, à la carte menu, car parking.

Address: 1 avenue Jean Jaurs.
CORINNE AND PHILIPPE DELET,
tel 44.44.19.56.

OMIECOURT, Somme 80320, Map 2 ⊗ ♀

AU BON ACCUEIL, RN 17

Menu: 52 to 65 Frs
Restaurant: closed Sundays.
Speciality: couscous.

Other points: bar, car parking.
Address: Route Nationale 17.
M. ALLAOUA BETROUNE, tel 22.85.42.49.

OVILLERS LA BOISSELLE, Somme 80300, Map 2 ⊗ ♀

LE POPPY, RD 929 between Bapaume and Albert

Places of interest: Mémorial de la Bataille de la Somme, basilique d'Albert.
Languages: German, English
Menu: 56 Frs
Restaurant: closed Mondays
Other points: bar, children welcome, à la carte

menu, garden terrace, pets allowed, car parking, traditional decor.
Address: 4 route de Bapaume.
M. GEORGES CANDENBULKE,
tel 22.75.45.45.

PERONNE, Somme 80200, Map 2 ⊗ ♀

LA CHAPELETTE – Chez Claude et Nicole, RN 17 between Roye and Péronne

Place of interest: Baie de Somme.
Menu: 55 Frs
Restaurant: closed Saturday afternoons and Sundays.
Other points: bar, credit cards accepted, children welcome, à la carte menu, pets allowed, car parking, traditional decor.
Address: 61 route de Paris.
CLAUDE AND NICOLE CHARPENTIER, tel 22.84.10.82.

PERONNE ASSEVILLERS, Somme 80200, Map 2 ⊗

L'ARCHE D'ASSEVILLERS, A 1 between Lille and Paris

Restaurant: lunch 10–5.30pm, dinner 5.30–11pm.
Other points: credit cards accepted, children welcome, self-service, garden terrace, pets allowed, car parking.
Address: Aire d'Assevillers Ouest.
Tel 22.85.20.35.

PONT REMY, Somme 80580, Map 2 ⊗♀

LE CONTINENTAL

Restaurant: closed in August.
Other points: bar.
Address: 9 rue Robert Bordeux.
MME GINETTE THRASSE, tel 22.27.12.89.

PROYART, Somme 80121, Map 2 ⊗♀⌂

LA RAPERIE, RN 29 between Amiens and Saint Quentin

Languages: English, Spanish
Menu: 49 to 98 Frs
Restaurant: closed Saturdays and Sundays (out of season).
Speciality: picardes.
Hotel: 8 rooms.
Other points: bar, credit cards accepted, children welcome, à la carte menu, pets allowed, car parking, traditional decor.
Address: Route Nationale 336.
MLLE FARIDA BENCHALAL, tel 22.85.37.30.

QUAEDYPRE, Nord 59380, Map 1 ⊗♀

L'GITANT, RD 916 between Lille and Dunkerque

Places of interest: Remparts de Bergues (Vauban), monts des Flandres, circuit des villages fleuris.
Languages: Dutch
Menu: 60 to 154 Frs
Restaurant: closed Saturdays.
Specialities: carbonnade flamande, potée Uleech.
Other points: bar, credit cards accepted, children welcome, lounge area, pets allowed, car parking, traditional decor.
Address: Chemin Départemental 916.
M. JOS LERMYTTE, tel 28.68.69.87.

RENESCURE, Nord 59173, Map 1 ⊗

LA CLE DES CHAMPS, RN 42 between St Omer and Hazebrouck

Places of interest: Cassel (10km), Andouarois (9km).
Menu: 40 Frs
Restaurant: lunch: 11.30–2pm. Closed Saturday afternoons and Sundays.
Other points: credit cards accepted, pets allowed, car parking, traditional decor.
Address: known as La Clé des Champs, 89 Route de Saint Omer.
MME MARLENE DEMAN-LAMIAUX, tel 28.49.81.12.

ROUBAIX, Nord 59100, Map 1 ⊗ ♈

LE CALAIS

Languages: German, English, Dutch
Menu: 50 Frs including wine
Restaurant: lunch 12–2.30pm, dinner
7.30–10.30pm. Closed Saturday afternoons,
Sundays, August and end December.

Other points: bar, credit cards accepted, pets
allowed, car parking.
Address: 2 quai de Calais.
MME JOSETTE VAZE, tel 20.26.00.35.

SAINT AUBIN EN BRAY, Oise 60650, Map 2 ⊗ ♈ ⌂

RELAIS DES FONTAINETTES, RN 31

Language: English
Restaurant: closed Sundays and first 2 weeks
of May.
Hotel: 5 rooms.

Other points: bar.
Address: known as Les Fontainettes.
M. JOSE ALBERT, tel 44.80.50.26.

SAINT INGLEVERT, Pas-de-Calais 62250, Map 1 ⊗

LA MURAILLE, RN 1 between Calais and Boulogne

Language: English
Menu: 60 Frs including a drink and coffee
Restaurant: lunch 11.45–2.30pm, dinner
7.30–9pm. Closed Saturdays, Sundays, and 2 to
3 weeks in August.

Other points: credit cards accepted, à la carte
menu, pets allowed, car parking.
Address: Route Nationale 1.
MME JOCELYNE SALMON, tel 21.33.75.44.

SAINT OMER, Pas-de-Calais 62500, Map 1 ⊗ ♈ ⌂

LA RENAISSANCE, RN 43

Places of interest: Marais Audomarois,
cathédrale, musées.
Languages: English and a little German
Menu: 50 Frs
Accommodation: 105 to 120 Frs
Restaurant: lunch 12–2pm, dinner 8–9pm.
Closed Saturday nights (except reservations),
Sundays and 3 weeks in August.

Hotel: 18 rooms: single 8, double 10.
Other points: bar, credit cards accepted, à la
carte menu, pets allowed, car parking,
traditional decor.
Address: 10 place du 11 Novembre.
HOTELS VANPYER, tel 21.38.26.55.

SAINT PAUL, Oise 60650, Map 2 ⊗ ♈

LE RELAIS SAINT PAUL, RN 31, on Beauvais, Rouen, Le Havre road

Places of interest: Parc d'attraction de Saint
Paul, abbaye de Saint Germer de Fly, Beauvais,
Gerberoy (village fleuri).
Menu: 55 Frs
Restaurant.

Other points: bar, children welcome, garden
terrace, pets allowed, car parking, traditional
decor.
Address: Route Nationale 31.
MME JEANNE-LISE FAURE, tel 44.82.20.19.

SAINT QUENTIN, Aisne 02100, Map 2 ⊗ ♈ ⌂

LE VASCO DE GAMA

Places of interest: Centre ville, Xenon.
Languages: English, German, Dutch,
Portuguese
Menu: 48 Frs
Accommodation: 75 to 98 Frs
Restaurant: dinner 7–10pm.

Hotel: 11 rooms: single 8, double 3. Showers,
private WCs, TV, phone.
Other points: bar, credit cards accepted,
children welcome, pets allowed, car parking.
Address: 30 place Cordier.
MME MARI ALICE, tel 23.68.22.84.

SAINT QUENTIN LAMOTTE, Somme 80880, Map 2   ⊗♀

A GROS JACQUES, RD 925 between Eu and Abbeville

Places of interest: Parc ornithologique (25km),
Marquenter.
Menu: 52 to 62 Frs
Restaurant: lunch 12–2.30pm. Closed Sundays
and 20 August to 5 September.

Other points: bar, credit cards accepted,
lounge area, garden terrace, pets allowed.
Address: Route Départementale 925.
MME JEANINE DECAYEUX, tel 22.60.41.14

SAINT RIQUIER, Somme 80135, Map 2   ⊗♀

LE CENTULOIS

Restaurant: closed Wednesdays.
Other points: bar.

Address: 70 rue du Général de Gaulle.
MME LILI COLINET, tel 22.28.88.15.

SALOUEL, Somme 80480, Map 2   ⊗♀

AUBERGE DU TROU NORMAND, RN 29

Languages: German, English
Restaurant: lunch 12–3pm, dinner 7–9pm.
Closed Saturday afternoons, Sundays and 2 to
26 August.

Other points: bar, children welcome,
traditional decor.
Address: 75 route de Rouen.
M. JEAN-MICHEL PICARD, tel 22.95.53.90.

SERIFONTAINE, Oise 60590, Map 2   ⊗♀⌂

LE RELAIS FLEURI, between Gournay en Bray and Gisors

Places of interest: Cathédrale, musée de la
tapisserie à Beauvais (40km), abbaye de Saint
Germer de Fly (10km).
Menu: 52,50 to 80 Frs
Accommodation: 90 to 160 Frs
Restaurant: lunch 12–2pm, dinner 7–9pm.
Closed Saturdays and Sundays.

Hotel: 9 rooms: single 3, double 6. Showers,
baths, private WCs.
Other points: bar, car parking.
Address: 22 rue Hacque.
MME ANNICK FONTAINE, tel 44.84.89.17.

SOREL EN VIMEU, Somme 80490, Map 2   ⊗♀

LE SYMPATIC, RD 903 between Beauvais and Paris

Place of interest: Château de Rambures.
Language: English
Menu: 55 to 77 Frs
Restaurant: lunch 11.30–3pm, dinner
6.30–10pm.

Other points: bar, children welcome.
Address: 1 route de Paris.
M. SERGE DELBECQ, tel 22.28.60.50.

STEENVOORDE, Nord 59114, Map 1 ⊗

CAFETERIA DE STEENVOORDE, A 25 in both directions

Places of interest: Le Mont Noir, Cassel, beaucoup d'anciens moulins à vent, la cristallerie d'Arques (Saint Omer).
Restaurant.

Other points: credit cards accepted, garden terrace, pets allowed, car parking.
Address: Aire de Saint-Laurent.
M. MICHEL JAMINION, tel 28.49.71.33.

TATINGHEM, Pas-de-Calais 62500, Map 1 ⊗ ♈

LE TRUCK WASH, RN 42 between Boulogne and Saint Omer

Place of interest: Cathédrale de Saint Omer.
Language: English
Menu: 55 Frs including coffee
Restaurant: lunch 12–2.30pm, dinner 7.30–9pm. Closed Saturday afternoons, Sundays and in August and December.

Other points: bar, credit cards accepted, children welcome, garden terrace, pets allowed, car parking.
Address: Zone Artisanale.
JACQUES AND CHRISTINE LEROY, tel 21.98.45.45.

TOURCOING, Nord 59200, Map 1 ⊗ ♈ 🏠

AU SIGNAL D'ARRET, exit Tourcoing les Francs, right at lights

Menu: 56 Frs
Accommodation: 85 to 135 Frs
Restaurant: lunch 11.30–3pm, dinner 7.30–9.30pm. Closed Saturdays, Sundays and second 2 weeks of August.
Hotel: 5 rooms: single 3, double 2. Showers, baths, private WCs, TV.

Other points: bar, credit cards accepted, children welcome, lounge area, pets allowed, car parking, traditional decor.
Address: 28 rue des Francs.
M. MICHEL GUILBERT, tel 20.26.56.74.

TROSLY BREUIL, Oise 60350, Map 2 ⊗ ♈

LA TERRASSE, RN 31 between Compiègne and Soissons

Places of interest: Château et forêt de Compiègne (10km), château de Pierrefonds (8km), le wagon de l'armistice.
Languages: German, Italian
Menu: 52 Frs
Restaurant: lunch 11.30–3.30pm, dinner 6.45–9.30pm. Closed Sundays and 15 days

in August.
Other points: bar, credit cards accepted, à la carte menu, garden terrace, pets allowed, car parking.
Address: 47 route de Reims.
M. ENSO DAL SACCO, tel 44.85.70.39.

VALENCIENNES, Nord 59300, Map 1 ⊗ ♈ 🏠

AUBERGE DE LA POTERNE, RN 29 exit Valenciennes south

Places of interest: Musée, fortifications, basilique.
Menu: 50 Frs
Restaurant: lunch 12–2pm, dinner 7.30–9.30pm. Closed Sundays (out of season) and for Christmas and New Year's day.

Hotel: 12 rooms: single 6, double 6.
Other points: bar, garden terrace, pets allowed, car parking.
Address: 9 boulevard Eissen.
M. JEAN DEMOLLE, tel 27.46.44.98.

VILLERS COTTERETS, Aisne 02600, Map 2 ⊗♈⌂

AU BOUT DU MONDE, RD 936

Places of interest: Musée Alexandre Dumas, château François I, musée du bois.
Menu: 52 to 110 Frs
Accommodation: 95 to 130 Frs
Restaurant: lunch 11.30–3pm, dinner 7–10pm. Closed Sundays and from 21 December to 5 January.
Specialities: confit, pierre gourmande, escargots Alexandre.
Hotel: 5 rooms: single 2, double 3.
Other points: bar, credit cards accepted, children welcome, à la carte menu, garden terrace, pets allowed, car parking, traditional decor.
Address: route de la Fern Milon.
MME MICHELE DORGE, tel 23.96.07.12.

WORMHOUT, Nord 59470, Map 1 ⊗

CAFE DE LA FORGE, Dunkerque

Menu: 40 to 60 Frs
Restaurant: lunch 12–2pm, dinner 7–9pm. Closed second 2 weeks of August.
Other points: children welcome, traditional decor.
Address: 84 Grand Place.
M. GUY DEPRIESTER, tel 28.65.62.33.

North West France

AGNEAUX, Manche 50180, Map 3

LE CARREFOUR SAINT GILLES, D 972

Places of interest: Mont Saint Michel, les remparts de Saint Lô (4km).
Languages: German, English
Menu: 50 to 75 Frs
Restaurant: dinner 7–9.30pm. Closed Sundays.

Speciality: fruits de mer.
Other points: bar, credit cards accepted, children welcome, pets allowed, car parking.
Address: Le Bourg, Saint Gilles.
M. JEAN-JACQUES BILLY, tel 33.05.24.50.

AMBENAY, Eure 27250, Map 3

HOTEL DE LA RISLE, RD 830 between Evreux and l'Aigle

Menu: 49 Frs
Restaurant: lunch 12–2pm, dinner 7.30–10pm. Closed Sundays.
Hotel: 6 rooms.

Other points: bar, credit cards accepted, traditional decor.
Address: 9 rue Guy Lacombe.
M. JEAN-LOUIS MARCILLY, tel 32.24.63.45

AMBREUMESNIL, Seine-Maritime 76550, Map 3

LE TORTILLARD, RD 152

Place of interest: Le manoir d'Ango.
Menu: 50 Frs
Restaurant.
Specialities: cassoulet, couscous.

Other points: bar, children welcome, à la carte menu, pets allowed, car parking.
Address: Hameau Ribeuf.
MME GILBERTE DOLBEC, tel 35.83.17.00.

ANETZ, Loire-Atlantique 44150, Map 5

LE RELAIS DE LA BARBINIERE, RN 23 between Angers and Nantes

Language: English
Menu: 46,50 Frs
Accommodation: 70 Frs
Restaurant: lunch 11.30–2pm, dinner 7–9.30pm. Closed Saturdays, Sundays and the week of 15 August.

Hotel: 4 rooms: single 2, double 2.
Other points: bar, credit cards accepted, car parking, traditional decor.
Address: La barbinière, Route Nationale 23.
MME SYLVIE DRONET, tel 40.83.11.25.

ANGERS, Maine-et-Loire 49100, Map 5

CHEZ JEAN-CLAUDE, between Paris and Nantes, exit Saint Serge

Places of interest: Château d'Angers, jardin des plantes, palais des congrès.
Menu: 54 Frs including wine
Accommodation: 120 Frs
Restaurant: lunch 11.30–2.30pm, dinner 7.30–11pm. Closed Saturdays, Sundays and in July and December.
Specialities: crêpes à la mode de Caen, poulet basquaise.

Hotel: 10 rooms: single 8, double 2. Showers, private WCs, TV.
Other points: bar, credit cards accepted, children welcome, lounge area, pets allowed, car parking.
Address: 7 boulevard Ayrault, Place Saint Serge.
M. JEAN-CLAUDE DEROUET, tel 41.43.88.99.

ANGERS, Maine-et-Loire 49100, Map 5 ⊗🍸

LE RELAIS DE L'ARCEAU, exit Angers towards Saumur

Places of interest: Château du Roi René, usine de Cointreau.
Language: English
Menu: 52 Frs
Restaurant: lunch 11.30–2.15pm. Closed Sundays.

Speciality: choucroute.
Other points: bar, credit cards accepted, children welcome, à la carte menu, pets allowed, car parking, traditional decor.
Address: 47 rue Guillaume Lekeu.
M. BRUNO HERANT, tel 41.43.86.25.

ARON, Mayenne 53440, Map 5 ⊗🍸🏠

LE RELAIS DES BRUYERES, RN 12 between Alençon and Mayenne

Place of interest: Bagnol de l'Orme (30km).
Language: German
Menu: 52 to 125 Frs
Accommodation: 120 to 180 Frs
Restaurant: closed Saturdays and in August.
Hotel: 9 rooms: single 7, double 2. Showers, TV.

Other points: bar, credit cards accepted, children welcome, à la carte menu, lounge area, garden terrace, pets allowed, car parking, traditional decor.
Address: Route Nationale 12.
M. JEAN-PIERRE BORDAS, tel 43.04.13.64.

AUTHEUIL AUTHOUILLET, Eure 27490, Map 3 ⊗🍸

CHEZ PIERROT, RD 316 and 836, exit Gaillon towards Evreux

Place of interest: La Vallée de l'Eure.
Restaurant: lunch 12–2pm. Closed Sunday afternoons and mid-August.
Other points: bar, garden terrace, car parking,

traditional decor.
Address: 17 rue de Pacy.
M. PIERRE DENOITTE, tel 32.34.67.67.

AUVERSE, Maine-et-Loire 49490, Map 5 ⊗🍸

CHEZ NANOU, RD 766 between Angers and Tours

Places of interest: Châteaux sur les bords de la Loire.
Language: English
Menu: 51 to 60 Frs
Restaurant: lunch 11.30–2pm, dinner 7–9pm. Closed Sundays (out of season) and first week of October.

Other points: bar, pets allowed, car parking, traditional decor.
Address: route de Noyant, Le Bourg.
MLLE VERONIQUE CHASSEAU, tel 41.82.20.13.

AVRANCHES, Manche 50300, Map 3 ⊗🍸

LES ROUTIERS, RN 176

Menu: 45 Frs
Restaurant: closed Sundays (out of season) and in September.

Other points: bar.
Address: 70 rue de la Constitution.
M. GEORGES HIPPOLYTE, tel 33.58.01.13.

BAGNEUX, Maine-et-Loire 49400, Map 5 ⊗🍸

RELAIS DE BOURNAN, RN 160 between Chôlet and Niort

Places of interest: Caves à champignons, château.
Menu: 55 Frs
Restaurant: lunch 11.30–2pm. Closed Saturday afternoons and Sundays (out of season).

Other points: bar, children welcome, pets allowed, car parking, traditional decor.
Address: 288 rue du Pont Fouchard.
MME JEANINE SANZAY, tel 41.50.18.02.

BAGUER PICAN, Ille-et-Vilaine 35120, Map 4

LE SAINT MICHEL, RN 176 4km from Dol de Bretagne

Places of interest: Le Mont Saint Michel (24km), Saint Malo (30km).
Menu: 45 Frs
Restaurant: closed Monday afternoons.
Hotel: 3 double rooms. Showers.

Other points: bar, credit cards accepted, showers, pets allowed, car parking, traditional decor.
Address: 12 rue de Paris.
M. MICHEL ROBERT, tel 99.48.37.48.

BALLEROY, Calvados 14490, Map 3

LE RELAIS DE LA FORET, RD 572 between Bayeux and Saint Lô

Language: English
Menu: 68 to 140 Frs
Accommodation: 180 to 190 Frs (pension 250 Frs, demi-pension 178 Frs)
Restaurant.
Hotel: 10 rooms, showers, TV.

Other points: bar, credit cards accepted, à la carte menu, car parking.
Address: L'Embranchement, Balleroy.
M. CHRISTIAN DESOBEAUX, tel 31.21.39.78.

BARRE EN OUCHE (LA), Eure 27330, Map 3

CHEZ JACKY ET CORINNE, RN 833 between Paris and Evreux

Place of interest: Château de Beaumesnil (8km).
Menu: 50 Frs
Restaurant: lunch 11.30–3pm, dinner 7–9pm. Closed Sunday afternoons, 8 days in August and 20 December to New Year's day.

Speciality: Escalope normande aux champignons.
Other points: bar, children welcome, pets allowed, car parking, traditional decor.
Address: Grande Rue.
M. JACKY SCIPION, tel 32.44.35.28.

BASSE INDRE, Loire-Atlantique 44610, Map 5

HOTEL BRETON, RD 107

Place of interest: Saint Herblain.
Menu: 45 Frs
Accommodation: 60 Frs
Restaurant: lunch 11–1pm, dinner 7–9pm. Closed weekends and in August.

Hotel: 12 rooms: single 2, double 10.
Other points: pets allowed, car parking.
Address: 10 quai Langlois.
M. YANNICK JAHENY, tel 40.86.01.65.

BAYEUX, Calvados 14400, Map 3

LA COLOMBE, RN 13

Places of interest: Cherbourg, plages du débarquement, cathédrale, musées.
Menu: 48 to 130 Frs
Restaurant: lunch 12–3pm, dinner 5–9pm. Closed Saturday nights and Sunday nights (out of season).

Speciality: fruits de mer.
Other points: bar, credit cards accepted, children welcome, à la carte menu, lounge area, garden terrace, pets allowed, car parking.
Address: 13 route de Caen.
M. GERARD HARDY, tel 31.92.13.65.

BAZOUGES SUR LE LOIR, Sarthe 72200, Map 5 ⊗ ♀

AUBERGE DU SOLEIL LEVANT, RN 23 between La Flèche and Angers

Language: English
Menu: 48 to 62 Frs
Restaurant: lunch 12–2pm, dinner 7–9pm. Closed Saturday afternoons, Sundays and 15 days in November.

Specialities: poulet estragon, choucroute.
Other points: bar, children welcome, à la carte menu.
Address: 79 rue du Maine.
M. DENIS BOREE, tel 43.45.33.47.

BEAUCE, Ille-et-Vilaine 35133, Map 4 ⊗ ♀

LES ROUTIERS – Aux Becs Fins, RN 12 between Paris and Brest

Place of interest: Château de Fougères.
Menu: 48 Frs
Restaurant: lunch 12–2pm, dinner 7.30–9.30pm. Closed Sundays, public holidays and in August.

Other points: bar, credit cards accepted, pets allowed, car parking, traditional decor.
Address: 19 route de Paris.
M. PIERRICK ROUX, tel 99.99.08.00.

BEAUMAIS, Calvados 14620, Map 3 ⊗ ♀

LE RELAIS DE BEAUMAIS

Menu: 50 Frs
Restaurant: closed Sunday afternoons and 15 days in February.

Other points: bar, car parking.
M. MICHEL LECOQ, tel 31.90.20.78.

BEAUMONT LE ROGER, Eure 27170, Map 3 ⊗ ♀

AUX AMIS, RD 13

Places of interest: Beaumont (6km), Brionne (14km), Bec Hellouin (20km), Neubourg (5km).
Menu: 50 Frs
Restaurant: lunch 11–3pm. Closed Sundays (except reservations) and 15 days in July.

Specialities: magret de canard au poivre, bourguignon, faux filet aux champignons.
Other points: bar, car parking, traditional decor.
Address: Bray.
MME MARGARET HERILS, tel 32.35.05.26.

BEAUVOIR EN LYONS, Seine-Maritime 76220, Map 3 ⊗ ♀

RELAIS NORMAND – Chez Françoise et Julien, RN 31 between Rouen and Reims

Places of interest: Châteaux de Wascueil et Martainville, Lyon.
Menu: 54 Frs including coffee
Restaurant: lunch 11–3pm, dinner 7–9.30pm. Closed Saturdays, Sundays, public holidays,

first week in May and last week in December.
Other points: bar, credit cards accepted, car parking, traditional decor.
Address: Les Carreaux, RN 31.
M. JULIEN JUE, tel 35.90.17.20.

BEAUVOIR SUR MER, Vendée 85230, Map 5 ⊗℞

AU RELAIS DU GOIS, RN 148 between Noirmoutiers and Le Gois

Place of interest: Le passage du Gois (unique en Europe) vers l'Ile de Noirmoutiers.
Menu: 55 to 160 Frs
Restaurant: lunch 12–2pm. Closed December.
Specialities: fruits de mer, poissons.
Other points: bar, credit cards accepted,

children welcome, à la carte menu, garden terrace, pets allowed, car parking, traditional decor.
Address: Route Nationale 148.
M. GILLES GRONDIN, tel 51.68.70.31.

BECON LES GRANITS, Maine-et-Loire 49370, Map 5 ⊗℞

LES GRANITS, RD 961 between Angers and Chateaubriant

Language: English
Menu: 47 to 130 Frs
Restaurant: lunch 11.30–2.30pm, dinner 7–10.30pm. Closed Saturdays.

Other points: bar, credit cards accepted, à la carte menu, pets allowed, car parking.
Address: 1 rue de Candé.
M. BRUNO MACE, tel 41.77.90.44.

BEDEE, Ille-et-Vilaine 35137, Map 4 ⊗℞🏠🍽☆

HOTEL DU COMMERCE, RN 12 between Rennes and Saint-Brieuc

Place of interest: Circuit de Brocéliande.
Language: English
Menu: 55 to 105 Frs
Accommodation: 100 to 138 Frs
Restaurant: lunch 12–2pm, dinner 7.30–9pm. Closed Saturday nights, Sundays and 3 weeks in August.
Specialities: coquilles Saint-Jacques à la Bretonne, gibelotte au cidre, poissons, lapin aux poireaux.

Hotel: 22 rooms: single 1, double 21. Showers, baths, private WCs, TV, phone.
Other points: bar, credit cards accepted, à la carte menu, self-service, pets allowed, car parking.
Address: 14 place de l'Eglise.
M. JEAN-LOUIS RIGOREAU, tel 99.07.00.37.

BEIGNON, Morbihan 56380, Map 4 ⊗℞🏠

LES ROUTIERS, RN 24 between Rennes and Lorient

Places of interest: Forêt Brocéliande, golf du Morbihan, Vannes, La Cité des Corsaires, écoles de Coëtquidan, musée.
Restaurant: lunch 12–2pm, dinner 7–9.30pm. Closed Saturdays after 3pm.
Specialities: fruits de mer, terrine du chef.

Hotel: 6 rooms, showers, TV, phone.
Other points: bar, credit cards accepted, à la carte menu, car parking, traditional decor.
Address: place de l'Eglise.
MME BERTHE-SIMONE LABBE, tel 97.75.74.37.

BELLENGREVILLE, Calvados 14370, Map 3 ⊗℞

LES ROUTIERS, RN 13

Restaurant: closed Sundays.
Other points: bar.

Address: 16 rue de Paris.
M. DESIRE DESMEULLES, tel 31.23.61.50.

BELLEVUE COETQUIDAN, Morbihan 56380, Map 4 ⊗℞🏠

L'UNION

Place of interest: Musée militaire du
Coëtquidan (1km).
Menu: 42 to 50 Frs
Accommodation: 90 to 130 Frs
Restaurant: lunch 12–2pm, dinner 7–9pm.
Closed Sundays and in August.

Hotel: 5 rooms, showers.
Other points: bar, credit cards accepted,
children welcome, pets allowed, car parking.
Address: 3 avenue Brocéliande.
M. OLIVIER GUERIN, tel 97.75.71.46.

BERNAY, Eure 27300, Map 3 ⊗�

L'ESCARBILLE, RN 138 between Rouen and Alençon

Places of interest: Basilique de Lisieux
(20km), musée de l'abbatial, musée de
l'automobile à Bec Heloin (20km).
Language: English
Menu: 45 to 75 Frs
Restaurant: lunch 12–1.30pm, dinner
7.30–9.30pm. Closed Sundays.

Other points: bar, credit cards accepted,
children welcome, à la carte menu, garden
terrace, pets allowed, car parking.
Address: 29 boulevard Dubus.
MME CHANTALE VERDONCK,
tel 33.43.60.43.

BERNAY, Eure 27300, Map 3 ⊗♂⌂

L'ESCALE, RN 13

Places of interest: Monastère à Bec Hellouin
(6km), Château Gaillard.
Menu: 52 Frs
Accommodation: 100 Frs
Restaurant: dinner 7–9pm. Closed Saturday
afternoons, Sundays and in July.

Hotel: 6 rooms: single 1, double 5. Showers,
TV.
Other points: bar, credit cards accepted,
children welcome, pets allowed, car parking.
Address: Carrefour de Malbrouck.
M. MICHEL SILLIAU, tel 32.44.79.99.

BESSE SUR BRAYE, Sarthe 72310, Map 5 ⊗♂⌂☆

LES ROUTIERS, RN 817

Place of interest: Château de Courtanvaux
(2km).
Menu: 46,50 to 50 Frs
Accommodation: 130 to 165 Frs
Restaurant: lunch 12–2pm, dinner 7–9.30pm.
Closed Sundays, in August and early
September.

Hotel: 12 rooms: single 8, double 4. Showers,
baths, private WCs, TV, phone.
Other points: bar, credit cards accepted, pets
allowed, car parking, traditional decor.
Address: 19 avenue de la Gare.
MME NADINE LENOIR, tel 43.35.30.22.

BEUZEVILLE, Eure 27210, Map 3 ⊗♂

CAFE DE L'ESPERANCE, RN 175 and CD 22

Language: English
Menu: 48 Frs
Restaurant: lunch 12–2pm, Saturdays,
Sundays and in August.
Specialities: couscous, choucroute, escalope
viennoise, lapin chasseur.

Other points: bar, pets allowed.
Address: 4 rue Pasteur.
MME DENISE DEGUINE, tel 32.57.70.60.

BEZU SAINT ELOI, Eure 27660, Map 3 ⊗♂

AUBERGE DE LA LEVRIERE, between Gisors and Rouen

Menu: 50 Frs
Restaurant: lunch 12–3pm, dinner 7–9.30pm. Closed Saturday lunch and in August/September.
Specialities: moules normandes, poissons.

Other points: bar, children welcome, à la carte menu, pets allowed, car parking, traditional decor.
Address: 42 route de Gisors.
M. YVES ROQUAIN, tel 32.55.07.12.

BIVILLE LA BAIGNADE, Seine-Maritime 76890, Map 3 ⊗ ♈

LA CUILLERE EN BOIS, RN 27

Restaurant: closed Wednesdays.
Other points: bar.

MME YVETTE GUERILLON, tel 35.32.88.81.

BLAIN, Loire-Atlantique 44130, Map 5 ⊗ ♈

LE RELAIS DU CHATEAU, RN 171 between Saint Nazaire (40km) and Rennes (80km)

Places of interest: Château de la Groulais, forêt de Gavres.
Menu: 48 Frs including wine
Restaurant: closed Sundays.
Other points: bar, credit cards accepted, pets

allowed, car parking.
Address: known as Le Gravier.
MLLE FRANCESCA BONHOMME, tel 40.79.97.11.

BOISNEY, Eure 27800, Map 3 ⊗ ♈ 🏠

CHEZ JEAN-PIERRE, RN 13 between Evreux and Lisieux

Places of interest: Basilique de Lisieux (32km), abbaye de Bec Hellouin (10km).
Menu: 48,50 Frs
Accommodation: 145 to 190 Frs
Restaurant: lunch 11–3pm, dinner 7–9.30pm. Closed Sundays.

Hotel: 7 rooms: single 3, double 4.
Other points: bar, children welcome, garden terrace, pets allowed, car parking.
Address: Route Nationale 13.
M. JEAN-PIERRE THOMAS, tel 32.46.23.43.

BOLBEC, Seine-Maritime 76210, Map 3 ⊗ ♈ 🏠

AUBERGE NORMANDE, N15

Menu: 50 Frs
Accommodation: 85 Frs
Restaurant: lunch 11.30–2.30pm, dinner 7–10pm. Closed Saturdays, Sundays, 15 days in August and 15 in December.
Hotel: 5 rooms: single 3, double 2. Baths.

Other points: bar, credit cards accepted, garden terrace, pets allowed, car parking.
Address: Route Nationale 15, Trouville-Alliquerville.
M. GERARD BAUDRIBOS, tel 35.31.15.21.

BONCHAMP LES LAVAL, Mayenne 53210, Map 5 ⊗ ♈ 🏠

RELAIS DE LA CORBINNIERE, RN 157 between Le Mans and Laval

Places of interest: Château de Laval (7km), château de Sainte Suzanne (30km), grottes de Saulges (30km), la vallée de la Mayenne.
Menu: 50 Frs
Accommodation: 80 to 100 Frs
Restaurant: closed Sundays (out of season).
Hotel: 6 rooms: single 2, double 4.

Other points: bar, credit cards accepted, children welcome, garden terrace, pets allowed, car parking, traditional decor.
Address: Route Nationale 157.
MME MICHELLE PERRIGAUD, tel 43.90.36.04.

BONNEVILLE SUR ITON (LA), Eure 27190, Map 3 ⊗♈

LE CAFE DES SPORTS, RN 830

Place of interest: Etang de la Noé.
Menu: 48 Frs
Restaurant: closed August and between
Christmas and New Year's day.

Other points: bar, car parking.
Address: 45 rue Jean Maréchal.
M. ROLAND FONTAINE, tel 32.37.10.16.

BOSGUERARD DE MARCOUVILLE, Eure 27520, Map 3 ⊗♈⌂

AUBERGE DE LA TETE D'OR, RN 138

Accommodation: 115 to 160 Frs
Restaurant.
Hotel: 10 rooms.

Other points: bar.
Address: Route Nationale 138.
MME COLETTE FOURNIER, tel 35.87.60.24.

BOUGUENAIS, Loire-Atlantique 44340, Map 5 ⊗♈

A LA FERME, RN 751, industrial zone of Cheviré (near port)

Places of interest: Vallée de la Loire, Nantes.
Menu: 47 to 51 Frs including wine and coffee
Restaurant: closed Saturdays and Sundays.
Other points: bar, pets allowed, car parking,

traditional decor.
Address: 65 rue de la Pierre.
M. YVON BURLOT, tel 40.65.23.58.

BOULOIRE, Sarthe 72440, Map 5 ⊗♈

LE P'TIT MARCHE, RN 157 between Le Mans and Saint Calais

Place of interest: Parc animalier de Pescheray.
Menu: 49 to 85 Frs
Restaurant: closed Thursdays and 20 October
to 20 November.
Other points: bar, credit cards accepted,

children welcome, garden terrace, pets allowed,
car parking, traditional decor.
Address: 82 rue Nationale.
M. FRANCIS HEMONNET, tel 43.35.40.04.

BOURG BEAUDOUIN, Eure 27380, Map 3 ⊗♈

AU PECHE MIGNON, RN 14 between Fleury sur Andelle and Rouen

Places of interest: Château de Martinville,
Rouen, château de Vascoeuil.
Menu: 50 Frs
Restaurant: closed Sundays.

Other points: bar, credit cards accepted,
children welcome, pets allowed, car parking.
Address: Route Nationale 19.
M. PASCAL LENOIR, tel 32.49.05.20.

BOURGNEUF EN MAUGES, Maine-et-Loire 49290, Map 5 ⊗♈⌂

RELAIS DE LA BOULE D'OR, RD 762

Menu: 45 to 140 Frs
Accommodation: 100 to 150 Frs
Restaurant: lunch 12–2pm, dinner 7–8pm.
Closed Wednesday afternoons.
Hotel: 5 rooms, showers, baths, private WCs.

Other points: bar, pets allowed, car parking,
traditional decor.
Address: 6 rue Notre Dame.
M. THIERRY VERON, tel 41.78.03.61.

BOURGNEUF EN RETZ, Loire-Atlantique 44580, Map 5 ⊗♀⌂

HOTEL DES TRADITIONS LE BOIRAT

Language: a little English
Restaurant: closed Saturdays.
Hotel: 6 rooms.

Other points: bar, car parking.
Address: 11 avenue de la Gare.
M. NOEL ROUSSELOT, tel 40.21.91.44.

BOURNEZEAU, Vendée 85480, Map 5 ⊗♀

LE RELAIS DU CHEVAL BLANC, RD 949 and 948 La Roche-sur-Yon/Fontenay-le-Comte

Places of interest: La Roche sur Yon (20km),
le Puy du Fou (35km), plages (20km).
Language: Spanish
Menu: 47 Frs
Restaurant.
Other points: bar, credit cards accepted,

children welcome, à la carte menu, garden
terrace, pets allowed, car parking, traditional
decor.
Address: 29 rue Jean Grolleau.
MME SYLVIA DEMESY, tel 51.40.71.54.

BRECE, Mayenne 53120, Map 5 ⊗♀

LE DOMINO

Menu: 49,50 Frs
Restaurant: lunch 12–2pm, dinner 7–9pm.
Other points: bar, credit cards accepted, pets

allowed, car parking, traditional decor.
Address: Le Bourg.
MME JANINE CARLIN, tel 43.08.62.72.

BRECOURT DOUAINS, Eure 27120, Map 3 ⊗♀

LE PACY VERNON, RN 181 between Pacy sur Eure and Vernon

Places of interest: Musée Claude Monet à
Giverny, parc ornithologique de Bernay.
Menu: 52 Frs
Restaurant: closed Sundays and in August.
Other points: bar, children welcome, garden

terrace, pets allowed, car parking, traditional
decor.
Address: Route Nationale 181.
M. ALAIN COTE, tel 32.52.44.67.

BRETEUIL SUR ITON, Eure 27160, Map 3 ⊗♀

CHEZ CLAUDE, RD 833

Places of interest: Châteaux, étang de Condé
sur Iton.
Menu: 52 Frs including wine and coffee
Restaurant: lunch 12–2pm. Closed Sundays
and in August.

Other points: bar, garden terrace, pets allowed,
car parking, traditional decor.
Address: Le Chesnay, Condé sur Iton.
M. CLAUDE BLANFUNE, tel 32.29.89.27.

BRETEUIL SUR ITON, Eure 27160, Map 3 ⊗♀

LE RELAIS DES MARES, RD 840

Places of interest: Rouen, Center Parc.
Menu: 51 Frs
Restaurant: dinner 7.30–11.30pm. Closed
Saturdays and Sundays.

Other points: bar, pets allowed, car parking,
traditional decor.
Address: Le Chesne.
M. DANICK GUIOT, tel 32.29.85.09.

BRETTEVILLE SUR DIVES, Calvados 14170, Map 3 ⊗❸♈

LE BRETTEVILLAIS, RD 16 between Saint Pierre sur Dives and Lisieux

Place of interest: Basilique de Lisieux.
Menu: 50 Frs
Restaurant.
Other points: bar, children welcome, lounge area, pets allowed, car parking, traditional decor.
MME PATRICIA DUFAILLY,
tel 31.20.13.31.

BRIONNE, Eure 27800, Map 3 ⊗♈🏠☆☆

HOTEL DU HAVRE between Bernay and Rouen

Place of interest: Château du XIIième siècle.
Menu: 50 Frs
Accommodation: 180 to 240 Frs
Restaurant: closed 24 December to 2 January.
Speciality: plats en sauce.
Hotel: 32 rooms, showers, baths, private WCs, TV.
Other points: bar, credit cards accepted, children welcome, à la carte menu, lounge area, garden terrace, car parking.
Address: 13 rue de la Soie.
M. JACKY PANE, tel 32.44.80.28.

BROGLIE, Eure 27270, Map 3 ⊗♈🏠

LES TOURISTES ET LES ROUTIERS, RN 138 between Alençon and Rouen

Menu: 55 to 78 Frs
Accommodation: 100 to 140 Frs
Restaurant: lunch 12–3pm, dinner 7–10pm. Closed Wednesdays and in October.
Specialities: rognons au porto, escalope normande, bourguignon.
Hotel: 5 rooms: single 4, double 1. Showers, private WCs.
Other points: bar, credit cards accepted, children welcome, à la carte menu, pets allowed, traditional decor.
Address: 47 rue Augustin Fresnel.
M. JEAN-LOUIS BUNEL, tel 32.44.60.38.

CAEN VENOIX, Calvados 14350, Map 3 ⊗♈🏠

LE VELODROME, RN 175 exit Caen on the Mont Saint Michel road

Places of interest: Abbaye, églises, musées.
Menu: 44 Frs
Accommodation: 105 Frs (60 Frs per extra bed)
Restaurant: lunch 11.30–2pm, dinner 7–8.30pm. Closed Saturday nights, Sundays and in August.
Hotel: 5 rooms: single 1, double 4. Showers.
Other points: bar, pets allowed.
Address: 9 avenue Henry Cheron.
M. DANIEL LEVIGOUREUX,
tel 31.74.40.71.

CAGNY, Calvados 14630, Map 3 ⊗♈🏠

HOTEL DE LA POSTE, RN 13 between Caen and Lisieux

Menu: 48 Frs
Accommodation: 120 to 150 Frs
Restaurant: dinner 7–8.30pm. Closed Saturday afternoons and Sundays.
Hotel: 5 rooms: single 3, double 2. Showers.
Other points: bar, credit cards accepted, pets allowed, car parking.
Address: 32 route de Paris.
MME ANNICK ROBENARD, tel 31.23.41.26.

CAGNY, Calvados 14630, Map 3   ⊗♀⌂

LE RELAIS DE CAGNY, RN 13

Menu: 47 to 135 Frs
Accommodation: 90 to 120 Frs
Restaurant: closed Saturday afternoons and
Sundays.

Hotel: 13 rooms, TV.
Other points: bar, car parking.
Address: 22 route de Paris.
MME BEATRICE BAYEUL, tel 31.23.41.27.

CALIGNY, Orne 61100, Map 3   ⊗♀

RELAIS DU PONT DE VERE, RD 962 between Flers and Caen

Places of interest: La vallée de la Veré, le
Mont de Cerisy belle étoile.
Menu: 54 Frs including wine or cider and
coffee
Restaurant: lunch 11.30–2.30pm, dinner
7–10pm. Closed Sundays (except reservations),

15 days in August and 1 week in December.
Speciality: tripes.
Other points: bar, credit cards accepted,
children welcome, pets allowed, car parking.
Address: Le Pont de Vère.
M. HENRI VIVIER, tel 33.65.65.60.

CALLAC DE BRETAGNE, Côtes-du-Nord 22160, Map 4   ⊗♀⌂

LES ROUTIERS, between Guingany and Carhaix

Places of interest: Callac et ses environs,
gorges du Corong, plan d'eau.
Language: a little English
Menu: 45 Frs
Accommodation: 90 to 130 Frs
Restaurant: lunch 12–2pm, dinner 7–8.30pm.
Closed Sundays (except reservations) and

15 days end August/early September.
Hotel: 10 rooms: single 8, double 2. Showers.
Other points: bar, children welcome, pets
allowed, car parking, traditional decor.
Address: 21 rue de la Gare.
MME MARIE-YVONNE RICHARD,
tel 96.45.51.10.

CAMBE (LA), Calvados 14230, Map 3   ⊗♀

LE BAR DES SPORTS, RN 13 between Bayeux and Cherbourg

Places of interest: Château de la Colombière,
les plages du débarquement.
Menu: 50 to 55 Frs
Restaurant: lunch 12–2pm, dinner 7–9pm.
Closed Mondays and 23 August to 10
September.

Other points: bar, credit cards accepted,
children welcome, pets allowed, car parking.
Address: Route Nationale 13.
JOLLIVET HOTELS, ROCADE D'ISIGNY,
tel 31.22.72.11.

CAMBRES FRESQUIENNES (LES), Seine-Maritime 76570, Map 3   ⊗♀

LES AMIS DE LA ROUTE, RN 27 between Rouen and Dieppe

Places of interest: Parc zoologique de Clères,
parc d'attractions de Bocasse.
Language: English
Menu: 53 Frs
Restaurant: lunch 11.30–3pm. Closed
Saturdays and Sundays.

Other points: bar, children welcome, garden
terrace, pets allowed, car parking.
Address: Route Nationale 27.
M. LUC LEDRAIT, tel 35.32.51.98.

CARCAGNY, Calvados 14740, Map 3 ⊗ ♎

AUX JOYEUX ROUTIERS, old RN 13 between Caen and Bayeux

Places of interest: Bayeux (8km), mémorial de la Paix à Caen (20km), les plages du débarquement(15km).
Languages: English, Italian
Menu: 50 Frs
Restaurant: lunch 11.45–2pm, dinner 7–9pm. Closed Saturdays and Sundays.

Specialities: boudin noir, tripes, petit salé, pâtisseries maison.
Other points: bar, credit cards accepted, children welcome, pets allowed, car parking, traditional decor.
Address: Le Hameau Saint Léger.
M. MICHEL PACARY, tel 31.80.22.01.

CARENTAN, Manche 50500, Map 3 ⊗ ♎

LE DERBY, RN 13 between Bayeux and Caen

Places of interest: Les plages du débarquement, église et mairie (cites classés), port de plaisance.
Menu: 45 to 49 Frs
Restaurant: dinner 7.30–9pm. Closed Saturday afternoons, Sundays, public holidays, 3 weeks at end September and first 2 in May.

Speciality: tripes maison.
Other points: bar, children welcome, pets allowed, car parking.
Address: 21 rue de la 101 Airborne.
M. MAURICE LEGUELINEL, tel 33.42.04.77.

CARPIQUET, Calvados 14650, Map 3 ⊗ ♎ 🏠

LE POURQUOI PAS between Caen and Cherbourg

Places of interest: Caen (2km), Bayeux.
Menu: 45 Frs including wine and coffee
Restaurant: lunch 11.30–2pm, dinner 6.30–8.30pm. Closed Saturday nights and Sundays.
Speciality: tripes à la mode de Caen.

Hotel: 4 rooms, showers, baths.
Other points: bar, garden terrace, car parking, traditional decor.
Address: 33 route de Bayeux, Bellevue.
M. DIDIER PREMPAIN, tel 31.73.84.84.

CAUDAN, Morbihan 56850, Map 4 ⊗ ♎

LE BOUTON D'OR, RD 81 between Quimper and Nantes, exit at Lorient

Places of interest: Port de plaisance, Lorient.
Language: English
Menu: 41 to 45 Frs
Restaurant: lunch 11.30–3pm. Closed Saturdays, Sundays and in August.

Speciality: couscous de poisson.
Other points: bar, lounge area, garden terrace, car parking.
Address: ZA Kergoussel.
MME JOELLE LE BAIL, tel 97.81.16.01.

CAUDEBEC LES ELBEUF, Seine-Maritime 76320, Map 3 ⊗ ♎

LE TIVOLI BAR on the road to Pont l'Arche

Menu: 50 Frs
Restaurant: lunch 11.30–2.30pm, dinner 6.30–8pm. Closed Sundays.
Other points: bar.

Address: 43 rue Félix Faure.
MME CLAUDETTE TOUCHARD,
tel 35.77.19.94.

CAULNES, Côtes-du-Nord 22350, Map 4   ⊗ ♈

LES ROUTIERS

Restaurant.
Other points: bar.
Address: 40 rue de la Gare.

MME MARIE-THERESE GAUDREL,
tel 96.83.94.14.

CAUVERVILLE EN ROUMOIS, Eure 27350, Map 3   ⊗ ♈

LA MEDINE, RN 175 towards Rouen

Places of interest: Château Robert le Diable,
maquis Barneville, pont de Tancarville.
Menu: 47,50 Frs including wine
Restaurant: lunch 11–6pm. Closed Saturdays,
Sundays and in August.
Specialities: choucroute, pizzas, couscous.

Other points: bar, children welcome, pets
allowed, car parking, traditional decor.
Address: Route Nationale 175.
M. JEAN-PIERRE FERRETTE,
tel 32.57.01.55.

CEAUCE, Orne 61330, Map 3   ⊗ ♈

LE RELAIS DE L'ETAPE, RD 962 between Caen and Laval, Laval and Nantes

Place of interest: Domfront (village fleuri).
Restaurant: lunch 11.30–2.30pm, dinner
7–10pm. Closed Sundays.
Speciality: fruits de mer (by arrangement).
Other points: bar, credit cards accepted,

children welcome, car parking, traditional
decor.
Address: 21 rue de Domfront.
MME MICHELE GERAULT, tel 33.30.84.04.

CHAIGNES, Eure 27120, Map 3   ⊗ ♈ ⌂

MA CAMPAGNE, RN 13

Language: English
Restaurant: closed Saturday nights and
Sundays.
Hotel: 14 rooms.

Other points: bar.
Address: Route Nationale 13.
M. GERARD DUCOAT, tel 32.36.95.52.

CHAILLE LES MARAIS, Vendée 85450, Map 5   ⊗ ♈

AU CHTI-MI, RN 137 between Nantes and La Rochelle

Place of interest: La Venise Verte.
Language: English
Menu: 52 to 62 Frs
Restaurant: lunch 11.30–2.30pm, dinner
7–9pm. Closed Saturday afternoons and
Sundays (out of season).

Other points: bar, credit cards accepted,
children welcome, pets allowed, car parking,
traditional decor.
Address: 13 rue Principale, Le Sableau.
M. JEAN-PIERRE TISON, tel 51.56.70.87.

CHALLANS, Vendée 85300, Map 5   ⊗ ♈

RELAIS DE LA NOUE, RN 148

Menu: 42 to 48,30 Frs
Restaurant: lunch 11.30–2.30pm, dinner
7.30–9pm. Closed Saturdays, Sundays and
3 weeks in August.

Other points: bar, children welcome, pets
allowed, car parking, traditional decor.
Address: place Victor Charbonnel.
MME MONIQUE MENEZ, tel 51.93.20.20.

CHAMBRETAUD, Vendée 85500, Map 5 ⊗

AUBERGE BEL'AIR, RN 160 between Cholet (18km) and La Roche sur Yon (52km)

Place of interest: Le Puy du Fou.
Languages: English, Italian
Menu: 52 to 150 Frs
Restaurant: lunch 12–3pm, dinner 7–10pm.
Speciality: fondue Bourguignone au vin rouge.
Other points: credit cards accepted, children

welcome, à la carte menu, garden terrace, pets allowed, car parking, traditional decor.
Address: route du Puy du Fou.
MME JACQUELINE MARTIN,
tel 51.67.51.61.

CHAMPAGNE, Sarthe 72470, Map 5 ⊗ 🍷

LE RELAIS DES FOUGERES, RN 157 between Le Mans and Saint Calais

Menu: 49,50 to 85 Frs
Restaurant: lunch 11.30–2pm, dinner 6.30–8pm. Closed Saturday afternoons and Sundays.
Other points: bar, credit cards accepted, à la

carte menu, garden terrace, pets allowed, car parking, traditional decor.
Address: route de Saint Calais.
M. ANTOINE MICHELIC, tel 43.89.50.96.

CHAMPTOCE SUR LOIRE, Maine-et-Loire 49170, Map 5 ⊗ 🍷 🏠

HOTEL LES RIVETTES, RN 23 Nantes to Angers, 25km from Angers on Route de Montjean, 150m off RN 23

Places of interest: La vallée de la Loire, château d'Angers, les vignobles, châteaux de la Loire.
Languages: English, Spanish
Menu: 40 Frs
Accommodation: 69 to 145 Frs
Restaurant: closed Saturdays, Sundays and 15 July to 15 August.

Specialities: tripes à l'Angevine, canard sauce muscade.
Hotel: 4 double rooms. Showers.
Other points: bar, self-service, garden terrace, pets allowed, car parking.
Address: route de Montjean.
MME AGNES CHENE, tel 41.39.91.75.

CHANGE, Mayenne 53810, Map 5 ⊗ 🍷

CHEZ CHRISTIANE, RN 30 between Laval and Fougère

Places of interest: Abbaye de Clermont, musée des chouants.
Restaurant: lunch 12–2.30pm, dinner 7–10pm.
Speciality: fruits de mer.
Other points: bar, credit cards accepted,

children welcome, car parking, traditional decor.
Address: Les Chênes Secs.
MME CHRISTIANE POUTEAU,
tel 43.02.39.26.

CHANGE, Mayenne 53810, Map 5 ⊗ 🍷

LE RELAIS DE NIAFLES, A 81 exit 3 Route Laval and Mayenne

Menu: 50 Frs
Restaurant: lunch 11–2.30pm, dinner 6.45–10.30pm. Closed Saturdays and Sundays.
Other points: bar, credit cards accepted, pets

allowed, car parking, traditional decor.
Address: Niafles.
M. PIERRE DADET, tel 43.53.76.15.

CHAPELLE CARO (LA), Morbihan 56460, Map 4

HOTEL DE LA GARE, RN 166

Place of interest: Vannes.
Restaurant: lunch 11–3pm, dinner 7–10pm.
Closed 25 December to 2 January.
Hotel: 4 rooms.

Other points: bar, children welcome.
Address: La Gare.
MME MARIE-CLAIRE BOULVAIS,
tel 97.74.93.47.

CHAPREPUS, Manche 50800, Map 3

LE RELAIS DE CHAMPREPUS, RD 924 between Villedieu (6km) and Granville (18km)

Places of interest: Le zoo de Champrépus
(300m).
Restaurant: lunch 12–2.30pm, dinner
7–8.30pm. Closed Wednesdays (out of season)
and 17 February to 4 March.
Specialities: papillote de saumon, terrine de
lapereau, poulet aux poireaux, cassoulet.

Other points: bar, credit cards accepted, à la
carte menu, garden terrace, pets allowed, car
parking, traditional decor.
Address: Le Bourg.
M. PATRICK JOUAUDIN, tel 33.51.42.32.

CHARTRE SUR LE LOIR (LA), Sarthe 72340, Map 5

RESTAURANT JEANNE D'ARC

Menu: 42 to 70 Frs
Accommodation: 100 Frs
Restaurant: lunch 12–2.30pm, dinner 7–9pm.
Closed Sundays.
Hotel: 5 rooms: single 4, double 1. Showers.

Other points: bar, children welcome, pets
allowed, car parking, traditional decor.
Address: 23 place Carnot.
M. JACQUES OLIVIER, tel 43.44.41.14.

CHASSILLE LOVE, Sarthe 72540, Map 5

LE PETIT ROBINSON, RN 157, Mans 25km

Place of interest: Grottes de Saulges (20km).
Menu: 55 Frs
Accommodation: 80 to 100 Frs
Restaurant: lunch 12–2pm, dinner 7–10pm.
Closed Saturdays and Sunday lunch and in
August.
Specialities: tête de veau sauce ravigote, tarte
tatin.

Hotel: 4 rooms, single 3, double 1.
Other points: bar, credit cards accepted, car
parking, traditional decor.
Address: Le Petit Robinson.
M. OLIVIER FOURNIGAULT,
tel 43.88.92.01.

CHATEAU GONTIER, Mayenne 53200, Map 5

RESTAURANT L'ETOILE – Chez Nicole et Nono, RN 162 between Laval and Angers

Places of interest: Châteaux, croisière sur la
Mayenne.
Menu: 44 Frs including wine
Restaurant: lunch 11.45–2.30pm, dinner
7–9pm. Closed Sundays, public holidays and in
August.

Other points: bar, credit cards accepted,
garden terrace, pets allowed, car parking.
Address: 43 rue Garnier.
M. NORBERT CORVE, tel 43.07.20.80.

CHATEAU L'HERMITAGE, Sarthe 72510, Map 5 ⊗ ᵧ

LA BELLE CROIX, RD 307

Place of interest: Le Lude.
Menu: 47,50 Frs
Restaurant: closed Sundays.

Other points: bar.
M. BRUNO DAVID, tel 43.46.35.73.

CHATEAUBRIANT, Loire-Atlantique 44110, Map 5 ⊗ ᵧ

CAFE DE LA POSTE, RN 171 between Laval and Paris

Place of interest: Châteaubriant.
Restaurant: lunch 12–2pm. Closed Mondays,
Wednesday afternoons and in August.

Other points: bar, pets allowed, car parking.
Address: 7 place Talhouât.
M. CLAUDE FRUCHARD, tel 40.28.62.36.

CHATEAUBRIANT, Loire-Atlantique 44110, Map 5 ⊗ ᵧ ⌂ ☆

PARIS – OCEAN, road to Laval, behind the station

Place of interest: Château.
Languages: English, Spanish
Menu: 35 to 115 Frs
Accommodation: 85 to 100 Frs
Restaurant: lunch 12–3pm, dinner 7.30–11pm.
Specialities: rognons de veau flambés, truite
Paris-Océan.

Hotel: 7 rooms: single 4, double 3.
Other points: bar, credit cards accepted,
children welcome, à la carte menu, garden
terrace, pets allowed, car parking.
Address: 25 rue d'Ancenis.
M. PATRICK GELEE, tel 40.81.21.79.

CHATEAUNEUF, Ille-et-Vilaine 35430, Map 4 ⊗ ᵧ ⌂

HOTEL DU LION D'OR, RN 137 between Rennes and Saint Malo

Places of interest: Dinan (12km), Saint Malo
(10km), Saint Suliac (4km), les bords de La
Rance (3km).
Language: English
Menu: 52 to 120 Frs
Accommodation: 130 to 280 Frs
Restaurant: lunch 12–2pm, dinner 7–10pm.
Closed November.
Speciality: grillades.

Hotel: 9 rooms: single 2, double 7. Showers,
baths.
Other points: bar, credit cards accepted,
children welcome, à la carte menu, garden
terrace, pets allowed, car parking.
Address: rue Principale Bourg.
MME GINETTE BRODBECKER,
tel 99.58.40.11.

CHATEAUTHEBAUD, Loire-Atlantique 44690, Map 5 ⊗ ᵧ ⌂

LA SAUCISSE VOLANTE, RN 137, Nantes 15km, to the south of the Loire

Places of interest: Nantes (15km), route des
vins.
Menu: 52,50 Frs
Accommodation: 78 Frs
Restaurant: lunch 12–2.30pm, dinner
7–10.30pm. Closed Saturday nights, Sundays
and 3 weeks in July or August.

Speciality: grillades.
Hotel: 5 rooms: single 1, double 4.
Other points: bar, credit cards accepted,
garden terrace, car parking, traditional decor.
Address: route de la Rochelle, Le Butay.
M. SERGE VIOLEAU, tel 40.06.63.55.

CHERBOURG, Manche 50100, see also Glacerie (La), Map 3

⊗ ℽ

LES ROUTIERS, RN 13

Languages: English, Spanish
Restaurant.
Other points: bar.

Address: 10 rue de l'Onglet.
MME VIVIANE COUVRIE, tel 33.53.08.15.

CHOLET, Maine-et-Loire 49300, Map 5

⊗ ℽ

CHEZ LA GUICHE, RN 160 near freight station

Place of interest: Chôlet.
Menu: 52 Frs including wine
Restaurant: dinner 7–9.30pm. Closed
Saturdays and Sundays.
Other points: bar, credit cards accepted, car

parking, traditional decor.
Address: 66 boulevard de Strasbourg.
M. CHRISTIAN GUICHETEAU,
tel 41.62.27.79.

CHOLET, Maine-et-Loire 49300, Map 5

⊗ ℽ ⌂

HOTEL RESTAURANT LES ROUTIERS, RN 160

Menu: 45 Frs
Accommodation: 70 to 90 Frs
Restaurant: lunch 12–2pm, dinner 7.30–9pm.
Closed Saturday nights, Sundays and 13 July to
13 August.

Hotel: 19 rooms: single 13, double 6.
Other points: bar, children welcome, pets
allowed, car parking.
Address: 13 place de la République.
M. MICHEL DUBILLOT, tel 41.62.11.09.

CHOLET, Maine-et-Loire 49300, Map 5

⊗ ℽ

LE RELAIS DES PRAIRIES, RN 160 opposite airport

Places of interest: Lac de Ribou (7km), lac du
Verdon (7km), Puy du Fou (25km).
Languages: German, English
Menu: 44 to 155 Frs
Restaurant: lunch 12–2pm, dinner 7.30–9pm.
Closed Saturdays (except reservations) and 25
December to 2 January.
Specialities: onglet à l'échalotte, côte de boeuf,

tête de veau.
Other points: bar, credit cards accepted,
children welcome, à la carte menu, garden
terrace, pets allowed, car parking.
Address: 3 boulevard du Pont de Pierre, Parc
des Prairies.
M. CLAUDE ALBERT, tel 41.58.09.39.

COEMONT-VOUVRAY, Sarthe 72500, Map 5

⊗ ℽ

LE BON COIN, RN 158 Loire valley

Restaurant: lunch 11.30–3pm. Closed Sundays
and in August.
Other points: bar, children welcome, garden

terrace, pets allowed, car parking, traditional
decor.
MME JOUANNEAU, tel 43.44.04.17.

COLOMBELLES, Calvados 14460, Map 3

⊗ ℽ ⌂

LES VIKINGS, RD 513

Menu: 51 to 90 Frs
Accommodation: 95 to 130 Frs
Restaurant: dinner 7–9.30pm. Closed Sundays and in August.
Hotel: 32 rooms, showers, private WCs.

Other points: bar, credit cards accepted.
Address: 3 route de Cabourg.
M. JEAN-CLAUDE MUSSON,
tel 31.72.18.83.

COLOMBY, Manche 50700, Map 3

CHEZ MEMENE, RD 2 between Valognes and Avranches

Menu: 48 Frs (two choices)
Restaurant: closed Mondays.
Other points: bar, car parking.

Address: Le Bourg, Valognes.
MME GERMAINE DELACOTTE,
tel 33.40.10.59.

COLPO, Morbihan 56390, Map 4

AUX DELICES DE L'OCEAN, between Vannes and Saint Brieuc

Languages: English, Spanish
Menu: 40 to 150 Frs
Accommodation: 79 Frs
Restaurant: lunch 12–2pm, dinner 7–9pm.
Closed Sunday nights and mid-June to mid-July.
Speciality: fruits de mer.

Hotel: 10 rooms: single 4, double 6. Showers.
Other points: bar, credit cards accepted, children welcome, à la carte menu, lounge area, pets allowed, car parking, traditional decor.
Address: 1 avenue de la Princesse.
M. JEAN-CLAUDE LE GUILLAN,
tel 97.66.82.21.

CONCOURSON SUR LAYON, Maine-et-Loire 49700, Map 5

AUBERGE DU HAUT LAYON, RD 160 between Tours and Nantes

Places of interest: Zoo (3km), village troglodytique (10km), jardin des roses.
Language: English
Menu: 54 to 75 Frs
Restaurant: lunch 12–2.30pm, dinner 7–9pm.
Closed Sunday nights.

Other points: bar, credit cards accepted, children welcome, à la carte menu, pets allowed, car parking, traditional decor.
Address: 7 Route Nationale.
M. BERNARD BATTAIS, tel 41.59.27.60.

CONDE SUR HUISNE, Orne 61110, Map 3

L'EUROPEENNE, RN 23 between Chartes and le Mans

Languages: English, Spanish, Italian
Menu: 50 Frs
Restaurant: lunch 12–2pm, dinner 6–10pm.
Closed Sundays (out of season) and 20 December to 6 January.
Speciality: Spanish.

Other points: credit cards accepted, garden terrace, pets allowed, car parking, traditional decor.
Address: La Fourche.
HOTELS L'EUROPEENNE, tel 37.52.53.18.

CONDE SUR NOIREAU, Calvados 14110, Map 3

HOTEL LES PROMENADES, RN 562 between Caen and Flers

Places of interest: Parc municipal, Suisse Normande.
Menu: 45 to 110 Frs
Restaurant: lunch 12–1.30pm, dinner 7.30–9pm. Closed Sundays, public holidays and in August.
Speciality: rognon de veau au Calvados.

Hotel: 6 rooms.
Other points: bar, credit cards accepted, children welcome, à la carte menu, self-service, garden terrace, pets allowed, car parking.
Address: 2 rue Motte de Lutre, Angle rue Saint Martin.
M. MICHEL JOMAT, tel 31.69.03.36.

CONNERRE, Sarthe 72160, Map 5

LA BICHE DOREE, RN 23 between Le Mans and Paris

Places of interest: Musée de l'automobile et circuit au Mans, le vieux Mans (18km), domaine animalier de Pescherau (7km), étang de Tuffé.
Languages: English, a little German
Menu: 50 Frs
Accommodation: 90 to 130 Frs
Restaurant: lunch 12–2.30pm, dinner 7–10pm.

Closed Saturdays and Sundays (except reservations).
Hotel: 10 rooms: single 6, double 4. Showers, baths.
Other points: bar, credit cards accepted, pets allowed, car parking.
Address: Route Nationale 23, La Belle Inutile.
M. DOMINIQUE HERAULT, tel 43.76.70.45.

CORNE, Maine-et-Loire 4925, Map 5

LE RELAIS DE LA CROIX BLANCHE, RN 147 between Tours and Nantes via Saumur

Places of interest: Château de Montgeoffroy à Maze (7km), château de Pignerolle, musée de la communication à Saint Barth.
Menu: 50 Frs
Restaurant: lunch 12–1.30pm, dinner 7.30–9pm. Closed Saturday nights, Sundays

and 1 week between Christmas and New Year's day.
Other points: credit cards accepted, pets allowed, car parking, traditional decor.
Address: Route Nationale 147.
M. JEAN-NOEL PIGNARD, tel 41.45.01.82.

CORON, Maine-et-Loire 49690, Map 5

LA BOULE D'OR between Chôlet and Saumur

Places of interest: Saumur, Angers, bords de la Loire.
Language: English
Menu: 50 to 150 Frs including wine and coffee
Restaurant: lunch 12–2pm, dinner 7–9pm. Closed Mondays.

Other points: bar, credit cards accepted, children welcome, à la carte menu, pets allowed, car parking, traditional decor.
MME ANNIE CHAUVEAU, tel 41.55.80.72.

CORPS NUDS, Ille-et-Vilaine 35150, Map 4

LES ROUTIERS, RN 163 between Rennes and Angers

Menu: 42 Frs
Restaurant: lunch 12–1.30pm. Closed Saturdays, Sundays and in August.

Other points: bar, credit cards accepted.
Address: 7 place de l'Eglise.
MME SOLANGE PIEL, tel 99.44.00.25.

COURGAINS, Sarthe 72260, Map 5

LA PETITE MARMITE, RD 19 towards Mamers

Places of interest: Les Alpes Mancelles, forêt perseigne.
Menu: 46 Frs
Restaurant: lunch 12–2pm, dinner 7–8pm. Closed Thursdays and in February.
Other points: bar, children welcome, garden terrace, pets allowed, car parking, traditional decor.
Address: Le Bourg.
MME MARIE-PIERRE VINCELET, tel 43.33.69.44.

COUTANCES, Manche 50202, Map 3   ⊗♟⌂

CLOSERIE DES LILAS

Languages: Portuguese, Spanish, English
Menu: 90 to 103 Frs
Restaurant.
Hotel: 14 rooms.
Other points: bar.
Address: 1 rue des Abattoirs.
M. GILLES LETOURNEUR, tel 33.45.53.23.

COUTANCES, Manche 50202, Map 3   ⊗♟⌂

LE RELAIS DU VIADUC, RN 171 between Granville and Saint Lô

Places of interest: Cathédrale de Coutances, château du Grato.
Language: English
Menu: 48 to 220 Frs
Accommodation: 90 to 220 Frs
Restaurant.
Specialities: poissons, langouste gratinée, tripes maison, gigot d'agneau.
Hotel: 7 rooms.
Other points: bar, car parking.
Address: 25 avenue de Verdun.
M. JEAN-MARC HARAU, tel 33.45.02.68.

COUVILLE, Manche 50690, Map 3   ⊗♟

LE BOURG NEUF, between Cherbourg and Valognes

Menu: 48 to 55 Frs
Restaurant: lunch 12–4pm, dinner 7–10pm. Closed Tuesday afternoons and in August.
Other points: bar, credit cards accepted, children welcome, à la carte menu, traditional decor.
Address: Le Bourg Neuf.
M. YVES ANQUETIL, tel 33.52.01.76.

COUYERE (LA), Ille-et-Vilaine 35320, Map 4   ⊗♟

AUBERGE CHANTECLAIR

Language: English
Menu: 45 to 65 Frs
Restaurant.
Other points: bar, à la carte menu.
Address: Le Pas.
M. YVES ROMMEL, tel 99.43.13.92.

CROISILLES, Calvados 14220, Map 3   ⊗♟

RELAIS DE LA FORGE, RD 962 between Caen and Flers

Place of interest: Le Pont du Hom.
Menu: 48 Frs
Restaurant.
Other points: bar, credit cards accepted,
children welcome, pets allowed, car parking.
Address: Le Bourg.
MME MONIQUE GIBON, tel 31.79.71.80.

CROISY SUR ANDELLE, Seine-Maritime 76780, Map 3

LE RELAIS DU COMMERCE, RN 31 between Rouen and Beauvais

Menu: 52 to 80 Frs
Restaurant: closed Sundays (out of season) and Christmas.
Specialities: côte normande, entrecôte, tarte aux pommes.

Other points: bar, children welcome, garden terrace, pets allowed, car parking.
Address: Route Nationale 31.
MME COLETTE BELIERE, tel 35.23.61.82.

CROIX MARE, Seine-Maritime 76190, Map 3

LE BON ACCUEIL, RN 15 between Rouen and Yvetot

Places of interest: Abbaye bénédictine de Fécamp (35km), parc régional de Bretonne, cathédrale de Rouen.
Menu: 55 Frs
Restaurant: closed Saturdays, Sundays, 15 days in May and 15 in winter.

Other points: bar, credit cards accepted, children welcome, garden terrace, pets allowed, car parking, traditional decor.
Address: Route Nationale 15.
M. CHRISTIAN LEMAITRE, tel 35.91.25.86.

CUON, Maine-et-Loire 49150, Map 5

LA POMM'DE PIN, RN 938

Menu: 48 to 118 Frs
Restaurant: lunch 11.30–2.30pm, dinner 7.30–10pm. Closed Monday afternoons and last 3 weeks of August.
Hotel: 4 rooms: single 2, double 2. Showers, baths, private WCs.

Other points: bar, credit cards accepted, children welcome, à la carte menu, lounge area, garden terrace, pets allowed, car parking, traditional decor.
Address: Route Nationale 938, Le Bourg.
MME YVETTE PECOT, tel 41.82.75.74.

DEAUVILLE, Calvados 14800, Map 3

AUBERGE DE LA CROIX SONNET, RD 74 St Gatien airport

Places of interest: Deauville (4km), Honfleur (9km).
Languages: English, Spanish, Italian
Menu: 50 to 132 Frs
Accommodation: 200 to 250 Frs
Restaurant: lunch 12–2pm, dinner 7.30–9.30pm. Closed Saturdays (out of season).

Specialities: moules, poissons.
Hotel: 4 single rooms. Showers, baths.
Other points: bar, children welcome, à la carte menu, garden terrace, pets allowed, car parking.
Address: La Croix Sonnet.
MME MARGUERITE PEDRAZZI, tel 31.88.19.62.

DENEE, Maine-et-Loire 49190, Map 5

LE PENALTY

Language: German
Restaurant: closed Sunday afternoons and Christmas to New Year.

Other points: bar.
Address: Place Muller.
M. ALAIN SAULGRAIN, tel 41.78.72.03.

DIEPPE, Seine-Maritime 76200, Map 3

CAFE DE L'AVENIR, RN 15

Place of interest: Dieppe.
Menu: 48 Frs
Restaurant: lunch 11–2pm. Closed Sundays and in August.

Other points: bar, pets allowed, car parking, traditional decor.
Address: 10 cours de Dakar, Port de Commerce.
M. BENOIT PAN, tel 35.84.18.10.

DINAN, Côtes-du-Nord 22100, Map 4

LA MARMITE, RN 176

Places of interest: Saint-Brieuc, le Mont Saint Michel, Cap-Fréhal, Dinan (vieille ville), Saint Malo.
Language: English
Menu: 45 to 75 Frs
Accommodation: 115 to 180 Frs
Restaurant: lunch 12–2pm, dinner 7.30–9pm. Closed Saturday nights, Sundays, 1 week at

Christmas and 3 in July.
Speciality: blancs de seiche à l'armoricaine.
Hotel: 5 rooms: single 3, double 2.
Other points: bar, credit cards accepted, children welcome, pet allowed, car parking.
Address: 91 rue de Brest.
M. GERARD BOUILLET, tel 96.39.04.42.

DINARD, Ille-et-Vilaine 35800, Map 4

L'EPICURIEN – Hôtel de la Gare

Menu: 50 to 80 Frs
Accommodation: 105 to 150 Frs
Restaurant: lunch 12–2.30pm, dinner 7.30–10pm. Closed Saturdays and Sunday nights.

Hotel: 9 rooms.
Other points: bar.
Address: 28 rue de la Corbinais.
M. MARC ARNOULT, tel 99.46.10.84.

DISSAY SOUS COURCILLON, Sarthe 72500, Map 5

RELAIS MAINE TOURAINE, RN 138

Places of interest: Châteaux de la Loire.
Restaurant.
Specialities: fruits de mer, terrines, pâtisserie maison.

Other points: bar, traditional decor.
Address: Route Nationale 138.
MME COLETTE PETIT, tel 43.44.09.08.

DIVES SUR MER, Calvados 14160, Map 3

LE BON GITE

Menu: 45 to 120 Frs
Restaurant: lunch 12–2.30pm, dinner 7–10.30pm. Closed Sunday afternoons and 25 to 31 December.

Specialities: couscous, paëlla.
Other points: bar.
Address: 71 rue du Général de Gaulle.
M. ALAIN BELKACEMI, tel 91.91.24.39.

DIVES SUR MER, Calvados 14160, Map 3

LE CAFE DU PARKING, near Port Guillaume

Places of interest: Village de Guillaume le conquérant, Dives sur Mer.
Menu: 50 Frs
Restaurant: lunch 12–2pm, dinner 7–9pm. Closed Sundays and in August.

Other points: bar, pets allowed, car parking, traditional decor.
Address: 2 rue des Frères Le Paule.
M. DANIEL CONSTANT, tel 31.91.24.25.

DOL DE BRETAGNE, Ille-et-Vilaine 35120, Map 4 ⊗♍🍽

LE RELAIS DE BELLE LANDE, RN 12

Places of interest: Le Mont Saint Michel
(26km), Saint Malo (25km).
Menu: 47 to 90 Frs
Restaurant.
Speciality: moules marinières, bouchots de la
baie.

Other points: bar, à la carte menu.
Address: 23 bis rue de Rennes.
M. JEAN-YVES BEUBRY, tel 99.48.06.14.

DOLO, Côtes-du-Nord 22270, Map 4 ⊗♍

CHEZ PAULETTE, RN 12 between Rennes and Saint Brieuc

Places of interest: Abbaye de Boquen, lacs de
Jugon, château de la Hunaudaye.
Language: English
Menu: 47 Frs
Restaurant: lunch 11.30–3pm, dinner 7–11
pm. Closed Sundays.

Other points: bar, credit cards accepted,
children welcome, pets allowed, car parking,
traditional decor.
Address: Les Vallées.
MME PAULETTE HERVÉ RENONCOURT,
tel 96.31.64.62.

DOMAGNE, Ille-et-Vilaine 35113, Map 4 ⊗♍

L'IMPREVU, RD 95 between Janze and Laval

Place of interest: Le vieux Vitré (15km).
Languages: English, Spanish, Italian
Menu: 50 Frs including coffee
Restaurant: closed Sunday afternoons and 14
July to 15 August.

Other points: bar, children welcome, à la carte
menu, garden terrace, pets allowed, car parking.
Address: 14 place de l'Eglise.
MME ANNICK CANTON, tel 99.00.05.69.

DOMFRONT, Orne 61700, Map 3 ⊗♍🏠🍽☆

LE RELAIS SAINT MICHEL, RN 176 exit Domfront

Places of interest: Eglise romaine du XIe
siècle, fouilles de la chapelle du XIe siècle, cité
médiévale.
Language: English
Menu: 50 to 140 Frs
Accommodation: 110 to 210 Frs (single), 140
to 250 Frs (double)
Restaurant: lunch 12–2pm, dinner 7.30–9pm.
Closed Friday nights, Sunday nights (out of
season) and 24 December to 15 January.
Specialities: andouillette aux poires, truites

flambées au calvados, pierrade basquaise,
aiguillette de canard au flan d'épinard, rognons
flambés.
Hotel: 13 rooms, showers, baths, private WCs,
TV, phone.
Other points: bar, credit cards accepted,
children welcome, à la carte menu, pets
allowed, car parking.
Address: 5 route du Mont Saint Michel.
M. MICHEL PROD'HOMME, tel 33.38.64.99.

DOMFRONT, Orne 61700, Map 3 ⊗♍🏠

LA CROIX DES LANDES, RN 12 and CD 908 to Ferté-Macé

Places of interest: Suisse normande (60km), le
Mont Saint Michel (80km), Saint Fraimbault
(20km), forêt d'Andaine (5km), centre de

loisirs de la Ferté-Macé (20km).
Languages: English, Spanish
Menu: 80 to 150 Frs

Restaurant: closed Sundays (out of season).
Hotel: 8 rooms, showers, baths, private WCs, TV, phone.
Other points: bar, credit cards accepted, children welcome, à la carte menu, pets allowed, car parking, traditional decor.
Address: La Croix des Landes.
M. CLAUDE LEVEAU, tel 33.38.51.35.

DOUE LA FONTAINE, Maine-et-Loire 49700, Map 5 ⊗ ♈

CHEZ PAUL, at roundabout for Poitiers, Saumurs, Cholet and Angers

Places of interest: Village troglodytique, caverne sculptée du XVIe siècle, jardin des roses, musée des vieux métiers, vignobles d'Anjou.
Language: English
Menu: 52 Frs
Restaurant: lunch 11–2pm, dinner 7–9pm. Closed Sundays (out of season) and 15 days in August.

Other points: bar, credit cards accepted, children welcome, garden terrace, pets allowed, car parking.
Address: Zone Industrielle, Route de Montreuil.
HOTELS TYPE-BASSANT, tel 41.59.03.33.

DURANVILLE, Eure 27230, Map 3 ⊗ ♈

LES ARCADES, RN 13 between Evreux and Lisieux

Place of interest: Lisieux.
Menu: 50 to 60 Frs
Restaurant: lunch 11.30–3.30pm, dinner 7–12pm. Closed Saturday 3pm to Sunday 10pm.

Other points: bar, credit cards accepted, children welcome, pets allowed, car parking.
Address: Route Nationale 13.
MME GENEVIEVE BOGA, tel 32.46.83.01.

ECALLES ALIX, Seine-Maritime 76190, Map 3 ⊗ ♈

AUBERGE DE LA FOURCHE, RN 15 Bis between Rouen and Le Havre

Restaurant: lunch 12–3pm, dinner 7–10pm. Closed Saturday 3.30pm to Monday 6am, and 15 December to first week of January.
Hotel: 3 rooms: single 2, double 1. Showers, private WCs.

Other points: bar, children welcome, à la carte menu, car parking, traditional decor.
Address: Hameau de Loumare.
M. SERGE VANNIER, tel 35.95.45.01.

ECARDENVILLE LA CAMPAGNE, Eure 27170, Map 3 ⊗ ♈ 🏠

AUBERGE DU RELAIS, RN 13 between Paris and Cherbourg

Places of interest: Château du champs de bataille, château d'Harcourt, abbaye du Bec Heloin.
Menu: 52 to 95 Frs
Accommodation: 90 to 110 Frs
Restaurant: lunch 11–3pm, dinner 6.30–10.30pm. Closed Saturday nights, Sundays (out of season) and between Christmas and New Year's day.

Specialities: tripes à la mode de Caen, spécialités normandes.
Hotel: 11 rooms: single 4, double 7. Showers.
Other points: bar, children welcome, à la carte menu, showers, garden terrace, pets allowed, car parking, traditional decor.
Address: Route Nationale 13.
M. JEAN-CLAUDE LOTHON, tel 32.35.05.32.

ECORPAIN, Sarthe 72120, Map 5   ⊗♍

LE RELAIS DE LA JAGOTIERE, RN 157 between Bouloire and Saint Calais

Menu: 50 Frs
Restaurant: lunch 12–2pm, dinner 7–9.30pm.
Other points: bar, pets allowed, car parking, traditional decor.

Address: La Jagotière.
MME MIREILLE GABORIT, tel 43.35.12.00.

ELVEN, Morbihan 56250, Map 4   ⊗♍🏠🍵☆

LE RELAIS DE L'ARGOUET, RN 166

Places of interest: Les tours d'Elven, le plus haut donjon de France, les grottes de Callac, le golf de Morbihan.
Language: English
Menu: 49 to 130 Frs
Accommodation: 110 to 160 Frs
Restaurant: lunch 12–2.30pm, dinner 7.30–10pm. Closed Saturdays (out of season) and first 2 weeks of October.

Specialities: fruits de mer et poissons.
Hotel: 12 rooms: single 7, double 5.
Other points: bar, credit cards accepted, children welcome, à la carte menu, garden terrace, pets allowed, car parking.
Address: 36 avenue de l'Argouet.
M. ANDRE LE DOUARIN, tel 97.53.32.98.

EMONDEVILLE, Manche 50310, Map 3   ⊗♍

LE COUP DE FREIN, RN 13

Places of interest: Cherbourg, les plages du débarquement, Saint Vaast le Hague, Le Val de Sarre, Ile de Tatihou.
Menu: 53 Frs including coffee
Restaurant: lunch 11.30–2.30pm, dinner 7.30–10.30pm. Closed Saturdays, Sundays and first 3 weeks of August.

Hotel: 3 rooms: single 1, double 2. TV.
Other points: bar, credit cards accepted, children welcome, car parking.
Address: Route Nationale 13.
MME THERESE JEAN, tel 33.41.22.74.

EPERRAIS, Orne 61400, Map 3   ⊗♍

LA PETITE VALLEE, RD 938 between Mortagne and Bellême

Places of interest: Forêt de Bellême avec sa fontaine gallo-romaine, les dolmens, haras.
Language: English
Menu: 45 to 58 Frs
Restaurant: closed Sundays (except reservations), 15 to 30 June and mid-December to mid-January.
Speciality: couscous (Saturdays with notice).

Other points: bar, credit cards accepted, children welcome, à la carte menu, garden terrace, pets allowed, car parking, traditional decor.
Address: La Petite Vallée.
MME MONIQUE GERMOND, tel 33.83.91.34.

EQUEURDREVILLE, Manche 50120, Map 3   ⊗♍🏠

RESTAURANT DE LA HAGUE, RD 901

Language: English
Menu: 42 Frs
Accommodation: 100 to 200 Frs
Restaurant: lunch 12–2.30pm, dinner
7.30–8.45 pm. Closed Saturdays, Sundays and
second 2 weeks of August.
Speciality: boeuf bourguignon.

Hotel: 20 rooms: single 13, double 7. Showers,
baths.
Other points: bar, credit cards accepted, pets
allowed, car parking.
Address: 120 rue de la Paix.
M. CLAUDE LAMY, tel 33.93.88.46.

ERBRAY, Loire-Atlantique 44110, Map 5 ⊗♈

LE SAINT HUBERT, between Châteaubriant and Angers

Places of interest: Château de Châteaubriant,
chapelle Glain, carrières des fusillés.
Menu: 56 Frs to 115 Frs including wine and
coffee
Restaurant: lunch 11–2.30pm, dinner
7–10.30pm. Closed Friday nights.

Speciality: fruits de mer (by arrangement).
Other points: bar, credit cards accepted,
children welcome, à la carte menu, garden
terrace, pets allowed, car parking.
Address: 1 place du Calvaire, La Touche.
M. BERNARD BELLANGER, tel 40.55.08.37.

ESSARTS (LES), Vendée 85140, Map 5 ⊗♈

LE RELAIS DU PINIER, RN 160

Place of interest: La Roche sur Yon.
Menu: 48 to 60 Frs
Restaurant: closed Saturdays and Sundays (out
of season).
Other points: bar, children welcome, à la carte
menu.

Address: Route Nationale 160.
MME JACQUELINE DUPONT,
tel 51.62.81.69.

ETALONDES, Seine-Maritime 76260, Map 3 ⊗♈

AU MILLE PATTES, RD 925 between Eu and Dieppe

Places of interest: Château et forêt d'Eu,
centrale nucléaire.
Menu: 50 Frs
Restaurant: lunch 11.30–3pm, dinner
9–11pm. Closed Sundays.

Other points: bar, credit cards accepted, pets
allowed, car parking, traditional decor.
Address: La Pipe.
M. JACKIE HULIN, tel 35.50.21.10.

ETREPAGNY, Eure 27150, Map 3 ⊗♈

RESTAURANT DES SPORTS

Language: English
Menu: 46 Frs
Restaurant: closed Sundays.

Other points: bar.
Address: 13 rue Saint Maur.
M. VINCENT RONCIL, tel 32.27.17.11.

EXMES, Orne 61310, Map 3 ⊗♈🏠

HOTEL DU COMMERCE, CD 14 between Paris and Rouen

Place of interest: Le Haras du Pin.
Menu: 50 to 85 Frs
Speciality: normandes.
Restaurant.

Hotel: 4 rooms: single 3, double 1.
Other points: bar, children welcome.
Address: 1 Grande Rue.
MME FERNANDE SIMON, tel 33.39.93.04.

EZY SUR EURE, Eure 27530, Map 3 ⊗🍷🏠

HOTEL TERMINUS, RN 12

Places of interest: Château d'Anet, musée
Dupeigne.
Languages: English, Spanish
Menu: 54 to 80 Frs
Accommodation: 120 to 170 Frs
Restaurant: lunch 12–2.15 pm. Closed
Saturdays and in August.

Specialities: boeuf bourguignon, cassoulet.
Hotel: 10 rooms: single 7, double 3. Showers,
TV.
Other points: bar, garden terrace, pets allowed,
car parking.
Address: 16 boulevard Ulysse Lavertue.
MME ANNIE VEISEN, tel 37.64.73.24.

FALAISE, Calvados 14700, Map 3 ⊗🍷🏠

LE RELAIS DES ROUTIERS, RN 158 exit Caen towards Le Mans

Places of interest: Falaise (ville touristique),
châteaux (dont celui de Guillaume le
Conquérant), églises.
Menu: 44 Frs
Accommodation: 95 to 125 Frs
Restaurant: lunch 12–2pm, dinner
7.30–8.30pm. Closed Sundays and in July.

Hotel: 5 rooms: single 3, double 2. Showers.
Other points: bar, credit cards accepted,
children welcome, à la carte menu, pets
allowed, car parking, traditional decor.
Address: 33 Avenue D'Hastings.
M. CHRISTIAN DURAND, tel 31.90.04.67.

FALAISE, Calvados 14700, Map 3 ⊗🍷

L'ESCALE, between Argentan and Caen

Place of interest: Château de Falaise.
Language: Swiss-French
Menu: 50 Frs including coffee
Restaurant: closed Sundays.

Other points: bar, children welcome, pets
allowed, car parking.
Address: 16 rue du Pavillon.
M. CLAUDE RUSSEAU, tel 31.90.12.67.

FALLERON, Vendée 85670, Map 5 ⊗🍷

CHEZ MARLENE

Places of interest: Les Iles de Noirmoutiers et
d'Yeu (35km).
Menu: 47 Frs
Restaurant: lunch 11–2pm. Closed Sundays
(out of season).

Other points: bar, credit cards accepted, pets
allowed, car parking, traditional decor.
Address: 54 rue Nationale.
MME MARLENE POTERLOT,
tel 51.35.50.22.

FAOUET (LE), Morbihan 56320, Map 4 ⊗🍷🏠

LE RELAIS DES HALLES, RN 782 between Lorient and Roscoff

Places of interest: Halles et chapelles du XVe
siècle.
Languages: English, Breton
Menu: 46 Frs
Accommodation: 75 to 120 Frs
Restaurant: lunch 12–2pm, dinner 7.30–9pm.
Closed Sundays and in September.

Hotel: 8 rooms: single 6, double 2. Showers,
private WCs.
Other points: bar, children welcome, phone,
pets allowed, car parking.
Address: 19 rue du Soleil.
M. ARMEL LE PUIL, tel 97.23.07.66.

FAOUET (LE), Morbihan 56320, Map 4   ⊗♀

LE TY GRAVIC, RD 769 between Lorient and Roscoff

Places of interest: Halles du XVe siècle, chapelle de Saint Barbe, chapelle de Saint Fiacre.
Languages: English, Italian, Finnish, Swedish
Menu: 46 Frs
Restaurant: closed Sundays.

Other points: bar, credit cards accepted, children welcome, pets allowed, car parking, traditional decor.
Address: Route de Gourin.
M. ALAIN HALTER, tel 97.23.07.04.

FENOUILLER, Vendée 85800, Map 5   ⊗♀⌂

LA MADELON, RN 754 between Nantes and Les Sables d'Olonne

Places of interest: Saint Gilles, Croix de Vie, port de pêche.
Language: English
Menu: 50 to 110 Frs including wine
Accommodation: 90 to 135 Frs
Restaurant: lunch 12–2pm, dinner 7.30–9pm.
Speciality: fruits de mer.

Hotel: 15 rooms: single 9, double 6.
Other points: bar, credit cards accepted, children welcome, garden terrace, pets allowed, car parking, traditional decor.
Address: 64 rue du Centre.
SNC POUVREAU-POUPART, tel 51.55.05.35.

FERRIERES EN BRAY, Seine-Maritime 76220, Map 3   ⊗♀⌂

HOTEL DU CHEMIN DE FER, RN 31

Places of interest: Rouen, Beauvais.
Menu: 45 Frs
Accommodation: 90 to 140 Frs
Restaurant: lunch 12–3pm, dinner 7.30–10.30pm. Closed Saturdays, Sundays, public holidays and 15 days early May.

Hotel: 10 rooms: single 4, double 6.
Other points: bar, pets allowed, car parking.
Address: 26 avenue de la Gare.
M. JEAN-SERGE FERET, tel 35.90.01.61.

FERTE BERNARD (LA), Sarthe 72400, Map 5   ⊗

L'ARCHE DE LA FERTE BERNARD, A 11 in both directions

Menu: 59 Frs
Restaurant: lunch 11–3.30pm, dinner 6.30–11.30pm.
Other points: credit cards accepted, children

welcome, à la carte menu, self-service, garden terrace, pets allowed, car parking.
Address: Aire de Villaines la Gonais.
M. GASTON BISSON, tel 43.93.41.02.

FLERS, Orne 61100, Map 3   ⊗♀⌂

HOTEL DES TOURISTES, RD 924 and 18

Place of interest: Bagnoles de l'Orne.
Language: Swiss-French
Menu: 42 to 60 Frs
Accommodation: 80 to 100 Frs
Restaurant: lunch 12–4pm, dinner 7–10pm. Closed Sundays and in August.
Speciality: tripes.

Hotel: 12 rooms.
Other points: bar, credit cards accepted, children welcome, à la carte menu, traditional decor.
Address: 80 rue de Paris.
M. MAURICE DUPONT, tel 33.65.25.57.

FLEURY SUR ORNE, Calvados 14123, Map 3 ⊗ ♈

LA POMME D'OR, RN 162 at Flers, towards Laval

Menu: 45 Frs
Restaurant: lunch 12–2pm. Closed Sundays, public holidays and in August.
Other points: bar, credit cards accepted, pets allowed, car parking.

Address: 20 route d'Harcourt.
MME EMILIENNE FRANCOIS, tel 31.82.36.87.

FONTAINE SAINT MARTIN (LA), Sarthe 72330, Map 5 ⊗ ♈

LE CHENE VERT, RN 23

Place of interest: Nantes.
Restaurant: lunch 11–3pm, dinner 7–10pm. Closed Saturdays, Sundays and in August.
Other points: bar, à la carte menu, car parking, traditional decor.

Address: Route Nationale 23.
MME MARIE-LOUISE FLAMEYGH, tel 43.87.80.84.

FOUCARMONT, Seine-Maritime 76340, Map 3 ⊗ ♈

CLUB ARLEQUIN, RN 28 between Neufchâtel en Bray and Blangy sur Bresle

Menu: 50 Frs
Restaurant: lunch 12–3pm. Closed Saturdays and Sundays.
Other points: bar, credit cards accepted, self-

service, garden terrace, car parking, traditional decor.
Address: 28 Route Nationale.
MME REGINE BENARD, tel 35.93.91.50.

FOUGERES, Ille-et-Vilaine 35300, Map 4 ⊗ ♈ 🏠 ☆

AUX AMIS DE LA ROUTE, RN 12 between Rennes and Saint Malo

Places of interest: Saint Malo, le Mont Saint Michel, parc, forêt et château de Fougères.
Languages: English, German
Menu: 55 Frs including a drink
Accommodation: 120 to 140 Frs
Restaurant: closed Sunday afternoons (out of season) and Saturdays, Sunday afternoons (in season).

Hotel: 15 single rooms.
Other points: bar, credit cards accepted, lounge area, garden terrace, car parking, traditional decor.
Address: 6 boulevard Saint Germain.
M. MICHEL BASTIEN, tel 99.99.07.62.

FROMENTEL, Orne 61210, Map 3 ⊗ ♈

LE RELAIS DE L'AIGLE D'OR, RD 924 between Argentan and Fler or Falaise and Laval

Place of interest: Bagnol de l'Orne (20km).
Menu: 48 Frs
Restaurant: closed Saturdays and Sundays.
Other points: bar, credit cards accepted,

children welcome, pets allowed, car parking, traditional decor.
MME MICHELE LEVALET, tel 33.96.21.00.

GAEL, Ille-et-Vilaine 35290, Map 4 ⊗ ♈ 🏠

LES ROUTIERS, between Dinan and Lorient

Place of interest: La forêt de Paimpont.
Menu: 46 Frs
Accommodation: 83 to 126 Frs
Restaurant: lunch 11.30–2.30pm, dinner
7–9pm. Closed Fridays after 3pm.
Specialities: tête de veau à l'ancienne
(Wednesdays), couscous et choucroute
(Thursdays).

Hotel: 5 rooms: single 1, double 4. Showers,
private WCs.
Other points: bar, credit cards accepted,
children welcome, phone, lounge area, pets
allowed, car parking, traditional decor.
Address: place des Tilleuls.
MME ANNICK REBILLARD, tel 99.07.72.39.

GISORS, Eure 27140, Map 3 ⊗ ♈

BAR DE L'AVENUE, RN 15

Language: English
Restaurant: closed Sundays and 15 to 30 August.
Other points: bar.

Address: Hôtels L'Estouffade Normande,
route de Dieppe.
M. ROUSSEL, tel 32.27.19.45.

GLACERIE (LA), Manche 50470, Map 3 ⊗ ♈

LE RELAIS DE LA GLACERIE, RN 13

Places of interest: Cherbourg, plages du
débarquement, La Hague.
Menu: 50 Frs
Restaurant: lunch 12–2pm, dinner 7.30–9pm.
Closed Saturdays, Sundays and 20 July to 8
August.

Other points: bar, credit cards accepted,
children welcome, à la carte menu, lounge area,
garden terrace, pets allowed, car parking.
Address: Route Nationale 13.
M. PAUL ROUPSARD, tel 33.44.13.54.

GLOS SUR RISLE, Eure 27290, Map 3 ⊗ ♈

RELAIS DE LA FORGE, RD 130 between Montfort and Brionne

Places of interest: Abbaye du Bec Hellouin
(6km), vallée de la Risle.
Menu: 35 to 50 Frs
Restaurant: dinner 7–8.30pm. Closed Sundays
and 8 days in February.

Other points: bar, credit cards accepted,
children welcome, self-service, pets allowed,
car parking, traditional decor.
Address: La Forge.
M. SERGE LANGLOIS, tel 32.56.16.34.

GODERVILLE, Seine-Maritime 76110, Map 3 ⊗ ♈

RELAIS DE SAINT SAUVEUR, CD 925 between Le Havre and Fécamp

Places of interest: Les falaises d'Etretat,
Fécamp.
Menu: 50 to 55 Frs
Restaurant: closed Saturdays.

Other points: bar, credit cards accepted,
garden terrace, pets allowed, car parking.
Address: Saint Sauveur d'Emalleville.
M. PHILIPPE GUERIN, tel 35.27.21.56.

GOUESNIERE (LA), Ille-et-Vilaine 35350, Map 4 ⊗ ♈ 🏠

AU RELAIS ROUTIERS, RD 4

Places of interest: Le Mont Saint Michel, Saint
Malo, Dinan.
Menu: 45 to 49 Frs including coffee
Restaurant: lunch 12–2pm, dinner 7.30–10pm.
Closed Sundays and second 2 weeks of August.
Hotel: 16 rooms: single 10, double 6. Showers,

baths, private WCs, TV, phone.
Other points: bar, pets allowed, car parking.
Address: 2 rue d'Halet.
MME MARIE-THE BOURGALAIS,
tel 99.58.80.57.

GOUSTRANVILLE, Calvados 14430, Map 3   ⊗♈

LE RELAIS DES ROUTIERS, RN 815

Restaurant: closed Sundays and in August.   M. DANIEL DUVAL, tel 31.79.21.90.
Other points: bar.

GRAINVILLE, Eure 27380, Map 3   ⊗♈

LE RELAIS DE GRAINVILLE, RN 14 between Paris, Rouen and Le Havre

Places of interest: Château-Gaillard (15km),   New Year's day.
Rouen (25km), les Andelys.   **Other points:** bar, credit cards accepted, pets
Menu: 47 Frs   allowed, car parking, traditional decor.
Restaurant: lunch 11.30–1.30pm, dinner   **Address:** 40 Route Nationale.
6–7.30pm. Closed Saturday afternoons,   MME EDWIGE LEGATT, tel 32.48.06.28.
Sundays and 1 week between Christmas and

GRAND FOUGERAY (LE), Ille-et-Vilaine 35390, Map 4   ⊗♈🏠☆

LE RELAIS DE LA BELLE ETOILE, RN 137

Language: English   **Other points:** bar.
Restaurant: closed Sundays.   **Address:** La Belle Etoile.
Hotel.   M. ROLAND PIROT, tel 99.08.42.59.

GRAVIGNY, Eure 27930, Map 3   ⊗♈🏠

HOTEL DES SPORTS

Languages: English, Spanish, Arabic   **Hotel:** 7 rooms: single 4, double 3. Showers,
Menu: 49 Frs   baths, private WCs.
Accommodation: 80 Frs   **Other points:** bar, children welcome, garden
Restaurant: lunch 12–2.30pm, dinner   terrace, pets allowed, car parking.
7.30–9.30pm. Closed Sundays.   **Address:** 109 avenue Aristide Briand.
Specialities: orientales, couscous.   M. TARIK SENOUCI, tel 32.33.16.19.

GREMONVILLE, Seine-Maritime 76970, Map 3   ⊗♈

LA CHAUMIERE, RN 15 between Rouen and St-Valéry-en-Caux

Places of interest: Eglise d'Yvetôt (5km), la   piquante, entrecôte à l'échalotte.
plage à Saint Valéry (25km), le chêne   **Other points:** bar, credit cards accepted,
d'Allouille Bellefosse.   children welcome, garden terrace, pets allowed,
Language: English   car parking, traditional decor.
Menu: 45 Frs   **Address:** place de l'Eglise, Motteville.
Restaurant: closed Tuesday and Wednesday   M. CHRISTIAN LE MASURIER,
afternoons.   tel 35.56.45.65.
Specialities: lapin au cidre, lanque à la sauce

GUE DE LA CHAINE (LE), Orne 61130, Map 3   ⊗♈

LE GUE ROUTIER, RD 955 between Alençon and Orléans

Places of interest: La Forêt Béllène.
Menu: 45 to 60 Frs
Restaurant: lunch 11.30–2.30pm, dinner
6.30–8pm. Closed Sundays and public holidays.

Other points: bar, pets allowed, car parking.
Address: Route de Mamers.
JEANNINE AND BERNARD HEROUIN,
tel 33.73.02.66.

GUENIN, Morbihan 56150, Map 4

LE RELAIS DE BON VALLON

Language: English
Restaurant.
Other points: bar, car parking.

Address: ZI de Bon Vallon.
M. JOEL LE HAZIF, tel 97.39.10.40.

GUERCHE DE BRETAGNE (LA), Ille-et-Vilaine 35130, Map 4

LE RELAIS DU PONT D'ANJOU, RN 178, Map 4

Menu: 43,50 to 82,50 Frs
Restaurant: closed Saturday nights.
Specialities: fruits de mer, couscous, paëlla.
Hotel: 12 rooms.

Other points: bar.
Address: 11 faubourg d'Anjou.
M. ANDRE MOUSSU, tel 99.96.23.10.

GUILBERVILLE, Manche 50160, Map 3

RESTAURANT LE POTEAU, RN 175

Languages: German, English
Restaurant: closed Saturdays, Sundays and
Christmas.

Other points: bar, car parking.
Address: Le Poteau.
M. FREDY MENANT, tel 33.56.73.10.

GURUNHUEL, Côtes-du-Nord 22390, Map 4

CHEZ GILBERTE, RN 787

Restaurant: closed July.
Other points: bar.

Address: Kérambellec.
M. YVES GEORGELIN, tel 96.21.81.00.

HAVRE (LE), Seine-Maritime 76600, Map 3

LE RELAIS DES ROUTIERS, RN 15

Places of interest: Le port, les bords de la mer.
Menu: 50 Frs
Restaurant: lunch 11.30–4pm, dinner
7–11pm. Closed Friday nights and
23 December to 7 January.
Speciality: fruits de mer.

Other points: bar, children welcome, self-
service, car parking, traditional decor.
Address: 57 Rue Marceau.
MME MARIE-PIERRE PRISER,
tel 34.74.06.32.

HAVRE (LE), Seine-Maritime 76600, Map 3

LE MARCEAU

Menu: 55 Frs
Restaurant: closed Sundays.
Other points: bar, children welcome, pets
allowed, car parking.

Address: 27 rue Marceau.
M. DOMINIQUE VALLERENT,
tel 35.53.17.80.

HAVRE (LE), Seine-Maritime 76600, Map 3 ⊗♉⌂

LE WELCOME, RN 13 Bis

Places of interest: Le port, les bords de la mer.
Menu: 90 to 180 Frs
Restaurant: lunch 12–3pm, dinner 7–11pm.
Specialities: huîtres, fruits de mer.
Hotel: 8 rooms, showers, baths, private WCs, phone.

Other points: bar, credit cards accepted, à la carte menu, self-service, car parking.
Address: 55–7 quai de Southampton.
MME MARIE-PIERRE PRISER,
tel 35.43.17.84.

HAVRE (LE), Seine-Maritime 76600, Map 3 ⊗♉

AU TELEPHONE, RN 13 Bis

Restaurant: closed Saturdays and Sundays.
Other points: bar.
Address: 173 boulevard Amiral Mouchez.

M. JEAN-CLAUDE BOUILLON,
tel 35.53.24.73.

HAVRE (LE), Seine-Maritime 76600, Map 3 ⊗

LE P'TIT COMPTOIR, in the area of St François

Menu: 56 to 78 Frs
Restaurant: lunch 12–2.15 pm, dinner 7.15–9.30pm. Closed Sundays, public holidays and 20 December to 15 January.

Speciality: choucroute aux 3 poissons.
Other points: children welcome.
Address: 31 rue du Général Faidherbe.
M. BERNARD RONDEL, tel 35.42.78.72.

HAVRE (LE), Seine-Maritime 76600, Map 3 ⊗♉

LE RELAIS, RN 13 Bis, left after car bridge

Place of interest: Le port.
Language: English
Menu: 54 to 140 Frs
Restaurant: lunch 11.45–2.30pm, dinner 6.45–10.30pm. Closed Sundays.
Specialities: magrets, saumon frais, viandes rôties et grillées.

Other points: bar, credit cards accepted, children welcome, à la carte menu, lounge area, pets allowed, car parking.
Address: 128 boulevard de Graville.
M. DIDIER EUDES, tel 35.24.54.48.

HAYE DU PUITS (LA), Manche 50250, Map 3 ⊗♉⌣

RESTAURANT DES AMIS, RN 800

Place of interest: Cherbourg.
Menu: 48 to 80 Frs
Restaurant: closed Saturday afternoons and Sundays (out of season).
Specialities: coq au vin, boeuf bourguignon, raie.

Other points: bar, credit cards accepted, à la carte menu, garden terrace, pets allowed, car parking.
Address: 16 rue du Château.
M. LOUIS LE FILLIASTRE, tel 33.46.03.42.

HAYE PESNEL (LA), Manche 50320, Map 3 ⊗♉⌣

LE RELAIS – Chez Armelle, RD 7

Menu: 48 to 80 Frs
Restaurant: closed Saturdays, Sundays (out of season) and in December.
Specialities: coquille Saint Jacques, escaloppe de veau à la crème.
Other points: bar, credit cards accepted,

children welcome, à la carte menu, traditional decor.
Address: rue de la Libération.
MME ARMELLE JACQUETTE ROGER, tel 33.61.50.83.

HERBERGEMENT (L'), Vendée 85260, Map 5 ⊗♀

LES ROUTIERS, RD 763 between Nantes and La Roche sur Yon

Menu: 47 Frs
Restaurant: lunch 11.45–2.30pm. Closed Thursday afternoons and in August.
Other points: bar, credit cards accepted,

children welcome, car parking.
Address: 17 rue Georges Clémenceau.
M. MICHEL BRETIN, tel 51.42.80.71.

HERBIERS (LES), Vendée 85500, Map 5 ⊗♀⌂☆☆

CHEZ CAMILLE, RD 38

Places of interest: Montchamps, Les Herbiers-South, Puy du Fou (9km), la mer (80km).
Menu: 55 to 100 Frs
Accommodation: 180 to 245 Frs
Restaurant: lunch 12–3pm, dinner 7–11 pm.
Hotel: 13 rooms: single 6, double 7. Showers, baths, private WCs, TV, phone.

Other points: bar, credit cards accepted, à la carte menu, lounge area, garden terrace, pets allowed, car parking.
Address: 2 rue Monseigneur Massé.
M. CAMILLE MASSE, tel 51.91.07.57.

HERBIERS (LES), Vendée 85500, Map 5 ⊗♀⌂☆

L'OREE DES BOIS VERTS, RN 160 between Angers and les Sables d'Olonne

Places of interest: Puy du Fou, l'étang de la Tricherie, abbaye de la Grainetière.
Menu: 45 Frs
Accommodation: 100 to 195 Frs
Restaurant: lunch 12–2pm, dinner 5.30–9pm. Closed Sundays, All Saints holiday and first 2 weeks of May.

Hotel: 11 rooms: single 8, double 3. Showers, baths, private WCs, TV, phone.
Other points: bar, credit cards accepted, lounge area, garden terrace, pets allowed, car parking, traditional decor.
Address: route des Sables.
M. RENE JOULIN, tel 51.91.00.18.

HERMITAGE (L'), Ille-et-Vilaine 35590, Map 4 ⊗♀

LE VILLAGE

Menu: 47 to 60 Frs
Restaurant: lunch 11–2pm, dinner 8–10pm. Closed Sundays and in August.
Other points: bar, credit cards accepted, pets

allowed, car parking, traditional decor.
Address: 23 rue de Rennes.
M. MICHEL BOISSEL, tel 99.64.03.31.

HEUGUEVILLE SUR SIENNE, Manche 50200, Map 3 ⊗♀🛏

LE MASCARET

Places of interest: Eglise gothique (sur place), la baie de la Sienne, parc zoologique (20km), cathédrale, jardin publique, port de Coutances (10km).
Menu: 50 to 120 Frs
Restaurant: closed Fridays.

Speciality: poissons.
Other points: bar, credit cards accepted, garden terrace, pets allowed, car parking, traditional decor.
Address: Le Presbytère.
M. GILBERT DESLANDES, tel 33.45.86.09.

HINGLE LES GRANITS (LE), Côtes-du-Nord 22100, Map 4 ⊗ ♉ ⌂

LES ROUTIERS, RN 166

Places of interest: Dinan, les côtes.
Language: English
Menu: 44 Frs
Restaurant: lunch 11.45–2pm. Closed Saturdays and in August.

Hotel: 6 rooms.
Other points: bar, car parking.
Address: rue de la Gare.
M. REMY PESSEL, tel 96.83.58.45.

HONFLEUR, Calvados 14600, Map 3 ⊗ ♉

LE MERLE BLANC

Language: English
Restaurant: closed Saturdays, August and 20 to 31 December.

Other points: bar.
Address: Honfleur.
MME DENISE RENAULT, tel 31.89.11.98.

HOTAUT LES BAGUES, Calvados 14250, Map 3 ⊗ ♉

LE RELAIS DE LA MANCHE, CD 9 between Caen and Granville

Menu: 48 Frs
Restaurant: lunch 11.45–2.30pm. Closed Saturdays, 15 days in June and 15 days end September.

Other points: bar, credit cards accepted, garden terrace, traditional decor.
Address: Grande Rue.
M. ROLAND JEANNE, tel 31.80.81.72.

HYENVILLE, Manche 50660, Map 3 ⊗ ♉ ⌂

LE RELAIS DE LA SIENNE, RD 971 between Coutances and Granville

Places of interest: Fonderie de cloches (30km), les plages, Villedieu les Poêles, four à chaux, le Mont Saint Michel.
Language: English
Menu: 50 to 85 Frs
Accommodation: 90 to 150 Frs
Restaurant: closed Sundays (out of season).

Hotel: 7 rooms: single 1, double 6. Showers.
Other points: bar, credit cards accepted, à la carte menu, garden terrace, pets allowed, car parking, traditional decor.
Address: Le Pont.
MME ELIANE MAYOR, tel 33.07.56.03.

JALLAIS, Maine-et-Loire 49510, Map 5 ⊗ ♉ ⌂ 🍴 ☆ ☆

LE GALANT VERT – LA CROIX VERTE, RD 765

Places of interest: Région viticole du Muscadet et de l'Anjou, musée de Cholet sur les Mouchoirs, Puy du Fou, musée de la guerre de Vendée, les bords de la Loire, zoo de Doué-la-Fontaine, les arènes.
Languages: English, German

Menu: 63 to 135 Frs
Accommodation: 120 to 240 Frs
Restaurant: lunch 12–2pm, dinner 7–10pm. Closed Friday nights (out of season).
Specialities: salade rillauds d'anjou chauds, pavé boeuf au Chinon.

Hotel: 20 rooms, showers, baths, private WCs, TV, phone.
Other points: bar, credit cards accepted, à la carte menu, lounge area, pets allowed, car parking, traditional decor.
Address: place de la Mairie.
M. PIERRE GAILLARD, tel 41.64.20.22.

JANZE, Ille-et-Vilaine 35150, Map 4

HOTEL RESTAURANT BAR METAYER, RN 777

Menu: 140 to 160 Frs
Restaurant: lunch 12–1pm, dinner 7–8.30pm.
Hotel: 7 rooms, showers, private WCs, TV, phone.
Other points: bar, car parking.
Address: 5 rue Jean-Marie Lacire.
M. MICHEL METAYER, tel 99.47.05.10.

JARZE, Maine-et-Loire 49140, Map 5

LE MOULINET, RN 766, Angers Tours via Seiches and Loir-Baugé

Menu: 46 Frs and 70 to 120 Frs
Restaurant: lunch 11.30–2.30pm, dinner 6.30–9.30pm. Closed Sunday nights.
Speciality: fruits de mer.
Other points: bar, car parking.
Address: Route Nationale 766.
M. DANIEL DOMAS, tel 41.95.47.52.

JOSSELIN, Morbihan 56120, Map 4

LA ROCHETTE – Les Routiers

Places of interest: Château de Josselin, musée de poupées.
Language: English
Menu: 43 to 70 Frs
Restaurant: lunch 12–2pm, dinner 7–9.30pm. Closed Saturdays and Sundays (out of season).
Other points: bar, credit cards accepted, children welcome, garden terrace, pets allowed, traditional decor.
Address: 128 rue Glatinier.
MME ANNIE LE CORRE, tel 97.22.27.29.

JOUE DU BOIS, Orne 61320, Map 3

LE RELAIS DU MANOIR, RN 12

Places of interest: Alençon, manoir de Joué du Bois, Forges, Château de Carrouges (XIVe siècle).
Languages: English, Serbo-Croat
Menu: 48 to 90 Frs
Restaurant: lunch 11.30–2.30pm, dinner 7–10pm. Closed Mondays.
Other points: bar, credit cards accepted, à la carte menu, garden terrace, pets allowed, car parking, traditional decor.
Address: Le Bourg.
MME VIOLAINE VULOVIC, tel 33.37.48.54.

JOUE EN CHARNIE, Sarthe 72540, Map 5

LE CHEVAL BLANC, RN 157 between Le Mans and Laval

Places of interest: Forêt de la Charnie, abbaye de Solesme, zoo de la Flèche, Le Mans, château de Sainte Suzanne, poterie à Molicorne.
Language: English
Menu: 45 to 130 Frs
Accommodation: 80 to 180 Frs
Restaurant: lunch 12–2.30pm, dinner 7–9pm. Closed Saturdays (out of season).

Speciality: choucroute.
Hotel: 10 rooms: single 4, double 6. Showers, baths, private WCs.
Other points: bar, credit cards accepted, children welcome, à la carte menu, garden terrace, pets allowed, car parking, traditional decor.
Address: Le Bourg.
M. DOMINIQUE BOURGON, tel 43.88.42.13.

JUMELLIERE (LA), Maine-et-Loire 49120, Map 5   ⊗ ☐ ⌂

LA BOULE D'OR, RD 961 between Angers and Cholet, 2km before Chemillé, turn right after 5km

Places of interest: Musée des vieux métiers (9km), musée de la vigne (8km), jardin des plantes médicinales (6km), train touristique (9km).
Menu: 48 to 170 Frs
Accommodation: 90 to 130 Frs
Restaurant: lunch 11.45–2pm, dinner 7–8.15pm. Closed Sundays.
Specialities: merlu au beurre blanc, coq d'Anjou rouge.

Hotel: 6 rooms: single 3, double 3. Showers, baths, private WCs.
Other points: bar, credit cards accepted, children welcome, pets allowed, car parking, traditional decor.
Address: 2 rue du Val de Loire.
MME JANINE SECHER, tel 41.64.33.23.

JURQUES, Calvados 14260, Map 3   ⊗ ☐

AU BON ACCUEIL, RD 577 exit at bend coming into Caen, interchange for Vire

Places of interest: Zoo de Jurques (3km), Bungy (10km), les gorges de la Vire.
Menu: 48 Frs including wine
Restaurant: lunch 11.45–2pm, dinner 7–9.30pm. Closed Sundays between 3pm and 5pm.

Other points: bar, credit cards accepted, children welcome, à la carte menu, pets allowed, car parking.
Address: route de Vire.
M. CHRISTIAN LESAGE, tel 31.77.81.17.

KERGONAN LANGUIDIC, Morbihan 56440, Map 4   ⊗ ☐

LE RELAIS ROUTIER, RN 24 between Lorient and Rennes

Places of interest: Ecomusée du village breton de Poul-Fetan (XVIe siècle), la vallée du Blavet.
Menu: 42 Frs
Restaurant: lunch 11.30–2pm. Closed Saturdays and in December.

Other points: bar, credit cards accepted, children welcome, garden terrace, pets allowed, car parking.
Address: 9 rue du Commerce.
M. ANDRE LE GARREC, tel 97.85.90.69.

LAMBALLE, Côtes-du-Nord 22400, Map 4   ⊗ ☐ ⌂ ⌷ ☆ ☆

LA TOUR D'ARGENT, RD 12 between Rennes and Saint-Brieuc

Places of interest: Saint Malo, le Mont Saint Michel, Dinan, Cap Fréhel, la côte, haras national.
Language: English
Menu: 75 to 168 Frs
Accommodation: 140 to 300 Frs
Restaurant: lunch 12–2.30pm, dinner 7–9.30pm. Closed Saturdays and first 2 weeks of June.
Specialities: fruits de mer, crevettes grillées,

canard à l'orange, blancs de seiches.
Hotel: 30 rooms: single 19, double 11. Showers, baths, private WCs, TV, phone.
Other points: bar, credit cards accepted, children welcome, à la carte menu, lounge area, garden terrace, pets allowed, car parking, traditional decor.
Address: 2 rue du Docteur Lavergne.
M. CLAUDE MOUNIER, tel 96.31.01.37.

LANDE SUR EURE (LA), Orne 61290, Map 3 ⊗♟

RELAIS DE LA TOUR, RD 151 and RD 36

Restaurant.
Other points: bar, pets allowed, car parking,
traditional decor.

Address: Le Bourg.
MME DENISE LEPRINCE, tel 33.73.65.00.

LANDERONDE, Vendée 85150, Map 5 ⊗♟

L'HORTENSE, RN 160 between La Roche sur Yon and Les Sables d'Olonne

Places of interest: La Roche sur Yon (10km),
les Sables d'Olonne (25km).
Menu: 47 to 170 Frs including wine
Restaurant: lunch 12–3pm, dinner 7–9pm.
Closed Monday evenings.
Specialities: coquilles Saint Jacques, terrine de
filet de sole, fruits de mer (by arrangement).

Other points: bar, credit cards accepted,
children welcome, à la carte menu, garden
terrace, pets allowed, car parking, traditional
decor.
Address: Route Nationale 160, known as Les
Loges.
M. MICHEL MIGRAN, tel 51.34.22.81.

LANDEVANT, Morbihan 56690, Map 4 ⊗♟🍽

LE RELAIS DU PELICAN, RN 165

Restaurant: closed Monday evenings, Tuesday
and October.
Other points: bar.

Address: 14 Route Nationale.
M. BOURN, tel 97.56.93.12.

LANESTER, Morbihan 56600, Map 4 ⊗♟🏠☆

LA ROTONDE, RN 24

Places of interest: Lorient, les plages.
Menu: 40 to 60 Frs
Accommodation: 90 to 140 Frs
Restaurant: lunch 12–2pm, dinner 7–9pm.
Closed Saturday afternoons, Sundays, 15 days
end August and 15 days at Christmas.
Hotel: 14 rooms: single 12, double 2. Showers,

private WCs.
Other points: bar, credit cards accepted, à la
carte menu, pets allowed, car parking,
traditional decor.
Address: 120 rue Jean Jaurès.
MME CECILE MERCIER, tel 97.76.06.37.

LANESTER, Morbihan 56600, Map 4 ⊗♟

LE RELAIS DU PONT DU BONHOMME RN 24 between Lorient and Carnac

Restaurant: lunch 11.30–2.30pm. Closed
August.
Other points: bar, children welcome, à la carte
menu.

Address: avenue du Pont du Bonhomme.
M. LUCIEN PHILIPPE, tel 97.76.51.23.

LANNION, Côtes-du-Nord 22300, Map 4 ⊗♟🏠

LA CROIX ROUGE, on the road to Morlaix

Menu: 47 to 140 Frs
Restaurant: lunch 11.30–3pm, dinner
7–9.30pm. Closed second 2 weeks of August.
Speciality: fruits de mer (Sundays).
Hotel: 15 rooms.

Other points: bar, credit cards accepted, pets
allowed, car parking.
Address: La Croix Rouge Ploumilliau.
M. CLAUDE BROZEC, tel 96.35.45.08.

LAVAL, Mayenne 53000, Map 5 ⊗ 🍸

DE LA GARE, RN 162 and RD 53

Place of interest: Le vieux Laval.
Restaurant: closed Mondays.
Other points: bar, garden terrace, pets allowed,
traditional decor.

Address: 107 avenue Robert Buron.
MME CLAUDIA HELBERT, tel 43.53.94.88.

LEGE, Loire-Atlantique 44650, Map 5 ⊗ 🍸

LE PARADIS, road to Challans through town centre

Places of interest: La côte Vendéenne, Saint
Jean de Mont, les Sables d'Olonne.
Menu: 50 to 150 Frs
Restaurant: lunch 12–2pm, dinner 7.30–9pm.
Closed Monday afternoons, Tuesday evenings
and 1 week for Christmas.

Speciality: grillades au feu de bois.
Other points: bar, credit cards accepted,
children welcome, à la carte menu, pets
allowed, car parking, traditional decor.
Address: 27 rue de l'Atlantique.
M. MICHEL CLOCHARD, tel 40.04.99.66.

LEUE (LA), Vendée 85210, Map 5 ⊗ 🍸 🏠

LES ROUTIERS, RN 137

Places of interest: Barrage de l'Angle
Guignard, maison de Lattre de Tassigny, Puit
du Fou, Château Clémenceau, bord de mer.
Menu: 50 to 58 Frs
Accommodation: 60 to 100 Frs
Restaurant: lunch 12–2.30pm, dinner
7.30–10pm. Closed Saturdays, Sundays and in
July.

Hotel: 7 rooms: single 4, double 3.
Other points: bar, credit cards accepted, car
parking.
Address: Route Nationale 137.
HOTELS CHARBONNEAU-DARIET,
tel 51.94.41.46.

LIGNOL, Morbihan 56160, Map 4 ⊗ 🍸 🏠

RELAIS DES VOYAGEURS, RD 782

Places of interest: Eglise de Kernascleden
(5km), étang de Priziac, zoo du Harlay (20km).
Menu: 44,50 Frs
Accommodation: 80 to 100 Frs
Restaurant: lunch 12–2pm, dinner 7–9pm.
Closed Monday afternoons.

Hotel: 7 rooms: single 4, double 3.
Other points: bar, credit cards accepted,
children welcome, pets allowed, car parking,
traditional decor.
Address: 4 rue de la Mairie.
M. BERNARD LE SOLLIEC, tel 97.27.03.48.

LISIEUX, Calvados 14100, Map 3 ⊗ 🍸 🏠

RELAIS PARIS/CHERBOURG, RN 13 towards Caen, exit Lisieux

Menu: 45 Frs
Restaurant: lunch 12–3pm, dinner
7.30–8.30pm. Closed September.
Hotel: 6 rooms, showers.
Other points: bar, children welcome, pets

allowed, car parking, traditional decor.
Address: 113 avenue du 6 Juin.
MME MARIE-THERESE PESTEL,
tel 31.62.06.38.

LOCMARIA GRAND CHAMPS, Morbihan 56390, Map 4 ⊗ 𝖸

LA MARMITE, RD 767 Vannes 10km, towards Pontivy

Place of interest: Le golf du Morbihan.
Menu: 45 to 200 Frs
Restaurant: lunch 11.30–3pm, dinner
6.30–10pm.
Other points: credit cards accepted, children

welcome, à la carte menu, self-service, pets
allowed, car parking.
Address: Collec.
M. JEAN-PIERRE JOULAUD,
tel 97.66.66.80.

LOIRE, Maine-et-Loire 49440, Map 5 ⊗ 𝖸

AU RENDEZ-VOUS DES ROUTIERS

Restaurant.
Other points: bar.

Address: 24 rue de la Libération.
M. PHILIPPE AUDOUIN, tel 41.94.10.83.

LONGUE, Maine-et-Loire 49160, Map 5 ⊗ 𝖸

LE RELAIS DES SOUVENETS, RN 147

Restaurant: closed Saturdays, Sundays and
end August.
Other points: bar, pets allowed, car parking.

Address: Les Souvenets.
MME REJANE TAUGOURDEAU,
tel 41.52.13.86.

LONGUE, Maine-et-Loire 49160, Map 5 ⊗ 𝖸

LE RELAX, RN 147 between Saumur (15km) and Anger (40km)

Places of interest: Saumur (les vignobles), les
châteaux de la Loire.
Menu: 55 to 135 Frs including wine
Restaurant: closed Sundays.
Other points: bar, credit cards accepted,

children welcome, à la carte menu, garden
terrace, pets allowed, car parking.
Address: Route Nationale 147.
M. CHEVRE, tel 41.52.68.81.

LORIENT, Morbihan 56100, Map 4 ⊗ 𝖸

L'ALBATROS

Menu: 45 Frs
Restaurant.
Other points: bar.

Address: 56 avenue de la Perrière.
MME MARIE LEGOUIC, tel 97.37.55.76.

LOUDEAC, Côtes-du-Nord 22600, Map 4 ⊗ 𝖸

LE STOP, RN 164 towards Rennes

Language: English
Menu: 45 to 75 Frs
Restaurant: closed Sundays.
Other points: bar, credit cards accepted,

traditional decor.
Address: Le Haut-Breuil.
M. YVES GICQUEL, tel 96.28.01.76.

LOUDEAC, Côtes-du-Nord 22600, Map 4   ⊗ � 🏠 ☆

LES ROUTIERS, RN 164

Places of interest: Saint Brieuc, lac de
Guerlédan (15km).
Language: English
Menu: 45 to 52 Frs
Accommodation: 72 to 130 Frs
Restaurant: lunch 12–2pm, dinner 7–9pm,
Sundays and in August (except hotel).
Speciality: fruits de mer.

Hotel: 40 rooms, showers, baths.
Other points: bar, credit cards accepted,
children welcome, phone, pets allowed, car
parking.
Address: 7 rue Lavergne.
M. DOMINIQUE LE COZANNET,
tel 96.28.01.44.

LOUVIERS, Eure 27400, Map 3   ⊗ �

LE RELAIS DES ROUTIERS, RN 154

Restaurant.
Other points: bar.
Address: 13 rue de Paris.

MME GUYLAINE QUESNEY,
tel 32.40.29.22.

LUCEAU, Sarthe 72500, Map 5   ⊗ ♕

LA CROIX DE PAILLE, RN 138 between Le Mans and Tours

Restaurant: closed Sundays (except group
dinners) and in August.
Other points: bar.

Address: Route du Mans, Château du Loir.
M. JACQUES-YVES MOREAU,
tel 43.44.05.50.

LUDE (LE), Sarthe 72800, Map 5   ⊗ ♕

LE RELAIS DES PECHEURS, RD 307

Places of interest: Châteaux.
Menu: 55 to 65 Frs
Restaurant: lunch 12–2.30pm, dinner
6.45–8pm. Closed Sundays (out of season) and
end August/early September.

Speciality: couscous.
Other points: bar, children welcome, garden
terrace.
Address: 14 boulevard de l'Hospice.
M. GILBERT MOIRE, tel 43.94.61.03.

MACHECOUL, Loire-Atlantique 44270, Map 5   ⊗ ♕ 🏠

LA BICYCLETTE D'ARGENT

Places of interest: Dolmens, châteaux, musées,
églises, abbaye, caves à vin.
Language: English
Restaurant: closed Saturday afternoons, Sunday
afternoons, 18 to 25 Feb and 22 Dec to 1 Jan.
Specialities: cuisses de poulet Bonne Femme,

rôti à la saumuroise, omelette Arc en Ciel.
Hotel: 9 rooms.
Other points: bar, car parking.
Address: 6 place du Pont.
MME MARIE-JOSEPH BAUDRY,
tel 40.78.50.48.

MAGNY LA CAMPAGNE, Calvados 14270, Map 3 ⊗ ♈

LA VALLEE D'AUGE, RD 40 between Caen and Saint Pierre sur Dive

Places of interest: Châteaux, monuments
historiques.
Menu: from 50 Frs
Restaurant: closed Tuesdays and in January.

Other points: bar, à la carte menu, pets
allowed, car parking, traditional decor.
MME MARIE-THERESE SEVIN,
tel 31.20.04.20.

MALE, Orne 61260, Map 3 ⊗ ♈ ⌂ ☆

LA BELLE RENCONTRE, RN 23 between Paris and Le Mans

Places of interest: Château, vallée du Perche.
Menu: 48 Frs
Accommodation: 95 to 190 Frs
Restaurant: dinner 7–10pm. Closed Sundays
(except groups or buses) and in August.
Hotel: 17 rooms: single 1, double 16. Showers,
private WCs, TV.

Other points: bar, credit cards accepted,
children welcome, garden terrace, car parking,
traditional decor.
Address: Le Gibet.
M. ANDRE CARLE, tel 37.49.68.85.

MARCILLE RAOUL, Ille-et-Vilaine 35560, Map 4 ⊗ ♈ ⌂

LES ROUTIERS, between de Combourg and Vitré

Places of interest: Le Mont Saint Michel
(30km), château de Combourg (10km).
Menu: 45 to 75 Frs
Accommodation: 85 to 105 Frs
Restaurant: lunch 11.30–2pm, dinner
7.30–9pm.
Hotel: 7 rooms: single 2, double 5. Showers,
baths.

Other points: bar, children welcome, à la carte
menu, pets allowed, car parking, traditional
decor.
Address: Le Bourg.
M. CHRISTIAN BELLEPERCHE,
tel 99.73.62.14.

MARCILLY LA CAMPAGNE, Eure 27320, Map 3 ⊗ ♈

LE RELAIS EUROPEEN, RN 154 between Evreux and Dreux

Place of interest: Aire d'Antan (2km).
Languages: German, English, Spanish
Restaurant: dinner 6–11 pm. Closed Saturdays
and Sundays.
Other points: bar, children welcome, garden

terrace, pets allowed, car parking, traditional
decor.
Address: Tivoly.
M. THIERRY VALLEE, tel 32.58.31.75.

MARIGNE LAILLE, Sarthe 72220, Map 5 ⊗ ♈

AUBERGE DU BON ACCUEIL, RN 138 between Le Mans and Tours

Menu: 49 to 150 Frs
Restaurant: lunch 12–2.30pm, dinner
7–9.30pm. Closed Wednesday afternoons.
Other points: bar, credit cards accepted, à la

carte menu, pets allowed, car parking.
Address: Route Nationale 138.
M. JEAN-LOUIS LOUDIERE, tel 43.42.12.01.

MARTIGNE FERCHAUD, Ille-et-Vilaine 35640, Map 4   ⊗ ♟ ⌂

LE POT D'ETAIN, RN 178

Restaurant: closed Saturdays and in August.
Hotel: 8 rooms.
Other points: bar, traditional decor.

Address: 10 grande rue.
MME YVONNE BOUTEILLER,
tel 99.47.90.12.

MARZAN, Morbihan 56130, Map 4   ⊗ ♟

LES RIVES DE VILAINE, RN 165, 1.5km to right after Roche Bernard bridge

Places of interest: Zoo de Branféré (18km),
barrage Darzal (6km), La Roche Bernard
(2km), le golf du Morbihan.
Menu: 40 to 100 Frs
Restaurant: lunch 11.45–2.30pm, dinner
7–8.30pm.
Specialities: fruits de mer, poissons au beurre

blanc (on request).
Other points: bar, credit cards accepted,
children welcome, garden terrace, pets allowed,
car parking, traditional decor.
Address: 13 rue de la Fontaine.
M. GILLES JOUAN, tel 99.90.63.22.

MATHIEU, Calvados 14920, Map 3   ⊗ ♟

RELAIS DE LA COTE DE NACRE, RD 7 exit Douvres la Délivrande

Menu: 51 to 60 Frs
Restaurant: lunch 12–3pm, dinner 7.30–9pm.
Closed Sunday afternoons and 20 December to
5 January.
Hotel: 2 rooms: single 1, double 1.

Other points: bar, traditional decor.
Address: 4 rue Augustin Fresnel.
M. MARC BEDEAU DE L'ECOCHERE,
tel 31.44.10.17.

MAY SUR ORNE, Calvados 14320, Map 3   ⊗ ♟ ⌂

L'AMMONITE, RD 562 between Caen and Flers

Places of interest: Vallée de l'Orne, Suisse
normande, plages du débarquement, route des
fromages.
Language: English
Menu: 50 to 94 Frs
Accommodation: 110 to 180 Frs
Restaurant: lunch 11.30–2.30pm, dinner
5–9.30pm. Closed Sundays (out of season) and
in August.

Hotel: 7 rooms: single 1, double 6. Showers,
baths.
Other points: bar, credit cards accepted,
children welcome, self-service, garden terrace,
pets allowed, car parking, traditional decor.
Address: 2 rue du Canada.
MME MARYVONNE HOREL,
tel 31.79.80.27.

MAYENNE, Mayenne 53100, Map 5   ⊗ ♟ ⌂

L'ESCALE, CD 35

Places of interest: Le Mans (château,
basilique, église, chapelle), le site gallo-romain
à Jublains (8km).
Menu: 49,50 Frs including wine
Accommodation: 92 Frs
Restaurant: lunch 11–2pm, dinner 7–9pm.
Closed Saturday nights and Sundays.

Hotel: 13 rooms: single 2, double 11.
Other points: bar, credit cards accepted,
children welcome, garden terrace, pets allowed,
car parking, traditional decor.
Address: route du Mans.
M. DOMINIQUE FORTIN, tel 43.04.19.14.

MENIL BROUT (LE), Orne 61250, Map 3 ⊗ ♈

LA BONNE FLANQUETTE, RN 12

Restaurant: closed Saturdays, Sundays and August.

Other points: bar, car parking.
MME CASTELIER, tel 33.27.10.03.

MESNIL DURAND (LE), Calvados 14140, Map 3 ⊗ ♈

LE RELAIS DE LA FORGE, RD 579 between Lisieux and Livarot

Places of interest: Basilique de Lisieux (12km), la vallée d'Auge.
Menu: 52 Frs
Restaurant: closed Sundays.
Other points: bar, credit cards accepted,

children welcome, garden terrace, pets allowed, car parking, traditional decor.
Address: Les Forges Mézières.
MME CHANTALE LE ROSIER,
tel 31.63.52.79.

MILLIERES, Manche 50190, Map 3 ⊗ ♈

RELAIS DES TOURISTES, main road from Lessay to St Lô between Perriers and Lessay

Places of interest: St Lô (20km), Lessaye (4km), visite de fromagerie (3km) et fabrique de jambon fumé avec dégustation.
Languages: English
Restaurant: closed Sundays.
Specialities: coq à la bière ou au vin.

Other points: credit cards accepted, children welcome, garden terrace, pets allowed, car parking.
Address: La Bezanterie.
M. GERARD LUNEL, tel 33.46.71.12.

MINIAC MORVAN, Ille-et-Vilaine 35540, Map 4 ⊗ ♈ ⌂

HOTEL DE LA GARE, between Rennes and St Malo

Places of interest: Le Mont Saint Michel, Dinard, St Malo.
Language: English, Italian
Restaurant.
Menu: 44 to 70 Frs
Accommodation: 120 to 175 Frs

Hotel: 9 rooms: single 5, double 4.
Other points: bar, car parking, traditional decor.
Address: La Costardais.
MARC SDF EFFLAM, tel 99.58.58.14.

MONNAI, Orne 61470, Map 3 ⊗ ♈ ⌂

LE CHEVAL BAI, RN 138

Restaurant: closed Sundays.
Hotel: 6 rooms.
Other points: bar.

Address: Route Nationale 138.
M. GILBERT ROUSSEL, tel 33.39.42.00.

MONT A LA QUESNE, Manche 50700, Map 3 ⊗ ♈

LE CLOS NORMAND, RN 13

Restaurant.
Other points: bar.

MME JOSIANE GERMAIN, tel 33.41.94.35.

MONT SAINT MICHEL (LE), Manche 50116, Map 3 ⊗ ♈ ⌂ ☆ ☆

HOTEL MOTEL VERT – La Rôtisserie, RN 776, last crossroads before the dyke

Places of interest: Le Mont Saint Michel (1.8km), la Côte d'Emeraude (Cancale, St Malo, Dinard, Dinan), Granville, Château de Fougères, Ile de Jersey (45km).
Languages: German, English, Italian
Menu: 53 to 195 Frs
Accommodation: 195 to 270 Frs
Restaurant: lunch 12–1.30pm, dinner 7–9pm. Closed in December and January.

Specialities: agneau, fruit de mer, omelette du Mont Saint Michel.
Hotel: 113 rooms, showers, baths, private WCs, TV, phone.
Other points: bar, credit cards accepted, children welcome, à la carte menu, garden terrace, pets allowed, car parking.
Address: route du Mont Saint Michel.
M. PHILIPPE FRANCOIS, tel 33.60.09.33.

MONTAUBAN DE BRETAGNE, Ille-et-Vilaine 35360, Map 4

HOTEL DE FRANCE, RN 12 and 164, town centre

Places of interest: Brocéliande, château féodal.
Language: English
Menu: 58 to 150 Frs
Accommodation: 110 to 205 Frs
Restaurant: lunch: 11.30–2pm, dinner 7–9.30pm. Closed Mondays (out of season) and from 20 December to 20 January.
Specialities: fruits de mer, coq au Muscadet, far breton, poissons.

Hotel: 12 rooms: single 8, double 4. Showers, baths, private WCs, TV, phone.
Other points: bar, credit cards accepted, children welcome, à la carte menu, lounge area, pets allowed, car parking, traditional decor.
Address: 34 rue du Général de Gaulle.
M. GABRIEL LE METAYER, tel 99.06.40.19.

MONTAUBAN DE BRETAGNE, Ille-et-Vilaine 35360, Map 4

RELAIS DE LA HUCHERAIS, RN 12 and 164

Language: English
Menu: 100 to 170 Frs
Restaurant: closed Sundays.
Hotel: 14 rooms.

Other points: bar, pets allowed, car parking.
Address: La Hucherais.
M. ALAIN MEHEUS, tel 99.06.40.29.

MONTAUDIN, Mayenne 53220, Map 5

HOTEL DE PARIS, RN 799

Places of interest: Le château de Fougères (17km), Pontmain (9km).
Language: English
Menu: 44 to 48 Frs
Accommodation: 135 to 185 Frs
Restaurant: closed Mondays.
Speciality: Brochet au beurre blanc.

Hotel: 5 rooms: single 3, double 2. Showers, private WCs, TV.
Other points: bar, credit cards accepted, children welcome, garden terrace, car parking.
Address: route d'Ernée
M. DANIEL DOUDARD, tel 43.05.30.79.

MONTMARTIN SUR MER, Manche 50590, Map 3

HOTELLERIE DU BON VIEUX TEMPS, RD 20, Granville

Places of interest: Baie de la Sienne (2km), les fours à chaux dans la commune, nombreux manoirs aux alentours, Granville (20km) avec la possibilité de visiter les îles de Chausey, Jersey et Guernesey.
Language: English

Menu: 58 to 200 Frs
Accommodation: 128 to 280 Frs
Restaurant: lunch 12–2pm, dinner 7.30–9.30pm. Closed Sunday nights (from All Saints Day to Easter).
Speciality: Cuisine au cidre et à la crème.

Hotel: 20 rooms: single 15, double 5. Showers, baths, private WCs, phone.
Other points: bar, credit cards accepted, children welcome, à la carte menu, garden terrace, pets allowed, car parking, traditional decor.
M. ERICK BOURBONNAIS, tel 33.47.54.44.

MONTOIR DE BRETAGNE, Loire-Atlantique 44550, Map 5   ⊗♈

LES NOES, RN 171, via expressway Nantes/Saint Nazaire

Places of interest: Port de Montoir, Saint Nazaire, parc régional de la Brière.
Menu: 50 Frs
Restaurant: lunch 11.45am–2pm, dinner 7–9pm. Closed Saturdays and Sundays.
Other points: bar, credit cards accepted, garden terrace, pets allowed, car parking.
Address: Route Nationale 171, Les Noës.
MME BRIGITTE LIBERGE, tel 40.45.55.67.

MONTPINCHON, Manche 50210, Map 3   ⊗♈

BAR DES AMIS

Menu: 46 Frs
Restaurant: lunch 12–2pm.
Other points: bar.
Address: Le Bourg.
M. JOEL HEBERT, tel 33.45.70.95.

MONTREUIL LE CHETIF, Sarthe 72130, Map 5   ⊗♈

AU RENDEZ-VOUS DES CHASSEURS, RD 310, Sillé-le-Guillaume, to Fresnay on the forest outskirts

Places of interest: Château Sainte Suzanne, grottes de Sauges, Fresnay, musée des coiffes, abbaye de champagne.
Menu: 48 to 80 Frs
Restaurant: lunch 12–2pm, dinner 7–9pm.
Other points: bar, credit cards accepted, children welcome, à la carte menu, self service, garden terrace, pets allowed, car parking, traditional decor.
Address: Le Grand Gué.
MME FRANCOISE BORDEAU, tel 43.33.39.90.

MORDELLES, Ille-et-Vilaine 35310, Map 4   ⊗♈

LE RELAIS, RN 24 between Rennes and Lorient

Place of interest: Brocéliande (15km).
Menu: 48 Frs
Restaurant: lunch 12–3pm. Closed August.
Other points: bar, credit cards accepted.
Address: La Croix Ignon.
M. MICHEL CAVELIER, tel 99.60.02.50.

MOREAC, Morbihan 56500, Map 4   ⊗♈⌂☆☆

LE RELAIS DU BARDERFF, RN 24 between Rennes and Lorient or Vannes and St Brieuc

Place of interest: La mer (30km).
Menu: 45 to 85 Frs
Accommodation: 210 to 360 Frs
Restaurant: lunch 12–2pm, dinner 7–10pm. Closed Sundays (out of season).
Hotel: 20 rooms: single 5, double 15. Showers, baths, private WCs, TV, phone.
Other points: bar, credit cards accepted, children welcome, à la carte menu, self service, lounge area, car parking.
Address: Z.I. du Barderff.
M. JEAN LAMOUR, tel 97.60.18.60.

MOREILLES, Vendée 85450, Map 5

LE CHEVAL BLANC, RN 137, main road from Nantes to Bordeaux

Places of interest: Le marais poitevin, l'Ile de Ré, la côte Vendéenne.
Menu: 59 Frs
Accommodation: 95 to 130 Frs
Restaurant: lunch 11.30–2pm, dinner 7–10pm. Closed Sundays (out of season) and 28 December to 17 January.

Specialities: mogettes, jambon vendéen.
Hotel: 5 rooms: single 1, double 4.
Other points: bar, credit cards accepted, children welcome, garden terrace, pets allowed, car parking.
Address: 9 route Nationale.
M. CHRISTIAN SARRAUD, tel 51.56.11.02.

MORTAGNE SUR SEVRE, Vendée 85290, Map 5

LE RELAIS DE LA GARE, RN 160

Restaurant: closed Saturday nights, Sundays and August.
Other points: bar.

Address: 52 route de Cholet.
M. JEAN-LUC ARROUET, tel 51.65.11.56

MORTREE, Orne 61570, Map 3

LE POINT DU JOUR, RN 158, between Argentan and Sees

Places of interest: Château de Mortrée, cathédrale de Sees, château de Sassy.
Language: English
Menu: 51 to 90 Frs
Restaurant: closed Saturday nights and Sundays.
Speciality: estoufade de volaille.

Other points: bar, credit cards accepted, children welcome, à la carte menu, garden terrace, pets allowed, car parking, traditional decor.
Address: 139 Grande Rue.
MME FABIENNE HUETTE, tel 33.35.35.22.

MOSLES, Calvados 14400, Map 3

RESTAURANT DE LA POSTE, RN 13, main road from Bayeux to Cherbourg

Places of interest: Les plages et le musée du débarquement, musée de la Tapisserie.
Menu: 49 to 68 Frs
Restaurant: lunch 11–2.30pm, dinner from 7pm. Closed Saturday afternoons and Sundays.

Other points: bar, credit cards accepted, children welcome, pets allowed, car parking.
Address: Route Nationale 13.
M. JACQUES LEROSIER, tel 31.22.33.79.

MOUZEUIL ST MARTIN, Vendée 85370, Map 5

CENTRAL ROUTIERS, RN 148 between Niort and Les Sables d'Olonne

Places of interest: Les marais poitevins, Puy du Fou.
Menu: 50 to 85 Frs
Accommodation: 70 to 90 Frs
Restaurant: lunch 12–2pm, dinner 8-9pm.
Hotel: 6 rooms: single 5, double 1. Showers,

private WCs, phone.
Other points: bar, children welcome, lounge area, garden terrace, pets allowed, car parking.
Address: 33 rue Louis Apraille.
M. JEAN-MARIE GUILBAUD, tel 51.28.72.44.

MOYON, Manche 50860, Map 3   ⊗♥

CARREFOUR DE PARIS – Super Routiers, CD 999, main road from St Lô to Villedieu les Poêles

Places of interest: Villedieu les Poêles, les roches de Ham (15km), la chapelle sur Vire (10km), château de l'Angotière, la vallée de la Vire, château de Cerisy la Salle, musée de Thorigny (20km).
Language: English
Menu: 40 to 50 Frs
Restaurant.

Specialities: pieds de veaux, oreilles de cochons.
Other points: bar, credit cards accepted, children welcome, à la carte menu, lounge area, garden terrace, pets allowed, car parking.
Address: Carrefour Paris.
M. JEAN-ROBERT FECAN, tel 33.05.59.74.

NANTES, Loire-Atlantique 44200, Map 5   ⊗♥🏠

A L'ANCRE D'OR, RN 43

Places of interest: Le château des ducs de Bretagne, le vieux Nantes (cathédrale), route du muscadet.
Menu: 41 to 49 Frs
Accommodation: 70 to 120 Frs
Restaurant: dinner 7–9.30pm. Closed Saturday afternoons, Sundays and in August.

Hotel: 5 rooms: single 2, double 3.
Other points: bar, credit cards accepted, à la carte menu, car parking.
Address: 55 boulevard Gustave Roch.
M. SERGE DESMORTIERS, tel 40.35.39.30.

NANTES, Loire-Atlantique 44200, Map 5   ⊗♥

AU RENDEZ-VOUS DES SPORTIFS, RN 43

Restaurant: closed Saturdays, Sundays and in July.
Specialities: paëlla, couscous.

Other points: bar, credit cards accepted.
Address: 40 quai de Malakoff.
M. BERNARD AUBERT, tel 40.47.75.39.

NANTES, Loire-Atlantique 44200, Map 5   ⊗♥

L'AVENIR, RN 23, on the banks of the Loire

Places of interest: Lac de Grand Lieu (20km), pont de Cheviré, safari.
Restaurant: lunch 11.30–2.30pm, dinner 7–10pm. Closed Saturdays, Sundays and mid-December.

Other points: bar, credit cards accepted, car parking, traditional decor.
Address: 1 rue de la Pompe.
MME VIVIANE BARON, tel 40.43.46.03.

NASSANDRES, Eure 27550, Map 3   ⊗♥

LE PARIS CAEN CHERBOURG INTERNATIONAL, RN 13

Place of interest: Abbaye de Bec-Hellouin.
Restaurant: closed Saturday afternoons and Sundays.
Other points: bar, credit cards accepted, pets

allowed.
Address: 11 Route Nationale 13.
M. PATRICE BOUTEL, tel 32.45.00.26.

NEUFCHATEL EN BRAY, Seine-Maritime 76270, Map 3   ⊗♥

RELAIS DES HAYONS, RN 28, main road from Paris to Dieppe

Places of interest: Neufchâtel en Bray, château Mesnières.
Menu: 45 to 70 Frs
Restaurant: lunch 11.30–3pm, dinner 6.30–11pm. Closed Sundays.
Speciality: normandaise.

Other points: bar, credit cards accepted, children welcome, à la carte menu, lounge area, pets allowed, car parking, traditional decor.
Address: Esclavelles.
M. JEAN-CLAUDE PIEDNOEL, tel 35.93.13.15.

NEUFCHATEL EN SAOSNOIS, Sarthe 72600, Map 5 ⊗♈⌂

LES ROUTIERS Tabac, RN 155

Restaurant: closed in August.
Hotel: 12 rooms.
Other points: bar.

MME CHRISTIANE CHAPELLIER, tel 43.97.74.10.

NEUVE LYRE (LA), Eure 27330, Map 3 ⊗♈⌂

LE RELAIS DES AMIS, between Evreux and l'Aigle

Menu: 49 Frs
Restaurant: closed Sundays and first 2 weeks of August.
Hotel: 5 rooms, showers.

Other points: bar, children welcome, garden terrace, pets allowed, car parking.
Address: Hameau de Chagny.
M. JEAN-CLAUDE GUYOT, tel 32.30.50.60.

NIEUL LE DOLENT, Vendée 85430, Map 5 ⊗♈

CHEZ JACQUES, RD 36 between la Roche sur Yon and les Sables d'Olonne

Place of interest: Les Sables d'Olonne.
Menu: 45 to 55 Frs
Restaurant: lunch 11.30–2.30pm. Closed Sundays.
Speciality: fraise de veau.

Other points: bar, credit cards accepted, pets allowed, car parking, traditional decor.
Address: 8 rue de Lattre de Tassigny.
M. JACQUES PINEL, tel 51.07.93.71.

NOE POULAIN (LA), Eure 27560, Map 3 ⊗♈

CHEZ MANU ET JOJO, CD 810 between Pontaumer and Bernay

Place of interest: Basilique de Lisieux (30km).
Menu: 52 Frs
Restaurant: closed Saturdays.

Other points: bar, credit cards accepted, car parking.
MME EMMANUEL LANGIN, tel 32.57.90.35.

NONANT LE PIN, Orne 61240, Map 3 ⊗♈⊷

LE RELAIS DES HARAS, RN 26, Argentan

Place of interest: Le Haras du Pin.
Menu: 50 Frs
Restaurant: lunch 11–3pm, dinner 7.30–10pm. Closed Sundays (except reservations) and in August.
Specialities: tripes maison, andouillette garnie.

Other points: bar, credit cards accepted, children welcome, pets allowed, traditional decor.
Address: Grande Rue.
M. JACQUES LAMPIN, tel 33.39.93.35.

NORT SUR ERDRE, Loire-Atlantique 44390, Map 5 ⊗♈⌂

HOTEL DES 3 MARCHANDS

Place of interest: La rive de l'Erdre.
Menu: 44 (wine inc) to 70 Frs
Accommodation: 80 to 130 Frs
Restaurant: lunch 11–3pm, dinner 6–9.30pm.
Closed from Saturday after 3pm to Monday
9am.
Hotel: 10 rooms: single 6, double 4.

Other points: bar, credit cards accepted,
children welcome, à la carte menu, pets
allowed, car parking, traditional decor.
Address: 3 place du Champ de Foire.
M. FRANCOIS ZAMGOTCHIAN,
tel 40.72.20.34.

NOTRE DAME DE GRAVENCHON, Seine-Maritime 76330, Map 3 ⊗ 𝕐

AU COUP DE FREIN, RD 428

Restaurant.
Other points: bar.

Address: rue Claude Bernard.
MME MARIE-JOSEE DAVID, tel 35 94 61 35.

NOYAL SUR VILAINE, Ille-et-Vilaine 35530, Map 4 ⊗ 𝕐 🏠

LE RELAIS 35, RN 157, old road between Paris and Rennes

Language: English
Menu: 48 Frs
Accommodation: 100 to 115 Frs
Restaurant: lunch 11–3pm, dinner 6–10pm.
Closed Saturday nights, Sundays and the week
of 15 August.

Hotel: 13 double rooms.
Other points: bar, credit cards accepted,
children welcome, à la carte menu, garden
terrace, pets allowed, car parking.
Address: 20 avenue du Général de Gaulle.
MME PASCALE SEFELIN, tel 99.00.51.20.

OCTEVILLE, Manche 50130, Map 3 ⊗ 𝕐

LE VENT D'AMONT, RN 3 and 900

Language: English
Restaurant: closed Mondays (after lunch).
Other points: bar, car parking.

Address: 1 rue Jules Ferry.
M. JACKY TRAVERS, tel 33.52.16.16.

OISSEAU LE PETIT, Sarthe 72610, Map 5 ⊗ 𝕐 🏠

HOTEL DE L'ESPERANCE, RN 138 between Le Mans and Alençon

Menu: 48 to 60 Frs
Restaurant: lunch 12–2pm, dinner 7.30–9pm.
Closed Saturdays, Sundays and in August.
Hotel: 4 rooms.

Other points: bar, children welcome, pets
allowed, car parking.
MME ANDREE BESNARD, tel 33.26.81.97.

OUISTREHAM, Calvados 14150, Map 3 ⊗ 𝕐

LE COIN DU PORT, RD 514

Places of interest: Les musées, les plages du
débarquement et le cimetière militaire.
Menu: 50 Frs
Restaurant: closed Sunday nights and from
24 December to 2 January.

Other points: bar, credit cards accepted,
children welcome, à la carte menu, self service.
Address: 90 avenue Michel Cabieu.
M. CLAUDE MORIN, tel 31.97.15.22.

OURVILLE EN CAUX, Seine-Maritime 76450, Map 3 ⊗ 𝕐 🏠

BAR DE LA PLACE

Restaurant: closed second 2 weeks of August.
Hotel: 10 rooms.
Other points: bar, car parking.

Address: Place Jean Picard.
M. JEAN-PIERRE POUCHET, tel 35.27.60.01.

PACE PAR ALENCON, Orne 61250, Map 3 ⊗🍷

LE RELAIS DES ROUTIERS, RN 12 to St Malo, Rennes and Alençon

Menu: 60 to 120 Frs
Restaurant: lunch 11.30-3pm, dinner 7–9pm.
Closed Saturday afternoons and Sunday
afternoons.
Specialities: Rillette, paté du chef.

Other points: bar, credit cards accepted, à la
carte menu, pets allowed, car parking.
Address: Damigni.
M. MARCEL BRUNEAU, tel 33.27.70.69.

PARIGNE, Ille-et-Vilaine 35133, Map 4 ⊗🍷

LE FRANCK'ELLE, RD 108 between Fougères and Louvigné

Places of interest: La forêt de Fougères et son
château, le Mont Saint Michel (23km), château
de Fretay (2km), le Rocher de Monthault
(cimetière américain).
Menu: 49 to 120 Frs
Restaurant: lunch 12–3pm, dinner 7–9pm.
Closed Monday afternoons and 15 days in
August.

Specialities: poulet aux écrevices, truite à la
hussade, fruits de mer.
Other points: bar, pets allowed, car parking,
traditional decor.
Address: 12 rue de la Mairie.
M. FRANCK ROUSSEL, tel 99.97.22.90.

PARIGNE LE POLIN, Sarthe 72330, Map 5 ⊗

LA CHESNAIE

Menu: 50 Frs
Restaurant: lunch 11.15–2pm, dinner
7–9.45pm. Closed Saturdays and Sundays.
Other points: credit cards accepted, pets

allowed, car parking.
Address: Route Nationale 23.
MME CHANTAL MARY, tel 43.87.90.70.

PARIGNY, Manche 50600, Map 3 ⊗🍷🏠

HOTEL DU CHEMIN DE FER, RD 977, main road from Caen to Rennes, between Mortain and St
Hilaire

Places of interest: Le Mont Saint Michel
(40km), lac de Vezins (8km), Villedieu (cité du
cuivre – 35km).
Menu: 47 Frs
Accommodation: 120 Frs
Restaurant: lunch 1pm, dinner 7–10pm.
Closed Sundays (out of season), and end of
December.

Hotel: 4 rooms: single 3, double 1. Showers,
baths, private WCs.
Other points: bar, credit cards accepted,
children welcome, à la carte menu, pets
allowed, car parking.
Address: La Gare.
M. GILBERT LECORNU, tel 33.49.10.55

PEDERNEC, Côtes-du-Nord 22540, Map 4 ⊗🍷

LE MAUDEZ, Lannion

Places of interest: La vallée du Perrier, le parc des loisirs (Armoripark), Le Ménez-Bré.
Menu: 30 to 78 Frs
Restaurant: Closed Sundays and in August.

Other points: bar, children welcome, à la carte menu, self-service.
Address: Maudez.
M. DENIS DUTILLET, tel 96.4 5.32.28.

PERCY, Manche 50410, Map 3   ⊗ 🍽 🏠

LE RELAIS DE LA GARE, RD 999, left at entrance to Percy coming into St Lô

Places of interest: Villedieu les Poëles (9km), le Mont Saint Michel (55km).
Menu: 45 Frs (lunch), 55 Frs (evening).
Accommodation: 80 to 100 Frs
Restaurant: lunch from 12pm, dinner 7–10pm. Closed Sundays, public holidays, and from 15 to 28 February.

Specialities: jambon fumé et omelette.
Hotel: 4 double rooms. Showers, private WCs.
Other points: bar, pets allowed, car parking.
Address: 4 rue de l'Ancienne Gare.
M. BERNARD GUILLOTTE, tel 33.61.20.96.

PETIVILLE, Calvados 14390, Map 3   ⊗ 🍽

LE COLOMBIER, RD 513, between Caen and Cabourg

Menu: 53 Frs
Restaurant: lunch 11.30–2.30pm. Closed Sundays and from 20 December to 6 January.

Other points: bar, credit cards accepted, children welcome.
M. GERARD BAUDEL, tel 31.78.00.67.

PIACE, Sarthe 72170, Map 5   ⊗ 🍽

LES DEUX RENARDS, RN 138 between Alençon (20km) and Le Mans (30km)

Place of interest: Les Alpes Mancelles (20km).
Menu: 47 to 54 Frs
Restaurant: lunch 11–2.30pm, dinner 7–10pm. Closed Saturdays and Sundays.

Other points: bar, credit cards accepted, children welcome, car parking.
Address: Route Nationale 138, Le Bourg.
M. JEROME BRILLIET, tel 43.97.02.16.

PICAUVILLE, Manche 50360, Map 3   ⊗ 🍽 🏠

HOTEL DES VOYAGEURS, RN 13, Cherbourg

Places of interest: Sainte Mère, Cherbourg.
Language: English
Menu: 44,70 to 115 Frs
Accommodation: 85 to 125 Frs
Restaurant: closed Sundays (out of season) and 15 days end December.
Specialities: moules marinières, soupe de poisson.

Hotel: 9 rooms.
Other points: bar, credit cards accepted, children welcome, à la carte menu, pets allowed, traditional decor.
Address: 43 rue de Périers.
MME FABIENNE FRANCOISE,
tel 33.41.00.59.

PIPRIAC, Ille-et-Vilaine 35550, Map 4   ⊗ 🍽 🏠 ☆

HOTEL DE LA TOUR D'AUVERGNE, RD 777

Places of interest: Châteaux, exposition de souffleurs de verre, village d'artisans, croisières sur l'Oust, chapelles.
Menu: 50 to 180 Frs

Accommodation: 90 to 140 Frs (supplement for infants)
Restaurant: lunch 12–2pm, dinner 7–9.30pm.

Closed Monday afternoons and 15 days in February.
Speciality: poissons au beurre blanc.
Hotel: 10 rooms, showers, private WCs, TV, phone.

Other points: bar, credit cards accepted, garden terrace, car parking, traditional decor.
Address: 7 rue de l'Avenir.
M. MICHEL GERARD, tel 99.34.34.85.

PLAINTEL, Côtes-du-Nord 22940, Map 4   ⊗ ♀ ⌂

A LA DESCENTE DES CHAOS

Language: English
Restaurant: closed Tuesday afternoons, Sunday afternoons and in August.
Hotel: 8 rooms.

Other points: bar.
Address: Gare de Plaintel.
M. JEAN-CLAUDE BONENFANT, tel 96.32.16.05.

PLAINTEL, Côtes-du-Nord 22940, Map 4   ⊗ ♀

LE SEBASTOPOL, RD 700, on the road to Loudéac

Places of interest: Quintin (7km), Saint Brieuc (12km), Loudéac (32km).
Language: English
Menu: 50 to 150 Frs
Restaurant.
Specialities: fer de mer, choucroute, cassoulet.

Other points: bar, credit cards accepted, children welcome, à la carte menu, pets allowed, car parking, traditional decor.
Address: route de Sébastopol.
M. THIERRY PODEUR, tel 96.32.15.74.

PLESTAN, Côtes-du-Nord 22640, Map 4   ⊗ ♀ ⌂

HOTEL DU CENTRE, RN 12, Saint Brieuc

Places of interest: Jugon les Lacs, la mer.
Menu: 48 to 78 Frs
Accommodation: 105 to 135 Frs
Restaurant: lunch 11.30–3pm, dinner 7.30–10pm. Closed Sundays.
Specialities: choucroute, paëlla, couscous et fruits de mer.

Hotel: 7 rooms: single 5, double 2.
Other points: bar, credit cards accepted, children welcome, à la carte menu, pets allowed, car parking, traditional decor.
Address: 5 rue de Penthièvre.
MME VIOLETTE MELINE, tel 96.34.10.96.

PLEUMEUR GAUTIER, Côtes-du-Nord 22740, Map 4   ⊗ ♀

CHEZ CINDY, CD 33, route de Tréguier

Places of interest: Cathédrale de Tréguier, Ile de Bréhat.
Menu: 48 to 105 Frs
Restaurant: lunch 12–2pm, dinner 7–9pm. Closed Saturdays and 3 weeks in August.
Speciality: couscous.

Other points: bar, credit cards accepted, children welcome, à la carte menu, garden terrace, pets allowed, car parking, traditional decor.
Address: route de Tréguier, La Croix Neuve.
M. HERVE LE FOLL, tel 96.92.42.19.

PLOERMEL, Morbihan 56800, Map 4   ⊗ ♀ ⌂

LES ROUTIERS, RN 24, after roundabout as you enter Ploermel

Menu: 50 to 120 Frs
Accommodation: 80 to 150 Frs
Restaurant: closed Saturdays and in September.
Hotel: 11 rooms.

Other points: bar, credit cards accepted, children welcome, car parking.
Address: route de Rennes.
MME SOLANGE RIO, tel 97.74.00.48.

PLOUAGAT, Côtes-du-Nord 22170, Map 4 ⊗♈⌂

CHEZ PIERRETTE, RN 12, take interchange to Quintin

Place of interest: Châtelaudren
Accommodation: 170 Frs
Restaurant: closed Saturdays to 3pm, Sundays and bank holidays.
Hotel: 12 rooms, showers, baths, private WCs, TV, phone.

Other points: bar, credit cards accepted, pets allowed, car parking.
Address: ZA de Fournello
HOTELS DROUIN RESTAURATION, tel 96.74.28.13.

PLOUER SUR RANCE, Côtes-du-Nord 22490, Map 4 ⊗♈⌐

LE BON ACCUEIL, RD 366 between Dinan and St Malo

Places of interest: Pont de la Rance, Dinan, St Malo, port de plaisance.
Menu: 48 to 120 Frs
Restaurant: lunch 120–2pm. Closed Monday afternoons, and in August.
Specialities: fruits de mer, poissons fumés maison.

Other points: bar, credit cards accepted, garden terrace, pets allowed, car parking.
Address: La Gourbanière.
M. THEOPHILE YRIS, tel 96.86.91.67.

PLOUGOUMELEN, Morbihan 56400, Map 4 ⊗♈

LE KENYAH, RN 165, expressway Vannes to Auray, exit Esso station

Places of interest: Auray (8km), Vannes (8km), Carnac (20km), Quiberon (30km).
Language: English
Restaurant: lunch 11.30–3pm, dinner 7–10.30pm. Closed Sundays.

Other points: bar, credit cards accepted, garden terrace, pets allowed, car parking.
Address: Zone commerciale du Kenyah.
M. JOEL BORILLER, tel 97.56.25.37.

PLOUGUENAST, Côtes-du-Nord 22150, Map 4 ⊗♈

LE RELAIS DU SQUARE, RN 168

Restaurant: closed Saturdays and in August.
Other points: bar.
Address: 5 rue d'Enfer.

MME SYLVIANE LAFON-SAGORY, tel 96.28.70.47.

PLOUNEVEZ MOEDEC, Côtes-du-Nord 22810, Map 4 ⊗♈⌂

AUX ROUTIERS – Le Relais du Beg-Ar-C'Hra, RN 12 between Morlaix and Guingamp

Places of interest: La mer (20km), lacs (10km).
Language: English
Menu: from 50 Frs
Accommodation: 100 to 150 Frs
Restaurant: lunch 12–2pm, dinner 7.30–10pm. Closed Saturdays, Sundays, from 1 to 10 May

and mid-August to mid-September.
Specialities: fruits de mer, poissons.
Hotel: 11 rooms, showers, baths.
Other points: bar, credit cards accepted, pets allowed, car parking, traditional decor.
M. JEAN-MARIE RUBEUS, tel 96.38.61.08.

PLOUNEVEZ QUINTIN, Côtes-du-Nord 22110, Map 4   ⊗�

LES ROUTIERS, RN 790 between Rostrenen and St Brieuc

Places of interest: Lacs, la vallée.
Menu: 48 to 60 Frs
Restaurant: lunch 11–2pm, dinner 7–8.30pm.
Closed Saturdays, and second 2 weeks of
August.

Other points: bar, credit cards accepted,
children welcome, pets allowed, car parking.
Address: place de l'Eglise.
MME GILDAS MARTIN, tel 96.24.54.05.

PLOURAY, Morbihan 56770, Map 4   ⊗♟

LE RELAIS DES SPORTS

Restaurant.
Other points: bar.

Address: 2 rue de l'Ellé.
MME LEANDRE LE LAIN, tel 97.23.90.18.

POLIGNE, Ille-et-Vilaine 35320, Map 4   ⊗♟

LE TIROUANEZ, RN 137 between Bain de Bretagne and Rennes

Menu: 45 Frs
Restaurant.
Other points: bar.

Address: Le Bourg.
M. YVES ROMMEL, tel 99.43.73.06.

PONT HEBERT, Manche 50880, Map 5   ⊗♟🏠

LE MADRILENE, RN 174

Restaurant.
Hotel: 6 rooms.
Other points: bar.

Address: Quartier du Pont la Meauffe.
MME MARIE-THERESE HAMET,
tel 33.56.44.18.

PONT-AUDEMER, Eure 27500, Map 3   ⊗♟

AU RENDEZ-VOUS DES CHAUFFEURS, RN 180

Restaurant: closed Sundays.
Hotel: 3 rooms.
Other points: bar.

Address: 4 rue Notre Dame du Pré.
M. RENAUD PIERREL, tel 32.41.04.36.

PONT-AUDEMER, Eure 27500, Map 3   ⊗♟

RELAIS DE SAINT PAUL, RN 180 between Pont Audemer and Bernay

Menu: 52 Frs
Restaurant: lunch 11.30–1pm. Closed
Saturdays, Sundays and first 2 weeks of
August.

Other points: bar, car parking, traditional
decor.
Address: Route de Saint-Paul, Les Saulniers.
M. CLAUDE VIRFOLLET, tel 32.41.16.17.

PONT-AUDEMER, Eure 27500, Map 3   ⊗♟

RELAIS DU BOULANGARD, RN 180

Restaurant.
Other points: bar.

M. FRANCIS EGRET, tel 32.57.01.27

PONTCHATEAU, Loire-Atlantique 44160, Map 5

LE RELAIS DE BEAULIEU, RN 165, main road from Nantes to Vannes

Places of interest: Le Calvaire de Pontchâteau, la Brière, la Baule, la Rohe Bernard, château de la Bretesche à Mussillac.
Languages: English, Italian
Menu: 65 to 145 Frs
Accommodation: 110 to 250 Frs
Restaurant: lunch 12–3pm, dinner 7–10pm. Closed Saturday nights and Sunday nights.

Specialities: anguilles au cidre, saumon grillé au beurre blanc, soupe de poissons, langoustes.
Hotel: 15 rooms: single 7, double 8. Showers, private WCs.
Other points: bar, credit cards accepted, children welcome, à la carte menu, pets allowed, car parking.
MME LOUISETTE PRAUD, tel 40.01.60.58.

PONTCHATEAU, Loire-Atlantique 44160, Map 5

L'AUBERGE DU CALVAIRE, RD 33, 4km from centre of Pontchâteau, towards Herbignac

Places of interest: Le Calvaire de Pontchâteau, parc régional de Brière, côte d'Amour, pont de Saint Nazaire.
Menu: 75 to 120 Frs
Accommodation: 180 to 250 Frs
Restaurant: lunch 12–2pm, dinner 7–9pm.
Specialities: anguilles au muscadet, merlun, beurre blanc.
Hotel: 122 rooms, showers, baths, private

WCs, TV, phone.
Other points: bar, credit cards accepted, children welcome, à la carte menu, garden terrace, pets allowed, car parking.
Address: 6 route de la Brière, lieu dit Le Calvaire.
MME GABRIELLE COUVRAND, tel 40.01.61.65.

PONTORSON, Manche 50170, Map 3

LE RENOVE, RN 175

Place of interest: Le Mont Saint Michel et sa baie.
Menu: 48 to 120 Frs
Accommodation: 130 to 220 Frs
Restaurant: lunch 12–3pm, dinner 7–10pm. Closed Sundays (out of season).
Hotel: 10 rooms: single 5, double 5. Showers,

private WCs.
Other points: bar, credit cards accepted, children welcome, à la carte menu, pets allowed, car parking.
Address: 4 rue de Rennes.
MME MARIE-CLAIRE PEPIN, tel 33.60.00.21.

PUTOT EN AUGE, Calvados 14430, Map 3

CHEZ MICHEL, RN 175

Menu: 52 to 55 Frs.
Restaurant: closed Saturdays, Sundays, 15 days in August and 15 days at Christmas.

Other points: bar, car parking.
Address: Dozulé.
M. MICHEL MARTIN, tel 31.79.20.29.

QUEVEN, Morbihan 56530, Map 4

LE RELAIS DE LA MAIRIE, RD 6

Restaurant.
Hotel: 8 rooms.
Other points: bar.

Address: rue Principale.
MME YVONNE LEGALLIC, tel 97.05.07.50.

RANDONNAI, Orne 61190, Map 3 ⊗♈⌂

HOTEL DU GRAND CERF, between l'Aigle and Nogent le Rotrou

Places of interest: Etoile du Perche (4km), abbaye de la Trappe (8km).
Menu: 46 to 60 Frs
Accommodation: 100 to 120 Frs
Restaurant: lunch 11.30–3pm, dinner 7–10pm. Closed Tuesday afternoons and first 2 weeks of June.
Specialities: langue sauce piquante, calamars à l'armoricaine, aile de raie au vinaigre, rognons au madère.
Hotel: 6 rooms: single 4, double 2. Showers, private WCs.
Other points: bar, credit cards accepted, children welcome, pets allowed, car parking, traditional decor.
Address: 5 route Sainte Anne.
M. DANIEL MILLIERE, tel 33.34.20.03.

RANES, Orne 61150, Map 3 ⊗♈⌂

HOTEL DU PARC, RN 916 between le Mont St Michel and la Bretagne

Places of interest: Suisse Normande (35km), Bagnole de l'Orne (20km), le Haras du Pin (40km), châteaux de Sassy et de Carrouges.
Menu: 60 to 160 Frs
Accommodation: 140 to 320 Frs
Restaurant: lunch 12–2pm, dinner 7–9pm. Closed Sundays.
Specialities: ris de veau Vallée d'Auge, coquelet au cidre.
Hotel: 7 rooms: single 4, double 3. Showers, baths, private WCs, TV.
Other points: bar, credit cards accepted, children welcome, à la carte menu, garden terrace, pets allowed, car parking, traditional decor.
Address: 9 rue du Parc.
M. ROGER CANTIN, tel 33.39.73.85.

REDON, Ille-et-Vilaine 35600, Map 4 ⊗♈⌂⌐☆

LE RELAIS, road to Rennes

Places of interest: Site mégalithique, site aquatique, parc zoologique.
Languages: English
Menu: 41 to 103 Frs
Accommodation: 120 to 140 Frs
Restaurant: lunch 12–2pm, dinner 7.30–10pm.
Hotel: 18 rooms, showers.
Other points: bar, credit cards accepted, children welcome, à la carte menu, pets allowed, car parking.
Address: route de Rennes.
M. NOEL FRANCOIS, tel 99.71.46.54.

RENAC, Ille-et-Vilaine 35660, Map 4 ⊗♈

RESTAURANT CREPERIE BEAUREGARD, RD 177 between Rennes and Redon

Places of interest: Site mégalithique de Saint Just, Redon (église).
Menu: 44 to 80 Frs
Restaurant: lunch 12–2pm, dinner 6–9pm. Closed Mondays and 8 days in February.
Other points: bar, credit cards accepted, à la carte menu, pets allowed, car parking, traditional decor.
MME MARIE-ANNICK BONNO, tel 99.72.07.83.

RIAILLE, Loire-Atlantique 44440, Map 5 ⊗♈

AU RENDEZ-VOUS DES PECHEURS, D 178 and D 33

Places of interest: Les châteaux et monuments.
Menu: 44 to 91 Frs
Restaurant: lunch 11.45–2.30pm, dinner 7–9pm. Closed Wednesday afternoons and from 28 July to 15 August.
Speciality: fruits de mer.

Other points: bar, credit cards accepted, children welcome, à la carte menu, garden terrace, car parking, traditional decor.
Address: place du champ de foire.
M. JOEL ASPOT, tel 40.97.80.95.

RICHEVILLE, Eure 27420, Map 3

RESTAUROUTE LE BALTO, RN 14, main road from Paris to Rouen

Places of interest: Château Gaillard (9km), les Andelys (9km), Vernon (20km), musée de Claude Monet à Giverny (23km).
Language: English
Menu: 46 to 117 Frs
Restaurant: dinner 6.30–9pm. Closed Sundays and in August.

Specialities: escaloppes normandes, filet au poivre.
Other points: bar, credit cards accepted, children welcome, à la carte menu, pets allowed, car parking, traditional decor.
Address: 4 Route Nationale 14.
M. PIERRE SADOK, tel 32.27.10.55.

RIVIERE ST SAUVEUR (LA), Calvados 14600, Map 3

LES OISEAUX DE MER, RN 180, in industrial zone of Honfleurs.

Places of interest: Honfleurs, Deauville (15km), Lisieux (33km).
Menu: 49 Frs
Restaurant: lunch 11–3pm, dinner 7–9pm. Closed Saturday afternoons, Sundays and in August.

Other points: bar, children welcome, pets allowed.
Address: 28 route des 4 Francs.
M. PASCAL QUESNEY, tel 31.69.11.62.

ROCHE SUR YON (LA), Vendée 85000, Map 5

HOTEL SULLY, RN 137

Places of interest: Haras, musée, barrage Papon.
Languages: English, Spanish
Menu: 165 to 300 Frs
Restaurant: lunch 12–3pm, dinner 7–11pm.
Speciality: jambon de Vendée et haricots blancs.

Hotel: 34 rooms: single 14, double 20. Showers, baths, private WCs, TV, phone.
Other points: bar, credit cards accepted, children welcome, à la carte menu, lounge area, pets allowed, car parking.
Address: Boulevard Sully.
MME NATHALIE MALIDIN, tel 51.37.18.21.

ROMAGNY, Manche 50140, Map 3

AUBERGE DES CLOSEAUX, RD 977, between Rennes and Caen in the direction of St-Hilaire-du-Harcouet

Places of interest: Le Mont Saint Michel (20km), la côte de Granville.
Menu: 54 to 135 Frs
Accommodation: 170 to 220 Frs
Restaurant: closed Sundays (out of season).
Specialities: pintade au cidre, crutacés, poissons.

Hotel: 10 double rooms. Showers, baths, private WCs, TV, phone.
Other points: bar, credit cards accepted, children welcome, à la carte menu, lounge area, garden terrace, car parking.
Address: Les Closeaux.
M. BERNARD CLOUARD, tel 33.59.01.86.

ROMAZY, Ille-et-Vilaine 35490, Map 4 ⊗♉

LE RELAIS, RN 175 between Rennes and le Mont Saint Michel

Places of interest: Le Mont Saint Michel (30km), château de Combourg (20km), château de Fougères (30km), parc d'attraction (30km).
Menu: 50 Frs
Restaurant: lunch 11–2.30pm, dinner 7–10pm. Closed Saturdays and Sundays.

Speciality: escalope normande.
Other points: bar, credit cards accepted, pets allowed, car parking.
Address: Le Bourg.
M. JEAN-CLAUDE MONCEL, tel 99.39.50.83.

RONAI, Orne 61160, Map 3 ⊗♉

LE PIERREFITTE, RN 158, main road from Argentan to Falaise, 9km from Argentan.

Places of interest: Falaise (10km), mémorial de Caen (39km).
Menu: 50 to 65 Frs
Restaurant: lunch 12–2pm, dinner 7–9pm. Closed Sundays, 15 days in February and 15 days in August.

Other points: bar, credit cards accepted, garden terrace, pets allowed, car parking, traditional decor.
M. YVES DELAUNAY, tel 33.35.95.06.

ROTS, Calvados 14980, Map 3 ⊗♉⌂

LE RELAIS DU COUP DE POMPE, RN 13

Places of interest: Cherbourg, Bayeux.
Languages: English, Spanish
Restaurant: lunch 12–2pm, dinner 7–9.30pm. Closed Saturday afternoons and Sundays.
Hotel: 5 rooms: single 2, double 3.

Other points: bar.
Address: 22 route de Caen.
M. VALENTIN CASTANDER, tel 31.26.63.56.

ROUANS, Loire-Atlantique 44640, Map 5 ⊗♉⌂

LA CHAUSSEE LE RETZ, Paimboeuf

Menu: 50 to 160 Frs
Accommodation: 100 to 140 Frs
Restaurant: lunch 12–3pm, dinner 7.30–10pm. Closed Saturdays (from October to Easter).
Specialities: grenouilles, anguilles grillées.
Hotel: 6 rooms: single 2, double 4. Showers,

private WCs.
Other points: bar, children welcome, à la carte menu, garden terrace, pets allowed, car parking.
Address: La Chaussée le Retz.
MME CLAUDETTE BITON, tel 40.64.22.23.

ROUDOUALLEC, Morbihan 56110, Map 4 ⊗♉

RESTAURANT TY KORN, Château du Faou, Quimper

Language: English
Menu: 46 Frs
Restaurant: lunch 11–3pm. Closed Sundays, 10 days in May and 15 days at Christmas.
Specialities: couscous, bourguignon, ragoût du pêcheur.

Other points: bar, credit cards accepted, children welcome, pets allowed, car parking, traditional decor.
MME MIREILLE GLET, tel 97.34.50.38.

ROUEN, Seine-Maritime 76100, Map 3 ⊗♀

RELAIS 207 – Chez Joëlle et Patrick, RN 13 and 14

Restaurant: closed Saturdays and Sundays
Other points: bar.

Address: 46 quai Cavelier de la Salle.
M. MEBARKI, tel 35.73.18.55.

ROUEN, Seine-Maritime 76100, Map 3 ⊗♀

LE LONDON BAR, RN 14 and 15, Rouen rive gauche

Menu: 52 Frs
Restaurant: lunch 11.30–3pm, dinner 7–10pm.
Closed Saturdays and Sundays.

Other points: bar, pets allowed, traditional decor.
Address: 55 quai Cavelier de la Salle.
M. DOMINIQUE MERCHI, tel 35.73.03.01.

ROUEN, Seine-Maritime 76100, Map 3 ⊗♀⌂

LES PLATANES, RN 13 and 14

Restaurant: closed Saturday nights, Sundays,
public holidays and 24 December to 2 January.
Hotel: 20 rooms.

Address: 57 avenue du Mont Riboudet.
M. ROGER SANNIER, tel 35.71.01.52.

ROUGE PERRIERS, Eure 27110, Map 3 ⊗♀

LE RELAIS DU PONT DE L'EURE, RD 137 between Le Neubourg and Brionne

Places of interest: Château d'Arcourt, abbaye
de Bec Helleoin.
Language: English
Menu: 50 to 85 Frs
Restaurant: lunch 12–2.30pm, dinner 7–9pm.
Closed Mondays.

Other points: bar, credit cards accepted,
children welcome, garden terrace, pets allowed,
car parking.
Address: 3 route d'Harcourt.
MME COLETTE LEPRINCE, tel 32.35.05.00.

ROUGEMONTIER, Eure 27350, Map 3 ⊗♀

LE LUDO, RN 175, main road from Rouen to Caen.

Places of interest: Parc de bretonne, four à
Pain (Haye de Routout), musée du sabotier,
moulin de pierre (Hauville), maison des métiers
(Bourneville).
Menu: 52 Frs
Restaurant: closed Saturdays after 2.30pm,

Sundays and in August.
Other points: bar, à la carte menu, pets
allowed, car parking.
Address: 175 Route Nationale.
M. JEAN-CLAUDE DUBOC, tel 32.56.85.22.

SABLES D'OLONNE (LES), Vendée 85100, Map 5 ⊗♀⌂

LES VOYAGEURS, RN 160 and 149

Menu: 43 to 120 Frs
Accommodation: 170 to 220 Frs
Restaurant: lunch 12–2pm, dinner 7.15–9pm.
Closed Friday nights and Saturdays (out of
season), 2 weeks end October and 1 week at
Christmas.

Hotel: 15 double rooms. Showers, private
WCs, phone.
Other points: bar, credit cards accepted, à la
carte menu, pets allowed, car parking.
Address: 17 rue de la Baudière.
M. CLEMENT PACORY, tel 51.95.11.49.

SABLES D'OLONNE (LES), Vendée 85100, Map 5 ⊗♈⌂

AU COQ HARDI, RD 949, La Rochelle

Places of interest: Les ports, la plage, la corniche et toute la côte atlantique.
Menu: 50 to 80 Frs
Accommodation: 150 to 200 Frs
Restaurant: lunch 12–2pm, dinner 7–8.30pm. Closed Saturdays, Sundays (out of season) and 20 September to 10 October.

Specialities: fruits de mer et poissons.
Hotel: 8 rooms: single 4, double 4.
Other points: bar, credit cards accepted, garden terrace, traditional decor.
Address: 7 avenue Alcide Cabaret.
MLLE FRANCOISE PAJOT, tel 51.32.04.62.

SACEY, Manche 50170, Map 3 ⊗♈⌂

LES VOYAGEURS, main road from Pontorson to Rennes and Fougères

Places of interest: Le Mont Saint Michel, le jardin des plantes à Avranches (12km).
Menu: 120 to 165 Frs
Restaurant: lunch 12–3pm, dinner 7–9pm.
Specialities: fruits de mer, homard à l'américaine (by arrangement).

Hotel: 6 rooms: single 2, double 4.
Other points: bar, credit cards accepted, children welcome, pets allowed, car parking, traditional decor.
Address: Le Bourg.
MME MARCELLE BELAN, tel 33.60.15.11.

SAINT AUBIN SUR SCIE, Seine-Maritime 76550, Map 3 ⊗♈

CHEZ FRANCOISE

Restaurant: closed Sundays and in August.
Other points: bar.
Address: rue du Gouffre.

MME FRANCOISE SOICHET,
tel 35.85.91.09.

SAINT BERTHEVIN, Mayenne 53940, Map 5 ⊗♈⌂☆☆

L'INTERNATIONAL, RN 157, main road from Laval to Rennes

Menu: 53 to 100 Frs
Accommodation: 100 to 145 Frs
Restaurant: lunch 12–3pm. Closed Sundays.
Hotel: 22 rooms: single 16, double 6. Showers, baths, private WCs, TV, phone.

Other points: bar, credit cards accepted, à la carte menu, self service, lounge area, pets allowed, car parking.
Address: known as L'Aulne, RN 157.
M. HENRI GARNIER, tel 43.69.31.74.

SAINT BOMER LES FORGES, Orne 61700, Map 3 ⊗♈

LE SAINT BOMER, RD 962 between Flers and Domfront

Places of interest: Cité ancienne de Domfront, circuit Lancelot du Lac, abbaye de Lonlay.
Menu: 45 to 100 Frs
Restaurant: lunch 11–3pm, dinner 7–9pm. Closed Monday evenings.

Other points: bar, credit cards accepted, children welcome, à la carte menu, pets allowed, car parking, traditional decor.
Address: Le Bourg.
M. PIERRE JANNIARD, tel 33.37.61.66.

SAINT BRANDAN, Côtes-du-Nord 22800, Map 4 ⊗♈

RELAIS JACOB, RD 190, on the road to Saint Brieuc

Places of interest: Marhalach, lac de Bosmeliac.
Menu: 50 to 80 Frs
Restaurant: lunch 11–3pm, dinner 7–10pm.
Closed Saturday afternoons, Sundays and in
August.

Other points: bar, children welcome, à la carte
menu, car parking, traditional decor.
Address: 47 rue de Launay.
M. PIERRE JACOB, tel 96.74.88.19.

SAINT BREVIN LES PINS, Loire-Atlantique 44250, Map 5 ⊗♈⌂

LA GUINGUETTE, Pont de Saint Nazaire

Places of interest: Pont de Saint Nazaire,
Pornic, océan.
Menu: 50 to 100 Frs wine and coffee included
Accommodation: 80 to 160 Frs
Restaurant: lunch 12–2pm, dinner 7–10pm.
Closed Saturdays, Sundays (out of season) and
from Christmas to New Year's day.
Speciality: plateau de fruits de mer.

Hotel: 18 rooms.
Other points: bar, credit cards accepted,
children welcome, garden terrace, pets allowed,
car parking, traditional decor.
Address: 137 avenue du Maréchal Foch, La
Courance.
MME PIERRETTE GIRAULT,
tel 40.27.21.95.

SAINT BRIEUC, Côtes-du-Nord 22000, Map 4 ⊗♈⌂☆

AU BEAUFEUILLAGE, RN 12

Restaurant: closed Sunday afternoons and
from 8 August to 1 September.
Hotel: 29 rooms.

Other points: bar.
Address: 2 rue de Paris.
M. CLAUDE ANDRIEUX, tel 96.33.09.16.

SAINT COME DU FRESNE, Calvados 14960, Map 3 ⊗♈

LE SANTA DE A

Places of interest: Les plages du débarquement
et château de Saint Come.
Menu: 45 to 85 Frs
Restaurant.
Speciality: fruits de mer.

Other points: bar, credit cards accepted,
children welcome, à la carte menu, self service,
pets allowed, car parking.
Address: 3 rue Panoramique.
MME ANDREA BOQUET, tel 31.21.15.70.

SAINT CYR EN PAIL, Mayenne 53140, Map 5 ⊗♈

LES ROUTIERS, RN 12 between Alençon and Mayenne

Places of interest: Le Mont des Avaloirs
(2km), château de Carrouges (20km), Pierre au
Loup (2km), la Corniche de Pail (2km).
Menu: 48 to 50 Frs
Restaurant: lunch 11.30–2.30pm, dinner
6.30–9pm. Closed Sundays and in August.

Other points: bar, children welcome, pets
allowed, car parking, traditional decor.
Address: Le Bourg, Pré en Pail.
MME ANTOINETTE DUPONT,
tel 43.03.03.21.

SAINT CYR EN TALMONDAIS, Vendée 85540, Map 5 ⊗♈

RESTAURANT DU CENTRE, RD 949 between Fontenay le Conte and Les Sables d'Olonne

Places of interest: Les Sables d'Olonne
(35km), parc floral et château dans le Bourg de
Saint Cyr.
Menu: 55 to 120 Frs

Restaurant: lunch 12–3pm, dinner 7–9pm.
Closed Thursdays after 2pm and 8 days in
January.
Other points: bar, credit cards accepted,

children welcome, à la carte menu, car parking, traditional decor.
Address: Route Départementale 949, Au Bourg.

M. JEAN-CLAUDE VAUCELLE, tel 51.30.82.84.

SAINT DENIS DE MAILLOC, Calvados 14100, Map 3

LA FORGE, RD 579, main road from Orbec to Lisieux

Places of interest: Basilique de Lisieux, château de St Germain de Livet, Deauville.
Menu: 48 Frs
Restaurant: lunch 11–2.30pm, dinner 6–8.30pm. Closed Saturdays, Sundays and second 2 weeks of August.

Other points: bar, garden terrace, pets allowed, car parking, traditional decor.
Address: Lisieux.
M. YVAN LEROY, tel 31.63.73.19.

SAINT DENIS DE MERE, Calvados 14110, Map 3

LE RELAIS DES LANDES, RD 562 between Caen and Flers

Places of interest: Clécy (10km), Flers (15km), Condé sur Noireau.
Menu: 49 Frs
Restaurant.

Other points: garden terrace, car parking, traditional decor.
Address: Route Départementale 562.
M. GERARD DEVRIESE, tel 31.69.07.06.

SAINT DENIS DES MONTS, Eure 27520, Map 3

LE LAMA, RN 138 between Rouen and Brionne

Place of interest: Le Bec Hellouin.
Menu: 52 Frs
Restaurant: lunch 11–3pm. Closed Saturdays, Sundays, 3 weeks in August and 10 days at Christmas.

Other points: bar, credit cards accepted, children welcome, pets allowed, car parking, traditional decor.
Address: Route Nationale 138.
M. CHRISTIAN CHUETTE, tel 32.42.60.10.

SAINT DENIS SUR SARTHON, Orne 61420, Map 3

HOTEL DE LA GARE – LES AMIS DES ROUTIERS, RN 12

Restaurant: closed Sundays.
Other points: bar.

Address: La Gare.
M. GUY ELLIEN, tel 33.27.30.03.

SAINT ERBLON, Ille-et-Vilaine 35230, Map 4

CHEZ MICHEL ET SYLVIE, RD 82, expressway Rennes to Nantes

Language: English
Menu: 47 Frs
Restaurant: lunch 12–2pm. Closed first 3 weeks of August.
Specialities: potée, couscous.

Other points: bar, car parking, traditional decor.
Address: Z.A. 3 allée des Leuzières.
M. MICHEL MARTIN, tel 99.52.28.40.

SAINT EVROULT DE MONTFORT, Orne 61230, Map 3

HOTEL DU RELAIS, RN 138 between Rouen and Alençon

Menu: 47 Frs
Accommodation: 80 to 150 Frs
Restaurant: lunch 11–3pm, dinner 7–10pm.
Closed Sundays.

Hotel: 5 rooms: single 2, double 3. Showers.
Other points: bar, car parking.
Address: Le Bourg.
M. DANIEL CONAN, tel 33.35.60.58.

SAINT GEORGES DES GARDES, Maine-et-Loire 49120, Map 5

LES ROUTIERS, RN 161 between Angers and Cholet

Menu: 48 Frs
Accommodation: 100 Frs
Restaurant.
Hotel: 6 rooms: single 4, double 2. Showers,
baths, private WCs.

Other points: bar, car parking.
Address: Chemillé.
M. LOUIS JOLIVET, tel 41.62.79.38.

SAINT GERMAIN SUR MOINE, Maine-et-Loire 49230, Map 5

LE TAILLIS DU VERGER, RN 249 on the Nantes to Cholet roadside

Menu: 50 Frs including coffee
Restaurant: lunch 11.30–2.30pm, dinner
7–10pm. Closed Sundays.
Other points: bar, credit cards accepted,
children welcome, garden terrace, pets allowed,

car parking.
Address: Carrefour du Petit Lapin, route de la
Renaudière.
M. PAUL ERAUD, tel 41.64.64.61.

SAINT GILDAS DES BOIS, Loire-Atlantique 44530, Map 5

LES ROUTIERS, RD 773 between Redon and Pontchâteau

Places of interest: Le Calvaire de Pontchâteau
(10 km), château de la Bretaiche.
Menu: 62 to 330 Frs
Accommodation: 110 to 125 Frs
Restaurant: lunch 12–2.30pm, dinner
8–9.30pm.
Specialities: plateau de fruits de mer, homard
grillé, beurre blanc.

Hotel: 10 single rooms.
Other points: bar, credit cards accepted,
children welcome, à la carte menu, TV, garden
terrace, pets allowed, car parking.
Address: 27 rue du Pont.
M. MICHEL GAIDANO, tel 40.01.42.15.

SAINT GILLES, Manche 50180, Map 3

LE RELAIS, RN 12

Languages: German, English
Restaurant: closed Saturdays, Sundays and
1 to 15 August.

Other points: bar, car parking.
Address: 23 rue de Rennes.
MME JEANINE ABIVEN, tel 99.64.63.04.

SAINT GREGOIRE, Ille-et-Vilaine 35760, Map 4

RESTAURANT DE L'ETANG

Menu: 46 to 200 Frs
Restaurant: lunch 11.30–3pm, dinner 7–9pm.
Closed Saturdays and Sundays.
Other points: bar, credit cards accepted, pets

allowed, car parking, traditional decor.
Address: rue de l'Etang au Diable.
M. MICHEL HUBERT, tel 99.38.49.43.

SAINT GUYOMARD, Morbihan 56460, Map 4

LE RELAIS DES DOLMENS DE LANVAUX, Rn 166 between Ploermel and Vannes

Places of interest: Les Landes de Lanvaux, Rochefort en Terre, le golf du Morbihan, Carnac.
Menu: 50 to 72 Frs
Accommodation: 140 to 170 Frs
Restaurant: lunch 11.45–2pm, dinner 7–9pm. Closed Saturday nights and Sundays (except group dinners).

Hotel: 7 rooms: single 1, double 6. Showers, private WCs.
Other points: bar, credit cards accepted, children welcome, à la carte menu, garden terrace, pets allowed, car parking, traditional decor.
Address: known as Le Passoir.
M. PIERRE LEGRAND, tel 97.93.81.05.

SAINT HELEN, Côtes-du-Nord 22100, Map 4

RELAIS DE LA CROIX DU FRENE

Restaurant: lunch 11.30–2.30pm, dinner 7–10.30pm. Closed Saturdays after 3pm, Sundays and public holidays.

Other points: bar.
Address: La Croix du Frene.
M. GUY GABILLARD, tel 96.83.25.02.

SAINT HILAIRE DE LOULAY, Vendée 85600, Map 5

LE RELAX, RN 137 between Nantes and La Rochelle, 30km from Nantes

Places of interest: Château, cave de Muscadet, jardin.
Languages: a little German, English
Menu: 60 to 144 Frs
Accommodation: 180 to 280 Frs
Restaurant: lunch 11.30–3pm, dinner 7–12pm. Closed Saturday lunch and 15 days in July.
Specialities: grillades au feu de bois, poissons au beurre blanc.

Hotel: 11 rooms: single 8, double 3. Showers, private WCs, TV, phone.
Other points: bar, credit cards accepted, children welcome, à la carte menu, garden terrace, pets allowed, car parking.
Address: Les Landes de Roussais.
M. LUC VAN WANGHE, tel 51.94.02.44.

SAINT JACQUES DE LA LANDE, Ille-et-Vilaine 35136, Map 4

LA GAITE, RD 177 exit at La Gaité on the road to Redon

Places of interest: Les étangs d'Apigné, le centre ville de Rennes.
Language: a little English
Menu: 46 Frs
Accommodation: 140 to 180 Frs
Restaurant: lunch 12–2.30pm, dinner 7.30–10pm. Closed Saturdays, Sundays and

public holidays (except group reservations).
Other points: bar, credit cards accepted, à la carte menu, pets allowed, car parking.
Hotel: 3 rooms, showers.
Address: 26 boulevard Roger Dodin.
M. YANNICK ECHELARD, tel 99.31.27.56.

SAINT JEAN DE BEUGNE, Vendée 85210, Map 5

L'OASIS, RN 137

Place of interest: Nantes.
Menu: 53 Frs
Restaurant: lunch 12–2pm, dinner 7.30–10pm. Closed Saturdays, Sundays, 15 days in August and for Christmas and New Year's day.

Other points: bar, car parking, traditional decor.
Address: Route Nationale 137.
M. GUY TEILLET, tel 51.27.38.80.

SAINT JEAN DE DAYE, Manche 50620, Map 3 ⊗ ℗

BAR DES SPORTS, RN 174 between St Lô and Carentan

Language: English
Menu: 48 Frs
Restaurant.
Other points: bar, à la carte menu, car parking.

Address: 9 rue de la Libération.
MME MARYVONNE TILLARD,
tel 33.55.46.42.

SAINT JEAN DE LA MOTTE, Sarthe 72510, Map 5 ⊗ ℗

CHEZ BEATRICE, RN 23 between Le Mans and Anger

Places of interest: le Lude (25km), circuit du
Mans (30km), poteries de Malicorne.
Language: English
Restaurant: lunch 11.30–2.30pm, dinner
7–10.30pm. Closed Sundays.

Other points: bar, credit cards accepted,
children welcome, car parking, traditional
decor.
Address: Route Nationale 23.
MME BEATRICE COLLIN, tel 43.45.72.02.

SAINT JEAN SUR COUESNON, Ille-et-Vilaine 35140, Map 4 ⊗

LA JUHUELLERIE, RN 24

Menu: 44 Frs
Restaurant: lunch 12–2pm, dinner 7.30–9pm.
Closed Saturdays, Sundays and mid-August to
September.

Address: La Juhuellerie.
MME MONIQUE GAREL, tel 99.39.11.85.

SAINT JEAN SUR VILAINE, Ille-et-Vilaine 35220, Map 4 ⊗ ℗ 🏠

LE RELAIS DU CHEVAL BLANC, RN 157

Restaurant.
Hotel: 10 rooms.
Other points: bar.

Address: 4 rue de Rennes.
M. ALAIN BELLEVIN, tel 99.00.32.67.

SAINT JULIEN LE FAUCON, Calvados 14140, Map 3 ⊗ ℗

LE CAFE DE LA GARE, RD 511 between Lisieux and Saint Pierre sur Dives.

Places of interest: Lisieux (14km), abbaye de
Saint Pierre sur Dives, château de Saint
Germain de Livet.
Menu: 49,50 Frs

Restaurant: closed Sundays and in August.
Other points: bar, children welcome, pets
allowed, car parking, traditional decor.
M. ROBERT GALLAIS, tel 31.63.62.91.

SAINT MARCEL, Eure 27950, Map 3 ⊗ ℗ 🏠

LE TERMINUS, between Vernon and Rouen

Places of interest: Le musée et jardin de
Claude Monet à Giverny (10km), château
Gaillard, les Andelys.
Menu: 53 Frs
Accommodation: 145 to 170 Frs
Restaurant: lunch 11.30–3pm, dinner
7.30–8.30pm. Closed Sundays, in August and
last week in December.

Hotel: 16 rooms: single 5, double 11. Showers,
baths.
Other points: bar, credit cards accepted,
children welcome, pets allowed, car parking,
traditional decor.
Address: 30 Route Nationale 15.
M. CLAUDE HARD, tel 32.52.50.07.

SAINT MARS LA BRIERE, Sarthe 72680, Map 5

AUBERGE DU MARAIS, RN 157 between Orléans and Le Mans

Places of interest: Château, forêt.
Menu: 50 Frs
Restaurant: closed Saturdays, Sundays and in August.

Other points: bar, credit cards accepted, garden terrace, pets allowed, car parking.
Address: Route Nationale 157.
M. REMY TRESSY, tel 43.89.87.30.

SAINT MARTIN DES BESACES, Calvados 14350, Map 3

LA RENAISSANCE, RN 175 between Avranches and Caen

Language: English
Menu: 55 to 75 Frs
Accommodation: 110 to 160 Frs
Restaurant: lunch 12–2.30pm, dinner 7–9.30pm. Closed Mondays (out of season) and in February.
Specialities: coquilles Saint Jacques, rognons au vieux calvados, faux filet au poivre.

Hotel: 8 rooms: single 6, double 2. Showers, private WCs.
Other points: bar, à la carte menu, garden terrace, pets allowed, car parking.
Address: Route Nationale 175, Le Bourg.
MME RENEE LEHERICEY, tel 31.68.72.65.

SAINT MARTIN OSMONVILLE, Seine-Maritime 76680, Map 3

LA GRANGE, RN 28 between Rouen and Neufchâtel en Bray

Place of interest: Forêt d'Eavy (5km).
Menu: 50 Frs
Restaurant: closed Sundays.
Other points: bar, credit cards accepted, children welcome, à la carte menu, garden

terrace, pets allowed, car parking, traditional decor.
Address: La Boissière.
MME DENISE DUBOIS, tel 35.34.14.34.

SAINT MEEN LE GRAND, Ille-et-Vilaine 35290, Map 4

LE RELAIS DU MIDI, RN 164 Rennes Montauban to Loudéac Carhaix

Menu: 42 Frs
Restaurant: lunch 12–2pm, dinner 7.30–9.30pm. Closed Saturdays, Sundays afternoons (out of season) and 2 weeks in August.
Hotel: 3 single rooms. Private WCs, TV, phone.

Other points: bar, credit cards accepted, pets allowed.
Address: 25 place Patton.
M. CHRISTIAN POSNIC, tel 99.09.60.02.

SAINT NICOLAS DE REDON, Loire-Atlantique 44460, Map 5

LES ROUTIERS, main road from Rennes to Redon

Places of interest: Roche Bernard, Rochefort en Terre, le golf du Morbihan.
Menu: 45 to 80 Frs
Restaurant: lunch 11.45–3pm, dinner 7–10pm. Closed Sundays and in August.

Speciality: couscous.
Other points: bar, children welcome.
Address: 84 avenue Jean Burel.
MME MARIE-ANNICK HEMERY, tel 99.71.01.96.

SAINT NOLFF, Morbihan 56250, Map 4 ⊗ ♈

LE RELAIS DE BELLEVUE, RN 166

Menu: 47 Frs
Restaurant: lunch 12–3pm, dinner 7–10.30pm.
Closed Sundays and in August.

Other points: bar, children welcome.
Address: Bellevue.
MME EDITH HUREAU, tel 97.45.44.04.

SAINT OUEN DU TILLEUL, Eure 27670, Map 3 ⊗ ♈

L'ESCALE – Auberge du Roumois, RD 313 between Bourgiheroulde and Elbeuf

Places of interest: Ancien monastère de Bel Helloin, château de Robert le diable, musée du sabotier, Rouen.
Language: English
Menu: 53,50 Frs
Restaurant.

Other points: bar, credit cards accepted, children welcome, garden terrace, pets allowed, car parking.
Address: rue des Canadiens.
MME SYLVIANE VALLEE, tel 35.87.70.19.

SAINT PAUL DU BOIS, Maine-et-Loire 49310, Map 5 ⊗ ♈

CHEZ GEGE ET MIMI, RN 748 between Vihiers and Niort (6km)

Menu: 45 to 135 Frs
Restaurant: lunch 11.30–2.30pm, dinner 6.30–9pm. Closed Tuesday afternoons.
Specialities: anguille à la crème, cuisses de grenouilles (by arrangement).

Other points: bar, children welcome, à la carte menu, pets allowed, car parking.
Address: La Réveillère.
M. GERARD BONNIN, tel 41.75.81.44.

SAINT PELLERIN, Manche 50500, Map 3 ⊗ ♈

LA FOURCHETTE, RN 13, main road from Caen to Cherbourg

Places of interest: Les plages du débarquement, la pointe du Cotentin.
Menu: 50 to 70 Frs
Restaurant: closed Sundays.
Specialities: pied de veau, rillettes, tripes.

Other points: bar, credit cards accepted, children welcome, à la carte menu, garden terrace, car parking, traditional decor.
Address: Carantan.
MME NICOLE LE ROUX, tel 33.42.16.56.

SAINT PHILBERT DE GRAND LIEU, Loire-Atlantique 44310, Map 5 ⊗ ♈ ⌂

LA BOULOGNE, RD 18

Places of interest: Abbatiales du IXe siècle (50m), lac de Grand Lieu (10km).
Menu: 42 to 100 Frs
Accommodation: 65 to 120 Frs
Restaurant: lunch 12–2pm, dinner 7–8.30pm. Closed Saturday afternoons, Sunday afternoons and first 2 weeks of August.

Hotel: 6 rooms: single 1, double 5. Showers, private WCs.
Other points: bar, credit cards accepted, children welcome, pets allowed, traditional decor.
Address: 11 place de l'Abbatiale.
M. BERNARD ANDRE, tel 40.78.70.55.

SAINT PIERRE DE QUIBERON, Morbihan 56510, Map 4 ⊗ ♈

LA CHALOUPE, RN 768 and 165, Quiberon

Places of interest: Les menhirs de Carnac, la côte sauvage de Quiberon et les îles.
Menu: 44 Frs
Restaurant: lunch 12–3pm. Closed Sundays (out of season) and from 15 October to 15 November.

Other points: bar, car parking.
Address: 10 rue Hoche, Kerhostin.
MME CHRISTIANE LE BELLOUR, tel 97.30.91.54.

SAINT PIERRE DU FRESNE, Calvados 14260, Map 3

CHEZ DOUDOU, RN 175, Mont Saint Michel

Language: English
Menu: 50 to 80 Frs
Restaurant: lunch 11–3pm, dinner 7–11pm. Closed Saturdays and Sundays.

Other points: bar, credit cards accepted, pets allowed, car parking.
Address: Les Haies Tigards.
M. LOIC LELEGARD, tel 31.77.80.89.

SAINT PIERRE LANGERS, Manche 50530, Map 3

LA GRILLADE, RD 973, main road from Granville to Avranches

Places of interest: Abbaye de la Lucerne (4km), Granville (3km), jardin des plantes, Avranches (15km).
Language: a little English
Menu: 48 to 50 Frs
Accommodation: 100 to 160 Frs
Restaurant: closed Sundays (out of season), and between Christmas and New Year's day.

Specialities: choucroute, couscous.
Hotel: 8 rooms.
Other points: bar, credit cards accepted, car parking.
Address: Hameau de la Havaudière.
M. MARC JOHAN, tel 33.48.12.63.

SAINT PIERRE LES ELBEUF, Seine-Maritime 76320, Map 3

LA SAUVAGINE

Language: English
Restaurant: closed Sundays, 15 days in January/February and 3 weeks in August.

Other points: bar.
Address: 611 Chemin du Halage.
M. PATRICK CLIVAZ, tel 35.78.37.70.

SAINT PIERRE SUR DIVES, Calvados 14170, Map 3

LE PRESSOIR, RD 40

Places of interest: Basilique de Lisieux (23km), les marches de Saint Pierre (ouvertes le lundi).
Language: English
Menu: 50 Frs
Restaurant: lunch 12–2.30pm, dinner 7–9pm.

Closed Saturday afternoons, Sundays.
Other points: bar, credit cards accepted, car parking.
Address: 17 route de Caen.
M. THIERRY BIGOT, tel 31.20.56.03.

SAINT QUAY PORTRIEUX, Côtes-du-Nord 22410, Map 4

LES ROUTIERS

Menu: 45 to 150 Frs
Accommodation: 100 to 120 Frs
Restaurant: lunch 12–3pm, dinner 7–9pm. Closed Sundays (out of season).
Speciality: couscous.

Hotel: 9 rooms, showers.
Other points: bar, credit cards accepted, garden terrace, pets allowed, car parking.
Address: 42 rue des 3 Frères Salaün.
M. CLAUDE BAILLEUL, tel 96.70.40.19.

SAINT QUENTIN LES ANGES, Mayenne 53400, Map 5 ⊗⍭⌂

LE RELAIS, main road from Rennes to Angers

Places of interest: Château de Craon, château de Mortiercrolles, Mine Bleue, musée Robert Tatin.
Languages: English
Menu: 46 to 150 Frs
Accommodation: 80 to 110 Frs
Restaurant: lunch 11.45–3pm, dinner 7–9.30pm. Closed last 3 weeks of August.
Specialities: coquille Saint Jacques à la Nantaise, filet de canard à la Craonnaise, filet de sandre grillé au beurre blanc.
Hotel: 9 rooms: single 5, double 4. Showers.
Other points: bar, credit cards accepted, children welcome, pets allowed, car parking, traditional decor.
Address: Le Bourg.
MME MARIE-ANNICK TROTTIER, tel 43.06.10.62.

SAINT REMY DE SILLE, Sarthe 72140, Map 5 ⊗⍭

LA COQUE, RD 304 between Le Mans and Sillé le Guillaume

Places of interest: Lac et forêt de Sillé le Guillaume, Saut du cerf.
Restaurant: lunch 12–3pm. Closed Sundays and in August.
Other points: bar, pets allowed, car parking, traditional decor.
Address: 11 bis route du Mans.
M. CLAUDE ROUZIER, tel 43.20.11.84.

SAINT ROMAIN DE COLBOSC, Seine-Maritime 76430, Map 3 ⊗⍭⌂

LE RELAIS DU FRESCOT, on the road to le Havre

Menu: 48 Frs
Restaurant: lunch 11.30–2.30pm. Closed Sundays.
Hotel: 7 rooms.
Other points: bar, à la carte menu, pets allowed, car parking.
Address: 18 Nationale.
M. JACQUES CHAPELET, tel 35.20.15.09.

SAINT SAMSON DE LA ROQUE, Eure 27680, Map 3 ⊗⍭

RELAIS NORD BRETAGNE, RN 815 A

Languages: English, Spanish
Restaurant: closed Saturdays and Sundays.
Other points: bar.
Address: route du Pont de Tancarville.
M. MARCEL POIRAUD, tel 32.57.67.30.

SAINT SYMPHORIEN DES MONTS, Manche 50640, Map 3 ⊗⍭⌂⌲

LE RELAIS DU BOIS LEGER, RN 176 between Alençon and le Mont Saint Michel

Places of interest: Lac de Vezins, Villedieu les Poêles, Bagnoles de l'Orne, le Mont Saint Michel, Eden Parc (300m).
Languages: English
Menu: 46 to 90 Frs
Accommodation: 100 to 160 Frs
Restaurant: lunch 12–2pm, dinner 7–9pm. Closed Sunday nights, 1 week in February and 3 in September.
Specialities: pintade aux pommes, pavé au cidre, terrine du chef.
Hotel: 10 rooms: single 4, double 6. Showers, baths.
Other points: bar, credit cards accepted, children welcome, à la carte menu, lounge area, garden terrace, car parking, traditional decor.
Address: Route Nationale 176, Le Bois Léger.
M. RAYMOND PINET, tel 33.49.01.43.

SAINT VIGOR LE GRAND, Calvados 14400, Map 3   ⊗Ϋ

CHEZ PEPONNE, between Bayeux and Cherbourg

Places of interest: Tapisserie de Bayeux,
musée du débarquement, cathédrale.
Menu: 45 to 49 Frs including coffee
Restaurant: lunch 11–4pm, dinner 6–11pm.
Closed Sundays and 15 days in August.

Other points: bar, credit cards accepted,
garden terrace, pets allowed, car parking.
Address: 3 rue du Pont Trubert.
MME MARIE-ANNICK VICTOIRE,
tel 31.92.28.39

SAINTE CECILE, Manche 50800, Map 3   ⊗Ϋ⌂

LE CECILIA, RD 924

Languages: English, German
Restaurant: lunch 12–1.30pm, dinner
7–8.30pm. Closed Saturdays and Sundays.
Hotel: 5 rooms, showers.

Other points: bar, credit cards accepted, car
parking.
Address: Le Bourg.
M. DANIEL LE HUBY, tel 33.61.07.81.

SAINTE CROIX HAGUE, Manche 50440, Map 3   ⊗Ϋ⌂

LE PETIT BACCHUS, RD 908 between Cherbourg and Baumont Hague

Places of interest: Pointe de Jobourg, côtes de
la Hague.
Accommodation: Pension 170 Frs and demi-
pension 140 Frs
Restaurant: lunch 12–3pm, dinner

7.30–9.30pm. Closed Saturdays and Sundays.
Other points: bar, credit cards accepted,
children welcome, pets allowed, car parking.
Address: Le Petit Bacchus.
M. CLAUDE CAVELLER, tel 33.52.77.52.

SAINTE FOY DE MONTGOMMERY, Calvados 14140, Map 3   ⊗Ϋ⌂

LE RELAIS DE MONTGOMERY, RN 179

Restaurant: closed Sundays
Hotel: 4 rooms.

Other points: bar.
MME PLANCKEEL, tel 31.63.53.02.

SAINTE LUCE SUR LOIRE, Loire-Atlantique 44980, Map 5   ⊗Ϋ⇨

LA BOUGRIERE, CD 68, A11 exit Thouaré Sainte Luce centre

Places of interest: Château des Ducs de
Nantes, jardin des plantes, quartier du Bouffay
(avec ses rues piétonnes), tour de Bretagne, le
vignoble, les bords de la Loire.
Languages: English, Spanish
Menu: 47,70 to 175 Frs
Restaurant: lunch 12–2.30pm, dinner
7–10.30pm. Closed Friday nights, Saturdays,
Sundays (except group dinners), August and

1 week between Christmas and New Year's
day.
Specalities: fruits de mer, poissons au beurre
blanc, grenouilles, anguilles, grillades.
Other points: bar, children welcome, à la carte
menu, garden terrace, pets allowed, car parking,
traditional decor.
Address: 4 rue du Pavillon.
M. PIERRE PERTUE, tel 40.25.60.84.

SAINTENY, Manche 50500, Map 3   ⊗Ϋ

LE RELAIS DES FORGES, CD 971

Menu: 43 Frs
Restaurant: lunch 12–2pm, dinner 7–8.00pm.

Closed Tuesdays and in August.
Other points: bar, credit cards accepted, pets

allowed, car parking.
Address: Les Forges.

MME FRANCINE COUSIN, tel 33.42.39.36.

SARTILLY, Manche 50530, Map 3   ⊗ 🍽

LE VIEUX LOGIS, between Avranches and Granville

Places of interest: La baie du Mont Saint
Michel, abbaye de la Lucerne, Granville,
Villedieu les Poëles.
Language: English
Menu: 53 Frs
Restaurant: lunch 12–1.30pm. Closed Sunday

afternoons, 10 days early March and 10 days
end October.
Other points: bar, pets allowed, car parking,
traditional decor.
Address: Grande Rue.
M. GERARD CADIOT, tel 33.48.80.31.

SAUMUR, Maine-et-Loire 49400, Map 4   ⊗🍽🏠🍵☆☆

HOTEL DE LA GARE, RN 152 opposite SNCF station

Places of interest: Les bords de la Loire,
château de Saumur, les coteaux de Saumur,
curiosités, habitations troglodytiques, musée des
champignons, musée des blindés, cave de vins.
Menu: 30 to 85 Frs
Restaurant: lunch 11–3pm, dinner 6–10pm.
Specialities: cuisses de poulet bonne femme,
rôti à la saumuroise.

Hotel: 21 rooms (+ 5 ordinaires), showers,
baths, private WCs, phone.
Other points: bar, children welcome, à la carte
menu, garden terrace, pets allowed, car
parking.
Address: 16 avenue David d'Angers.
M. JACQUES GAUDICHEAU,
tel 41.67.34.24.

SAVENAY, Loire-Atlantique 44260, Map 5   ⊗🍽

RELAIS 165, RN 165, main road from Nantes to Vannes

Place of interest: La mer (25km).
Menu: 47 Frs
Restaurant.

Other points: bar, pets allowed, car parking.
Address: Le Pas de l'Aulne, Prinquiau.
M. CLAUDE BOURGINE, tel 40.56.64.99.

SEGRE, Maine-et-Loire 49500, Map 5   ⊗🍽🏠

LE RELAIS DU COMMERCE, RN 775 on the road to Cholet

Places of interest: La mine bleue, Noyant la
Gravoyère.
Restaurant.
Hotel: 6 single rooms.

Other points: bar, children welcome, lounge
area, garden terrace, car parking.
Address: 1 place de la Gare.
M. EMILE GEORGET, tel 41.92.22.27.

SENE, Morbihan 56860, Map 4   ⊗🍽🏠🍵☆

RELAIS ROUTIERS, RN 165 between Vannes and Lorient

Places of interest: Le golf du Morbihan, port
de plaisance, plages.
Menu: 40 to 150 Frs
Accommodation: 78 to 160 Frs
Restaurant: lunch 12–3pm, dinner 7–9.30pm.
Closed 24 December to 2 January.
Speciality: fruits de mer.

Hotel: 45 rooms: single 30, double 15.
Showers, baths.
Other points: bar, credit cards accepted,
children welcome, lounge area, pets allowed,
car parking.
Address: 46 route de Vannes, Le Poulfanc.
S.A. PENRU, tel 97.47.47.97.

SILLE LE GUILLAUME, Sarthe 72140, Map 5 ⊗🍷🏠

HOTEL DE PARIS, between Le Mans and Laval

Places of interest: Les grottes de Saulges
(15km), les Alpes Mancelle (20km), Saint
Léonard des Bois.
Menu: 47,50 to 96 Frs
Accommodation: 80 to 170 Frs
Restaurant: lunch 11.30–3pm, dinner 7–10pm.
Closed Sundays.

Hotel: 4 rooms: single 3, double 1. Showers.
Other points: bar, credit cards accepted,
children welcome, à la carte menu, pets
allowed, car parking, traditional decor.
Address: 12 place de la Gare.
M. PASCAL PAINEAU, tel 43.20.11.38.

SOMMERY, Seine-Maritime 76440, Map 3 ⊗🍷

LE MONTESTRUC

Menu: 45 to 55 Frs
Restaurant: lunch 11.30–3pm, dinner 7–10pm.
Closed Tuesday evenings.
Speciality: moules frites.
Other points: bar, credit cards accepted,

children welcome, à la carte menu, pets
allowed, car parking, traditional decor.
Address: La Cavée.
M. JEAN-LUC EDET, tel 35.90.56.16.

SORINIERES (LES), Loire-Atlantique 44840, Map 5 ⊗🍷🏠

LE RELAIS – Chez Pierrette et Jean, RN 137 and 178 sur la route de La Roche sur Yon

Menu: 41 to 110 Frs
Accommodation: 95 Frs
Restaurant: lunch 12–3pm, dinner 7.30–10pm.
Closed Sundays and from 20 December to 15
January.
Specialities: couscous, entrecôte, grillade.

Hotel: 7 rooms: single 5, double 2.
Other points: bar, children welcome, à la carte
menu, garden terrace, pets allowed.
Address: 16 rue du Général de Gaulle.
M. JEAN LOUIS BENOIT, tel 40.31.22.91.

SOURDEVAL, Manche 50150, Map 3 ⊗🍷🏠

AU BON ACCUEIL – Les Routiers, main road from Caen to Vire

Places of interest: Le Mont Saint Michel,
Avranches, musée du granit.
Language: English
Menu: 80 to 120 Frs
Accommodation: 47 to 100 Frs
Restaurant: closed Sundays (except
reservations).

Hotel: 5 rooms: single 3 (2 with showers),
double 2.
Other points: bar, credit cards accepted, à la
carte menu, garden terrace, pets allowed,
traditional decor.
Address: 1 place du Champ de Foire.
M. DANIEL DELAUNAY, tel 33.59.62.91.

SOURDEVAL LES BOIS, Manche 50450, Map 3 ⊗🍷

CHEZ COLETTE, RN 799

Places of interest: Abbaye d'Hambye (2km),
Villedieu les Poëlles.
Menu: 40 Frs
Restaurant: lunch 12–2pm.

Other points: bar, pets allowed, car parking.
Address: known as La Croix
MME COLETTE DUFOUR, tel 33.61.77.99.

SUZAY, Eure 27420, Map 3 ⊗℉

LE RELAIS MODERNE, RN 14, main road from Paris to Rouen

Menu: 55 to 60 Frs
Restaurant.
Other points: bar, children welcome, garden

terrace, pets allowed, car parking.
M. JEAN-CLAUDE LAURENT,
tel 32.55.65.01.

TALMONT SAINT HILAIRE, Vendée 85440, Map 5 ⊗℉⌂

HOTEL DU CENTRE, RD 949 between Les Sables d'Olonne and Luçon

Places of interest: Château de Talmont, musée
automobile.
Menu: 100 to 180 Frs
Restaurant: closed Saturdays and in October.
Speciality: fruits de mer.
Hotel: 12 rooms, showers, private WCs, TV,
phone.

Other points: bar, credit cards accepted,
children welcome, à la carte menu, garden
terrace, pets allowed, car parking.
Address: 1 rue du Centre.
M. MICHEL LE BLOND, tel 51.90.60.35.

TESSY SUR VIRE, Manche 50420, Map 3 ⊗℉

LES ROUTIERS, RD 13, Granville

Places of interest: Les gorges de la Vire, St Lô,
Villedieu, Coutances.
Menu: 45 Frs
Restaurant: dinner 7–8.30pm. Closed
Thursday afternoons and Sundays.

Other points: bar, credit cards accepted,
children welcome, pets allowed, car parking,
traditional decor.
Address: place du Marché.
M. MAURICE ROBERT, tel 33.56.35.25.

THEIL (LE), Orne 61260, Map 3 ⊗℉

BAR DE L'ARCHE

Restaurant.
Other points: bar.

Address: La Rouge.
M. GERARD LEROUX, tel 37.49.62.92.

THOMER LA SOGNE, Eure 27240, Map 3 ⊗℉

RELAIS 154, RN 154 between Dreux and Evreux

Place of interest: Cathédrale d'Evreux.
Language: English
Menu: 53 Frs
Restaurant: lunch 11–3pm, dinner 7–10pm.
Closed Sunday afternoons and 2 weeks in
August.

Other points: bar, credit cards accepted,
children welcome, garden terrace, pets allowed,
car parking.
Address: route d'Orléans.
MME NICOLLE VANDECANDELAERE,
tel 32.67.41.00.

THOREE LES PINS, Sarthe 72800, Map 5 ⊗℉⌂

RESTAURANT DES PECHEURS, CD 306

Places of interest: Zoo de La Flèche, le Lude,
châteaux et musée.
Languages: English, German.
Restaurant: closed Wednesday afternoons and

3 weeks in August.
Speciality: poissons.
Hotel: 4 double rooms. Showers, baths.
Other points: bar, credit cards accepted,

children welcome, à la carte menu, pets allowed, car parking, traditional decor.

Address: Le Bourg.
M. MARCEL GUILLAUME, tel 43.45.03.79.

TOLLEVAST, Manche 50470, Map 3

LES CHEVRES, RN 13

Places of interest: L'arsenal, la Hague, le port.
Language: English
Menu: 50 Frs
Restaurant.
Speciality: pieds de veau.

Other points: bar, credit cards accepted, pets allowed, car parking, traditional decor.
Address: Route Nationale 13.
M. CLAUDE YSSAMBOURG,
tel 33.43.77.92.

TOTES, Seine-Maritime 76890, Map 3

LE NORMANDY, RN 27

Places of interest: Parc zoologique de Clères (12km), musée automobile de Clères, parc d'attraction du Bacasse.
Menu: 55 to 85 Frs
Restaurant: closed Saturdays and Sundays.

Other points; bar, credit cards accepted, children welcome, pets allowed, car parking.
Address: route d'Yvetôt.
M. ALAIN MONTIER, tel 35.32.99.54.

TOTES, Seine-Maritime 76890, Map 3

LES AMIS REUNIS, RN 27

Restaurant.
Other points: bar.

Address: route de Dieppe.
M. MICHEL GUILBERT, tel 35.79.91.27.

TOURVILLE SUR ARQUES, Seine-Maritime 76550, Map 3

LA FALAISE, RN 27

Languages: English, Italian, Spanish
Menu: 65 to 75 Frs
Restaurant: closed Saturdays, Sunday nights (out of season).
Hotel: 12 rooms: single 6, double 6.
Other points: bar, credit cards accepted,

children welcome, pets allowed, car parking, traditional decor.
Address: Bas de Tourville.
MME MICHELINE CAPEYROU-BOTTE,
tel 35.85.44.77.

TRAIT (LE), Seine-Maritime 76580, Map 3

LE JEAN BART – Les Routiers, RD 982 between Duclair and Caudebec en Caux

Places of interest: Abbaye de Saint Wandrille, pont de Bratonne, pont de Tancarville.
Languages: German, English
Menu: 43 Frs
Restaurant: lunch 11.30–3.30pm, dinner 6–10pm. Closed Sundays and last 3 weeks of August.
Specialities: langue sauce piquante, boudin noir maison, onglet à l'échalotte.

Hotel: 3 rooms: single 1, double 2. Showers, baths.
Other points: bar, credit cards accepted, children welcome, à la carte menu, lounge area, garden terrace, pets allowed, car parking.
Address: 488 rue Jean Bart.
M. JEAN MAHIER, tel 35.37.22.47.

TREBEURDEN, Côtes-du-Nord 22560, Map 4

RESTAURANT DES SPORTS, RN 12, in front of the mairie, towards Perros-Guirec

Places of interest: La côte de granit rose, Euradom, le planétarium, l'aquarium, centre ornithologique.
Language: English
Restaurant: lunch 11.45–1.45pm. Closed Tuesday afternoons (out of season) and second 2 weeks of August.

Other points: bar, credit cards accepted, children welcome, pets allowed, car parking, traditional decor.
Address: 24 rue des Plages.
M. ANDRE COURAGEUX, tel 96.23.50.12.

TREFFENDEL, Ille-et-Vilaine 35380, Map 4 ⊗♉

LE RN 24, RN 24 between Rennes and Lorient

Places of interest: La vallée de Broccliaude, forêt.
Menu: 45 Frs
Restaurant: lunch 11.30–3pm, dinner 6.30–10.30pm. Closed Sundays.

Other points: bar, credit cards accepted, children welcome, garden terrace, pets allowed, car parking.
Address: La Gare.
MME GUILLEMOT, tel 99.61.00.62.

TREGUIDEL, Côtes-du-Nord 22290, Map 4 ⊗♉

LE BOUTOU, between Saint Brieux and Paimpol

Places of interest: Le zoo de Trégomeur, le nouveau pont de Saint Guay Pontrieux.
Menu: 48 Frs
Restaurant.

Other points: bar, car parking.
Address: Le Bourg.
MMES PAULETTE AND JOSSELINE ALGERI, tel 96.70.02.42.

TREILLIERES, Loire-Atlantique 44119, Map 5 ⊗♉

LE PIGEON BLANC, RN 137 and D 537, Rennes

Place of interest: La vallée de l'Erdre.
Menu: 51,50 to 120 Frs
Accommodation: 180 Frs
Restaurant: closed Sundays.
Hotel: 3 rooms, showers, private WCs, TV.

Other points: bar, credit cards accepted, children welcome, pets allowed, car parking, traditional decor.
Address: known as Le Pigeon Blanc.
MME REGINE PLAT, tel 40.94.67.22.

TREMOREL, Côtes-du-Nord 22230, Map 4 ⊗♉

LES ROUTIERS, RN 164 between Loudéac and Pontivy

Menu: 43 Frs
Restaurant: closed Monday afternoons.
Other points: bar, credit cards accepted,

children welcome, car parking.
Address: Le Bourg.
M. YVON SOHIER, tel 96.25.21.70.

TRIGAVOU, Côtes-du-Nord 22490, Map 4 ⊗♉

LE MILL'PATT

Restaurant: closed Monday nights.
Other points: bar.

Address: Le Bourg.
M. LOIC RENAULT, tel 96.27.84.14.

TRINITE SURZUR (LA), Morbihan 56190, Map 4 ⊗♉⌂

AUBERGE DE LA VIEILLE FONTAINE, RN 165 between Vannes and la Roche Bernard

Places of interest: Le golf du Morbihan, château du Plessis, Vannes.
Language: English
Menu: 42 Frs
Accommodation: 120 to 150 Frs
Restaurant: lunch 12–2pm, dinner 7–10pm.
Specialities: fruits de mer, plats régionaux, poissons, potée.

Hotel: 7 rooms: single 5, double 2. Showers, private WCs, TV, phone.
Other points: bar, credit cards accepted, children welcome, à la carte menu, lounge area, garden terrace, pets allowed, car parking.
Address: La Vieille Fontaine.
M. DIDIER LE RAY, tel 97.42.01.01.

TRONQUAY (LE), Calvados 14490, Map 3 ⊗ 🍷

AU ROUTIER SYMPA, RD 572 between Bayeux and St Lô

Places of interest: Musée et château de Bayeux, musée de la mongolfières.
Menu: 47 Frs
Restaurant: lunch 11.15–2.30pm, dinner 7–9.30pm. Closed Saturday afternoons and Sundays.

Other points: bar, credit cards accepted, à la carte menu, lounge area, pets allowed, car parking.
Address: La Commune.
M. DANIEL MERIEL, tel 31.92.38.68.

UROU ET CRENNES, Orne 61200, Map 3 ⊗ 🍷 🏠

LE CLOS FLEURI, RN 26

Place of interest: Le Haras du Pin.
Languages: English, German
Menu: 75 to 100 Frs
Restaurant: dinner 7–9pm. Closed Sundays.
Hotel: 9 rooms: single 3, double 6. Showers, baths.

Other points: bar, credit cards accepted, children welcome, pets allowed, car parking, traditional decor.
Address: route de Paris.
M. GILBERT ESTELLE, tel 33.67.08.85.

VALLET, Loire-Atlantique 44330, Map 5 ⊗ 🍷 🏠

RESTAURANT DE LA GARE, RD 756 and 763, on bypass around the centre of Vallet

Places of interest: Nantes (20km), château de Clisson, zoo de la Boissière du Doré, musée Pierre Abeliard au Vallet.
Language: English
Menu: 47 to 75 Frs
Accommodation: 140 to 200 Frs
Restaurant: lunch 11.30–2.30pm, dinner 7–9.30pm. Closed Sundays and public holidays (except the hotel).

Specialities: fruits de mer, poisson de la Loire au beurre blanc, navarin au muscadet.
Hotel: 25 rooms: single 11, double 14. Showers, private WCs, TV.
Other points: bar, credit cards accepted, children welcome, lounge area, garden terrace, pets allowed, car parking.
Address: 43 rue Saint Vincent.
M. MICHEL JOUY, tel 40.33.92.55.

VALOGNES, Manche 50700, Map 3 ⊗ 🍷

AU PETIT MONT ROUGE, RN 13

Restaurant: closed Saturdays, Sundays and in August.
Other points: bar, pets allowed, car parking.

Address: 14 boulevard de la Victoire.
MME MONIQUE LE BLOND, tel 33.40.11.80.

VANNES, Morbihan 56000, Map 4 ⊗ 🍷 🏠

LE RELAIS DE LUSCANEN, RN 165, on Nantes–Brest express exit at Vannes

Places of interest: La côte Bretonne, le golf du Morbihan.
Language: English
Menu: 44 Frs including wine
Accommodation: 110 Frs
Restaurant: lunch 11.30–3pm, dinner 7–11pm. Closed Sundays and 15 days in August

Hotel: 24 rooms: single 12, double 12. Showers, baths, private WCs.
Other points: bar, credit cards accepted, children welcome, à la carte menu, lounge area, pets allowed, car parking.
Address: Zone artisanale de Luscanen.
M. JEAN-MARIE GITEAU, tel 97.63.45.92.

VENDEUVRE, Calvados 14170, Map 3

⊗🍴🏠🍽

LE RELAIS DE VENDEUVRE

Places of interest: Le château de Vendeuvre, musée de meubles miniatures (unique en Europe), musée du fromage, cidreries, château de Falaise.
Language: a little English
Menu: 50 to 145 Frs
Accommodation: 100 to 180 Frs
Restaurant: lunch 11–2pm, dinner 6–9pm. Closed Saturdays
(except weddings and group dinners), 3 weeks at Christmas and 3 weeks in August/September.

Specialities: coq au cidre, truite au cidre, canard au muscadet.
Hotel: 11 rooms: single 1, double 10. Showers, baths, private WCs.
Other points: bar, credit cards accepted, children welcome, à la carte menu, garden terrace, pets allowed, car parking, traditional decor.
Address: place de la Gare.
M. ANDRE DENIS, tel 31.40.92.77.

VERN SUR SEICHE, Ille-et-Vilaine 35770, Map 4

⊗🍴

WELCOME BAR, between Rennes and Angers

Places of interest: Chateaubriand, la vallée de la Seiche.
Language: English
Menu: 45 Frs
Restaurant: lunch 12–2pm, dinner 7–10pm. Closed Sundays.

Speciality: couscous maison.
Other points: bar, credit cards accepted, pets allowed, car parking, traditional decor.
Address: Le Clos Berquet.
M. PHILIPPE BROSSAULT, tel 99.62.83.18.

VERNEUIL SUR AVRE, Eure 27130, Map 3

⊗🍴

RELAIS DE L ESPERANCE

Restaurant.
Other points: bar.

Address: 65 porte de Breteuil.
M. AGULLO, tel 32.32.12.81.

VERNON, Eure 27200, Map 3

⊗🍴

DU HAMEAU FLEURI, RN 15 between Bonnières and Rouen.

Places of interest: Le musée et jardin Claude Monet à Giverny (8km), château de Bizy.
Menu: 48 to 76 Frs
Restaurant: lunch 11.30–2.30pm, dinner 7–9pm. Closed Saturdays.

Other points: bar, credit cards accepted, children welcome, à la carte menu, pets allowed, car parking, traditional decor.
Address: 88–90 avenue de Rouen.
MME CHANTAL DEKIMPE, tel 32.51.84.69.

VERNON, Eure 27200, Map 3

⊗🍴

AU MIDI MOINS CINQ, RN 15, main road from Vernon to Paris.

Place of interest: Le musée de Claude Monet à Giverny (5km).
Menu: 60 Frs
Restaurant: lunch 11.30–2.30pm, dinner 7–10.30pm.
Specialities: couscous, paëlla, bouillabaisse.

Other points: bar, credit cards accepted, children welcome, à la carte menu, pets allowed, car parking, traditional decor.
Address: Le Petit Val.
MME JOELLE BUCQUET, tel 32.51.08.41.

VERNON, Eure 27200, Map 3

HOTEL DE FRANCE, Rouen

Places of interest: Le musée de Claude Monet à Giverny, château Bizy et Gaillon, musée et collégiale de Vernon.
Menu: 50 to 130 Frs
Accommocation: 100 Frs
Restaurant: lunch 11–4pm, dinner 6.30–10pm. Closed Sundays (except group reservations) and between Christmas and New Year's day.

Speciality: normandes.
Hotel: 10 rooms.
Other points: bar, credit cards accepted, children welcome, à la carte menu, garden terrace, pets allowed, car parking.
Address: 70 route de Rouen.
MME MONIQUE BONTE, tel 32.51.53.55.

VESLY, Eure 27870, Map 3

CHEZ JACKY, RD 181

Menu: 48 to 75 Frs
Restaurant.
Other points: bar, credit cards accepted,

children welcome, car parking.
Address: 35 Grande Rue.
M. JACKY FRICHOT, tel 32.55.62.37.

VILDE GUINGALAN, Côtes-du-Nord 22980, Map 4

LA BORGNETTE, main road from Dinan to St Brieuc, 9km from Dinan

Place of interest: Dinan (9km).
Menu: 45 Frs
Restaurant: lunch 11–3pm, dinner 7–10pm. Closed Sundays, Thursday mornings.

Other points: bar, credit cards accepted, children welcome, pets allowed, car parking.
Address: La Borgnette.
M. ALAIN LAMBARD, tel 96.27.61.10.

VILLEBAUDON, Manche 50410, Map 3

LES ROUTIERS, RD 999, main road from Cherbourg to Rennes

Places of interest: Abbaye d'Hambye, Villedieu, les roches du Ham, pont de Soulenne (saut à l'élastique).
Menu: 50 to 85 Frs
Accommodation: 100 to 150 Frs
Restaurant: lunch 12–3pm, dinner 7–9.30pm.
Specialities: St Pierre à l'oseille, steak

au poivre.
Hotel: 3 single rooms. Showers, private WCs.
Other points: bar, credit cards accepted, children welcome, self-service, garden terrace, car parking, traditional decor.
MME AGNES OSOUF, tel 33.61.20.52.

VILLEDIEU LES POELES, Manche 50800, Map 3

HOTEL DES VOYAGEURS, between Caen and Avranches

Places of interest: Le Mont Saint Michel, Villedieu (fonderie de cloches, musées du vélo et du meuble, zoo), Granville.
Menu: 50 Frs
Accommodation: 120 to 140 Frs
Restaurant.

Hotel: 6 rooms: single 3, double 3.
Other points: bar, children welcome, garden terrace, car parking.
Address: 36 rue du Maréchal Leclerc.
M. BERNARD MAGUSTO, tel 33.51.08.98.

VILLERS BOCAGE, Calvados 14310, Map 3

HOTEL DE LA GARE, RN 175

Places of interest: Les plages du débarquement, Bayeux, Suisse Normande.
Menu: 55 to 95 Frs
Accommodation: 120 to 160 Frs
Restaurant: lunch 11.30–2pm, dinner 7–9pm. Closed Sundays.
Specialities: poule au riz, pintade vallée d'Auge, tripes calvados, blanquette à l'ancienne.

Hotel: 10 rooms: single 5, double 5. Showers, private WCs.
Other points: bar, credit cards accepted, children welcome, garden terrace, car parking, traditional decor.
Address: 6 rue du Maréchal Foch.
MME PAULETTE GOLASSE-MARIE, tel 31.77.00.23.

VILLERS SUR MER, Calvados 14640, Map 3

LE NORMAND, RD 813, main road from Caen to Deauville

Places of interest: Lisieux, Caen, Honfleur, le Mont Saint Michel.
Menu: 52 to 89 Frs
Accommodation: 185 Frs
Restaurant: lunch 12–2pm, dinner 7–9pm. Closed Sundays (out of season) and from mid-September to mid-October.

Speciality: fruits de mer.
Hotel: 8 double rooms. Showers, TV.
Other points: bar, credit cards accepted, children welcome, à la carte menu, pets allowed, car parking.
Address: 44 rue du Maréchal Foch.
M. DOMINIQUE BRETEAU, tel 31.87.04.23.

VIMOUTIERS, Orne 61120, Map 3

HOTEL DE LISIEUX, RN 179

Place of interest: Le chemin du camembert.
Menu: 75 to 105 Frs
Restaurant: closed Saturday afternoons, Sunday nights and second 2 weeks of August.

Hotel: 5 rooms: single 2, double 3. Showers.
Other points: bar.
Address: 37 avenue Lyautey.
MME YVETTE LARIVIERE, tel 33.39.02.62.

VIRE, Calvados 14500, Map 3

HOTEL DE FRANCE, main road from Caen to Rennes

Places of interest: Lac de la Dathée, parc de loisirs, forêt de Saint-Sever, zoo de Jurques, Suisse Normande.
Language: English
Menu: 60 to 90 Frs
Accommodation: 155 to 320 Frs
Restaurant: lunch 12–2pm, dinner 7–9.30pm. Closed from end December to 10 January.
Specialities: ris de veau Vallée d'Auge,

escalope normande, tarte aux pommes flambées au calvados.
Hotel: 50 double rooms. Showers, baths, private WCs, TV, phone.
Other points: bar, credit cards accepted, children welcome, à la carte menu, lounge area, pets allowed, car parking.
Address: 4 rue d'Aignaux.
M. ROGER CARNET, tel 31.68.00.35.

VIRE, Calvados 14500, Map 3

L'AVENIR, Rennes

Menu: 40 to 58 Frs
Restaurant: lunch 12–2.30pm. Closed Sundays and in December.
Specialities: tripes, escalope normande.

Other points: bar, à la carte menu, pets allowed, car parking.
Address: 28 rue Emile Chenel.
M. HERVE GAUTHEROT, tel 31.67.76.94.

VIRONVAY, Eure 27400, Map 3

L'ARCHE DE VIRONVAY, A 13

Places of interest: Honfleur, Deauville, Etretat, les plages du débarquement, côte normande.
Language: English
Menu: 57 Frs
Restaurant: lunch 10–6pm, dinner 6–11pm.
Speciality: jambon braisé sauce madère.

Other points: bar, credit cards accepted, self service, garden terrace, pets allowed, car parking, traditional decor.
Address: Aire de Vironvay. Dans les deux Sens.
Tel 32.40.21.51.

VIVY, Maine-et-Loire 49680, Map 5

RESTAURANT SAINT PAUL, RN 147 between Saumur and Le Mans

Place of interest: Saumur et sa région.
Languages: a little English
Menu: 50 to 150 Frs
Accommodation: 110 to 200 Frs
Restaurant: lunch 12–2.30pm, dinner 7.30–10pm.
Speciality: brochet au saudre de Loire au beurre blanc.

Hotel: 27 rooms: single 2, double 25. Showers, baths, private WCs, TV, phone.
Other points: bar, credit cards accepted, children welcome, à la carte menu, lounge area, garden terrace, pets allowed, car parking.
Address: 30 rue Nationale.
MME MARIE-LOUISE BIDET, tel 41.52.50.13.

VOIVRES (LES), Sarthe 72210, Map 5

RELAIS LE TAMARIS, RD 23

Menu: 51 Frs
Accommodation: 75 Frs
Restaurant: closed Sunday nights.
Hotel: 5 rooms: single 2, double 3.

Other points: bar, children welcome, self service, car parking.
Address: route de la Suze.
M. PATRICK LEGUY, tel 43.88.52.60.

YERVILLE, Seine-Maritime 76760, Map 3

L'ESCALE ROUTIERE, RN 29, main road from Le Havre to Amiens

Menu: 55 Frs
Restaurant: lunch 11–3pm, dinner 7.30–10pm. Closed from Friday 6pm to Saturday noon and in August.

Other points: bar, credit cards accepted, à la carte menu, pets allowed, car parking.
Address: route d'Yvetôt.
M. CHRISTIAN DELAHAYE, tel 35.96.80.45.

YVETOT, Seine-Maritime 76190, Map 3

HOTEL DE FECAMP

Menu: 120 to 150 Frs (pension to 170 Frs)
Restaurant.
Hotel: 5 rooms.

Other points: bar, car parking.
Address: 25 rue Clovis Cappon
CORBINEAU-LAMARE, tel 35.95.44.40.

YVRE L'EVEQUE, Sarthe 72530, Map 5 ⊗ ♈

LA MAISON DU BON CAFE, RN 23, Le Mans East

Menu: 48 to 55 Frs
Restaurant: lunch 12–2pm, dinner 7–8.30pm.
Closed Wednesday afternoons and in August.

Other points: bar, children welcome.
Address: 25 route du Mans, Bener.
MME ANNICK SIMON, tel 43.84.54.63.

North East France

ANCERVILLE, Meuse 55170, Map 17 ⊗ ⍭ 🏠 ☆

LE RELAIS, RN 4 between Paris and Strasbourg

Places of interest: Lac du Dër (25km), Vaucouleur, Donrémy, Colombelle les deux Eglises, Bar le Duc.
Menu: 55 to 75 Frs
Accommodation: 110 to 150 Frs
Restaurant: lunch 12–2pm, dinner 7–9pm. Closed Saturday afternoons, Sunday afternoons and 15 to 30 September.
Specialities: tête de veau, andouillettes, choucroute.

Hotel: 12 rooms: single 7, double 5. Showers, baths, private WCs.
Other points: bar, credit cards accepted, children welcome, à la carte menu, self-service, car parking, traditional decor.
Address: 59 route de Saint Dizier.
MME RENEE LANGE, tel 29.75.30.13.

APPOIGNY, Yonne 89380, Map 15 ⊗ ⍭

Station Service Shell LE RELAIS DE L'AMITIE, RN 6 between Sens and Paris

Places of interest: Auxerre, les rives de l'Yonne, collégiale Saint Pierre.
Menu: up to 60 Frs
Restaurant: lunch 12–2.30pm, dinner 7–10pm. Closed Sundays, August (restaurant only).

Other points: bar, credit cards accepted, car parking, traditional decor.
Address: 21 route d'Auxerre.
M. PHILIPPE SAUR, tel 86.53.21.76.

ARC LES GRAY, Haute-Saône 70100, Map 16 ⊗ ⍭

LES ROUTIERS

Restaurant: closed Sundays.
Other points: bar.
Address: 4 place Aristide Briand, La Croisée

MME HENRIETTE DEMOULIN, tel 84.65.37.23.

ARCES, Yonne 89320, Map 15 ⊗ ⍭ 🏠 ☆

RELAIS DE LA FORET D'OTHE, RD 905

Restaurant.
Hotel: 8 rooms.
Other points: bar.

Address: 15 place de l'Eglise.
MME YOLANDE MISURA, tel 86.88.10.44.

ARCHES, Vosges 88380, Map 17 ⊗ ⍭ 🏠 ☆ ☆

LA TRUITE RENOMMEE

Places of interest: Epinal-Remiremont, musée de l'imagerie à Epinal.
Languages: English, German, Italian
Menu: 49 to 110 Frs
Accommodation: 190 to 210 Frs
Restaurant: lunch 12–2.30pm, dinner 7–11pm. Closed Saturday afternoons.
Speciality: truite fumée vosgienne.

Hotel: 8 rooms: single 6, double 2. Showers, baths, private WCs, TV, phone.
Other points: bar, credit cards accepted, pets allowed, car parking, traditional decor.
Address: 1 rue d'Epinal.
MME JOSSELINE HAGENAUER, tel 29.32.79.13.

ARGENTEUIL SUR ARMANCON, Yonne 89160, Map 15 ⊗ ⍭

CAFE DE LA MARE, CD 109 and 118 between Lézinnes and Ancy-le-Franc

Places of interest: Château d'Ancy-le-Franc (8km), sites très pitoresques (50 à 80km).
Menu: 56 Frs
Restaurant: lunch 12–2pm, dinner 7–9pm. Closed Saturday mornings.

Specialities: jambon au Chablis, coq au vin.
Other points: bar, children welcome, pets allowed, car parking, traditional decor.
MME MARIE-MADELEINE MESTANIER, tel 86.75.08.60.

ARNAY LE DUC, Côte-d'Or 21230, Map 15   ⊗♀⌂

RELAIS ROUTIERS LE SAINT PRIX, RN 6 towards Chalon sur Saone

Places of interest: Château de Neufchâteau, château de Rochepot, hospice de Beaune.
Languages: English, Italian
Menu: 54 to 70 Frs
Accommodation: 120 to 140 Frs
Restaurant: lunch 11.45–2pm, dinner 7.30–10pm. Closed Sundays.

Speciality: boeuf bourgignon.
Hotel: 6 rooms, showers.
Other points: bar, credit cards accepted, garden terrace, car parking, traditional decor.
Address: Sivry.
M. ROBERT TONELLI, tel 80.84.81.74.

ASFELD, Ardennes 08190, Map 18   ⊗♀

LE SOLEIL D'OR

Languages: German, English
Menu: 48 Frs
Restaurant: lunch 11.30–2pm, dinner 7–10.30pm.
Specialities: couscous, paëlla.

Other points: bar, car parking.
Address: 28 rue Chantereine.
MME VERONIQUE MODAINE, tel 24.72.97.57.

ATHIS, Marne 51150, Map 18   ⊗♀⌂

AU BON ACCUEIL, between Chalon sur Marne and Epernay

Places of interest: Visite des caves et coteaux champenois (Reims, Epernay – 13km), la vallée de la Marne.
Menu: 50 Frs
Accommodation: 70 to 140 Frs
Restaurant: lunch 11.30–2.30pm, dinner 7.30–9pm. Closed Sundays and in August.

Hotel: 5 rooms: single 2, double 3. Showers, private WCs.
Other points: bar, credit cards accepted, garden terrace, pets allowed, car parking, traditional decor.
Address: 12 Route Départementale.
M. DANIEL BOURSCHEIDT, tel 26.57.62.61.

AUBETERRE, Aube 10150, Map 18   ⊗♀

LES TILLEULS, RN 77

Places of interest: Lac, forêt d'Orient, cathédrale de Troyes.
Menu: 45 to 52 Frs
Restaurant.

Other points: bar, credit cards accepted, à la carte menu, car parking.
M. RAYMOND MIELLE, tel 25.37.51.11.

AUMETZ, Moselle 57710, Map 17   ⊗♀⌂

CAFE DE LA POSTE, RN 52

Language: Italian
Menu: 42 Frs
Accommodation: 90 to 120 Frs

Restaurant: lunch 12–3pm, dinner 7–9pm. Closed Tuesday afternoons.
Speciality: Italian.

Hotel: 7 rooms.
Other points: bar, credit cards accepted, pets allowed, car parking.

Address: 15 rue Foch.
MME LINDA COSSA, tel 82.91.91.71.

AUTECHAUX, Doubs 25110, Map 16 ⊗ ♀

RELAIS DE L'AUTOROUTE – Chez Simone, A36 exit at Baume les Dames towards Lure and Vesoul

Places of interest: Grottes de la glacière, gouffre de Pouchey, saut du Doubs (Villers le Lac), lac de Bonnal, château de Belvoir.
Languages: a little English, Spanish
Menu: 54 Frs including a drink and coffee
Restaurant: lunch 11–3pm, dinner 7–12pm. Closed Sundays, public holidays and 15 days

in August.
Specialities: croûtes aux champignons, fondue aux 3 fromages, canard à l'ananas.
Other points: bar, children welcome, garden terrace, car parking, traditional decor.
MME SIMONE COURTIAL, tel 81.84.01.14

AUVILLERS LES FORGES, Ardennes 08260, Map 18 ⊗♀⌂

ARRET DES ROUTIERS, RN 43

Restaurant.
Hotel: 6 rooms.
Other points: bar.

Address: Mon Idée.
MME NICOLE BONNAIRE, tel 24.54.32.77.

AUXERRE, Yonne 89000, Map 15 ⊗♀⌂⊖☆

LE SAINTE NITASSE, RN 65

Places of interest: Monuments du moyen âge d'Auxerre, Avallon, Vezelay, Joigny.
Language: English
Menu: 53 to 85 Frs
Accommodation: 100 to 130 Frs
Restaurant: lunch 12–2.30pm, dinner 7.30–10.30pm. Closed Saturdays and Sundays.

Hotel: 31 double rooms. Baths, private WCs.
Other points: bar, credit cards accepted, à la carte menu, garden terrace, pets allowed, car parking, traditional decor.
Address: Route de Chablis.
MME CORINE COURAULT, tel 86.46.95.07.

BEAUMONT SUR VESLE, Marne 51360, Map 18 ⊗♀⌂⊖☆☆

LA MAISON DU CHAMPAGNE, RN 44 between Reims and Chalons sur Marne

Places of interest: Caves de champagne, vignobles, vestiges de 14–18, Fort Pompelle.
Languages: German, English, Flemish
Menu: 68 to 180 Frs
Accommodation: 110 to 300 Frs
Restaurant: lunch 12–2.15pm, dinner 7–9.30pm. Closed Sunday nights, Mondays, 15 days in February and 15 in October.
Specialities: terrine maison, rognons de veau au ratafia, soufflé au marc, terrine du chef,

canard aux griottes.
Hotel: 13 rooms: single 9, double 4. Showers, baths, private WCs, TV, phone.
Other points: bar, credit cards accepted, children welcome, à la carte menu, garden terrace, pets allowed, car parking, traditional decor.
Address: 2 rue du Port.
M. MARC BOULARD, tel 26.03.92.45.

BEAUNE, Côte-d'Or 21200, Map 15   ⊗🍷

TRUCKSTORE CAFE, A 6 between Paris and Lyon, in both directions

Place of interest: Archéodrome (sur autoroute).
Languages: German, English, Spanish
Menu: 58 Frs
Restaurant.

Other points: bar, credit cards accepted, à la carte menu, lounge area, garden terrace, pets allowed, car parking.
Address: Aire de Service de Beaune Tailly. Tel 80.21.40.78.

BEAUNE, Côte-d'Or 21200, Map 15   ⊗🍷

LE MALMEDY, RN 74

Menu: 55 Frs
Restaurant: lunch 12–2pm. Closed Sundays and in August.
Specialities: coq au vin, boeuf bourguignon.

Other points: bar, car parking, traditional decor.
Address: 6 rue du Lieutenant Dupuis. MME YVETTE PECOUT, tel 80.22.14.74.

BEAUNE, Côte-d'Or 21200, Map 15   ⊗🍷🏠🍲☆☆☆

RELAIS DE BEAUNE, A 6 on the bridge across autoroute, in both directions

Place of interest: Archéodrome (sur autoroute).
Restaurant.
Hotel: 150 rooms, showers, baths, private WCs, TV, phone.

Other points: bar, credit cards accepted, children welcome, à la carte menu, self-service, lounge area, garden terrace, pets allowed, car parking.
Address: Aire de Service de Beaune. Tel 80.21.46.24.

BEAUNE, Côte-d'Or 21200, Map 15   ⊗🍷

CAFE DE FRANCE, RN 74

Places of interest: Hospices de Beaune, marché aux vins.
Menu: 52 Frs
Restaurant: lunch 12–2pm. Closed Sundays and in August.

Specialities: boeuf bourguignon, coq au vin.
Other points: bar, children welcome, pets allowed, traditional decor.
Address: 13 faubourg Bretonnière. M. JEAN-PIERRE LE PAYEN, tel 80.22.25.44

BEAUNE, Côte-d'Or 21200, Map 15   ⊗🍷🏠

AUBERGE DE LA GARE, RN 74

Restaurant: closed Sundays, public holidays and in August.
Hotel: 6 rooms.
Other points: bar.

Address: 11 avenue des Lyonnais. HOTELS AUBERGE DE LA GARE, tel 80.22.11.13.

BELLEVILLE SUR MEUSE, Meuse 55100, Map 17   ⊗🍷

CHEZ DEDE, road to Charleville

Places of interest: Verdun, les champs de bataille, Douaumont.
Languages: English, Italian
Menu: 47,50 Frs

Restaurant: lunch 11.30–3pm. Closed Sunday afternoons, afternoons of public holidays and 8 days in September.

Other points: bar, pets allowed, car parking, traditional decor.

Address: 164 avenue du Général de Gaulle. M. ANDRE BUFFELO, tel 29.84.57.85.

BINING, Moselle 57410, Map 17

⊗ ⸜

AUBERGE AU TILLEUL

Places of interest: Ligne Maginot, musée du cristal de Saint Louis (30km), citadelle de Bitche (20km).
Languages: German, English
Menu: 58 to 120 Frs
Restaurant: lunch 12–2pm, dinner 7–10pm. Closed Thursdays and second 2 weeks of September.

Specialities: baeckoffe, couscous, paëlla, choucroute.
Other points: bar, credit cards accepted, children welcome, à la carte menu, car parking.
Address: 2 rue du Tilleul.
M. GILLES EHRE, tel 87.09.74.86.

BLACY, Marne 51300, Map 18

⊗ ⸜

LE RELAIS DE LA MAISON BLANCHE

Places of interest: La Route du champagne vers Epernay, lac du Der (20km).
Menu: 53 to 75 Frs
Restaurant: closed Saturday 3pm to Monday 5am.

Other points: bar, credit cards accepted, car parking.
Address: 8 route de Paris.
MME CLAUDINE SIMIONI, tel 26.74.44.98.

BLAGNY, Ardennes 08110, Map 18

⊗ ⸜

LES ROUTIERS, RN 381 between Montmedy and Lomuy

Places of interest: Châteaux, Belgique (15km), vallée de la Meuse.
Menu: 60 Frs
Restaurant: lunch 11.30–3pm, dinner 7.30–10pm. Closed Saturdays and in August.

Other points: bar, children welcome. pets allowed, car parking.
Address: 37 Route Nationale.
M. GERARD LEMAITRE, tel 24.22.00.23.

⊗
BLENOD LES PONT A MOUSSON, Meurthe-et-Moselle 54700, Map 17   ⸜

CHEZ FERNANDE, RN 57 A 4 near exit autoroute

Place of interest: Les portes d'or de la place Stanislas de Nancy.
Languages: German, Portugues.
Menu: 48 Frs
Accommodation: 80 Frs (1 person) to 100 Frs (2 persons)
Restaurant: lunch 11–2.30pm, dinner 7–11pm. Closed Saturday afternoons, Sundays and in August.

Specialities: couscous, paëlla, choucroute, potée lorraine.
Hotel: 2 double rooms. Showers.
Other points: bar, credit cards accepted, children welcome, garden terrace, pets allowed, traditional decor.
Address: 88 avenue Victor Claude.
MME LOUISETTE PEREIRA, tel 83.81.03.54.

BOUILLY, Aube 10320, Map 18

⊗ ⸜ 🏠 ☆

AU RELAIS MONTAIGU, RN 77

Places of interest: Auxerre, Troyes, musées, lacs, forêt d'Orient, églises.
Menu: 50 to 80 Frs
Accommodation: 80 to 130 Frs
Restaurant: lunch 12–2 pm.
Hotel: 13 rooms: single 5, double 8. Showers.

Other points: bar, credit cards accepted, children welcome, phone, lounge area, garden terrace, pets allowed, car parking, traditional decor.
Address: 300 rue au Fébvres, Souligny.
M. RENE BRAUX, tel 25.40.20.20.

BOUXWILLER, Bas-Rhin 67330, Map 17

AU SOLEIL, RD 6 and 7

Places of interest: Bouxwiller (musée), Lichtenberg.
Languages: German, English
Menu: 35 to 150 Frs
Accommodation: 130 to 250 Frs
Restaurant: lunch 11.30–2.15pm, dinner 7.30–9.15pm. Closed Wednesdays, Sunday nights, early July, and February except school holidays.

Specialities: choucroute, coq au Riesling, Sandre à l'oseillto.
Hotel: 16 rooms: single 2, double 14. Showers, baths, private WCs, TV, phone.
Other points: bar, credit cards accepted, à la carte menu, pets allowed, car parking.
Address: 71 Grand Rue.
M. CHARLES JAEGER, tel 88.70.70.06.

BRIENNE SUR AISNE, Ardennes 08190, Map 18

LES ROUTIERS

Places of interest: Reims (15km), parc des Aillettes (20km).
Language: English
Menu: 52 Frs
Restaurant.

Specialities: côtes de boeuf, andouillettes.
Other points: bar, car parking.
Address: 9 rue d'Obernai.
M. PASCAL RAMBEAUX, tel 24.38.95.92.

BRIENON SUR ARMANCON, Yonne 89210, Map 15

LES ROUTIERS DE BOURGOGNE, between Joigny and Saint Florentin

Places of interest: Joigny (22km), Auxerres (20km), Chablis (20km).
Languages: English, Polish, Russian
Menu: 50 Frs
Accommodation: 80 to 100 Frs
Restaurant: closed Saturday afternoons and Sundays.

Hotel: 9 rooms: single 7, double 2. Showers.
Other points: bar, credit cards accepted, garden terrace, pets allowed, car parking, traditional decor.
Address: 21 route de Joigny.
M. CHRISTIAN DUSSART, tel 86.43.00.63.

BUCEY LES GY, Haute-Saône 70700, Map 16

CAFE DE LA GARE, RD 474 between Dijon and Vesoul

Menu: 57 Frs
Restaurant: lunch 11.30–2pm, dinner 7.30–9.30pm. Closed Sunday afternoons.
Speciality: croûte aux champignons.
Other points: bar, credit cards accepted,

children welcome, garden terrace, pets allowed, car parking, traditional decor.
Address: rue de la Gare.
MME YVETTE BOLE-BESANCON, tel 84.32.92.02

CHAINTRIX, Marne 51130, Map 18

LE CARO'S

Language: English
Menu: 54 to 130 Frs
Restaurant: lunch 11.45–1.45pm, dinner
7–9.30pm. Closed Sundays.

Other points: bar, car parking.
Address: route de Paris.
MME CAROLINE COUDERT,
tel 26.66.43.80.

CHALLUY, Nièvre 58000, Map 15 ⊗ 🍷 🏠

RELAIS DU PONT CARREAU, RN 7

Restaurant.
Hotel: 4 rooms.
Other points: bar.

MME FERNANDE TAILLEMITTE,
tel 86.21.00.02.

CHALONS SUR MARNE, Marne 51000, Map 18 ⊗ 🍷

AU MONT SAINT-MICHEL, RN 77 Troyes then A 26

Places of interest: Les caves de champagne.
Languages: English, Spanish
Menu: 46 to 137 Frs
Restaurant: closed Sunday nights.
Specialities: champenoise, antillaise.

Other points: bar, credit cards accepted,
children welcome, à la carte menu, lounge area,
pets allowed, car parking.
Address: 31 route de Troyes, RN 77.
SNC QUEIGE ET MAZEAU, tel 26.68.05.08

CHAMPAGNOLE, Jura 39300, Map 16 ⊗ 🍷

LES ROUTIERS, between Paris and Genève

Places of interest: Les cascades de la Billaude
(500m), celles du Hérisson (10km), de
nombreux lacs.
Menu: 50 Frs
Restaurant: lunch 12–2pm. Closed Sundays

and 15 days in August.
Other points: bar, car parking.
Address: La Billaude, Commune du Vaudioux.
M. GEORGES CHAGRE, tel 84.51.60.33.

CHAMPIGNEULLES, Meurthe-et-Moselle 54250, Map 17 ⊗ 🍷

AUBERGE FLEURIE, RN 4

Places of interest: Nancy (3km) (la place
Stanislas, musée lorrain, musée du fer).
Language: German
Menu: 55 Frs
Restaurant: lunch 11–2pm, dinner 7–10pm.
Closed Sundays.

Other points: car parking.
Address: Fonds de Toul, Les Baraques –
Nancy East.
MME SEVERINE BROUGIERE,
tel 83.98.52.32.

CHAMPLOST, Yonne 89210, Map 15 ⊗ 🍷

AU BON ACCUEIL, RD 905 between Sens and Dijon

Places of interest: Le mont Avrollot, site
archéologique.
Menu: 53 to 65 Frs
Restaurant: closed Sundays.

Other points: bar, car parking.
Address: 23 Route Nationale 5.
SNC DUTERIEZ – LE LEUCH,
tel 86.43.14.71

CHANTENAY SAINT IMBERT, Nièvre 58240, Map 15 ⊗ 🍷

AU BON ACCUEIL, RN 7 between Moulin and Nevers

Places of interest: Château de Saint Augustin (16km), parc animalier, parc d'attractions, forêt de Tronçais, arborétom de Balaine.
Menu: 51 Frs
Restaurant: lunch 12–2pm, dinner 7–9.30pm. Closed Saturday lunch, Sundays and in August.
Specialities: truite à la bourbonnaise,

omelette bûcheronne, paté aux pommes de terre.
Other points: bar, children welcome, à la carte menu, garden terrace, pets allowed, car parking, traditional decor.
Address: St Pierre le Moutier.
MME LUCETTE VACHER, tel 86.39.61.95.

CHATELET SUR RETOURNE, Ardennes 08300, Map 18

LE RELAIS PONT ROYAL

Place of interest: Région de champagne.
Menu: 52 to 150 Frs
Restaurant: closed Tuesdays.

Other points: credit cards accepted.
Address: Châtelet sur Retourne.
M. YVES DETRUISEAUX, tel 24.38.93.27.

CHATILLON EN BAZOIS, Nièvre 58110, Map15

HOTEL DU RELAIS, RD 978

Restaurant: closed Sundays and public holidays.
Hotel: 7 rooms.

Other points: bar.
M. JEAN-JACQUES CHARPRENET,
tel 86.84.13.79.

CHATILLON SUR SEINE, Côte-d'Or 21400, Map 15

BAR RESTAURANT LE CHARIOT, RN 71 between Troyes and Dijon

Places of interest: Le vase de Vix, l'église de Saint Vorles.
Language: English
Menu: 47 to 70 Frs
Restaurant: lunch 12–2pm, dinner 7–9pm. Closed Sundays and 4 to 18 August.

Specialities: coq au vin, boeuf bourguignon.
Other points: bar, credit cards accepted, à la carte menu, pets allowed, traditional decor.
PAULETTE AND NADINE BUNCEY, SNC LACROIX, tel 80.91.09.82

CHAUDENEY, Meurthe-et-Moselle 54200, Map 17

LE MIRABELLIER, A 31

Places of interest: Luxembourg, Metz, Nancy.
Languages: German, English
Menu: 53 Frs
Restaurant.

Other points: children welcome, self-service, car parking.
Address: Aire de Service de Toul-Dommartin.
M. JOEL FRERES, tel 83.64.64.01.

CHAUMONT, Haute-Marne 52000, Map 18

BELLEVUE RELAIS ROUTIERS, RN 67 exit Chaumon towards St Dizier

Places of interest: Chaumont (basilique Saint Jean, viaduc, hôtel de ville), Colombey les deux Eglises (25km).
Menu: 55 Frs
Accommodation: 80 to 150 Frs
Restaurant: lunch 12–2.30pm, dinner 7–9.30pm. Closed Sundays and in September.
Speciality: tripes maisons.

Hotel: 8 rooms, showers, baths.
Other points: bar, credit cards accepted, children welcome, à la carte menu, lounge area, garden terrace, pets allowed, car parking, traditional decor.
Address: Route Nationale, Brethenay.
MME MICHELINE BOURGOIN,
tel 25.32.51.02.

CHAUMONT, Haute-Marne 52000, Map 18 ⊗ ♀

CHEZ JEAN, RN 19

Restaurant.
Other points: bar.

Address: 29 avenue Carnot.
M. JEAN CORROY, tel 25.03.06.57.

CHAUMONT, Haute-Marne 52000, Map 18 ⊗ ♀

LA HALTE DU VIADUC, RN 65

Places of interest: Viaduc, Colombey les deux
Eglises.
Language: English
Menu: 55 Frs including wine
Restaurant: lunch 11.30–3pm, dinner
6.30–11pm. Closed Saturdays and Sundays.

Speciality: tête de veau.
Other points: bar, credit cards accepted, pets
allowed, car parking.
Address: Route de Paris.
M. SERGE RICHOUX, tel 25.03.55.59.

CHELSEY, Côte-d'Or 21430, Map 15 ⊗ ♀ 🏠

LES ROUTIERS – Chez Ursula et Bernard, RN 6 midway between Saulieu and Arnay le Duc

Places of interest: Musée de l'Art de la Table à
Arnay le Duc, Saulieu.
Languages: German, English
Menu: 59 to 70 Frs
Accommodation: 90 to 210 Frs
Restaurant: lunch 12–3pm, dinner 7–9pm.
Closed Saturdays, Sundays and 3 weeks in
August.

Speciality: pintade rôtie.
Hotel: 5 rooms: single 3, double 2. Showers.
Other points: bar, children welcome, à la carte
menu, pets allowed, car parking, traditional
decor.
Address: Route Nationale 6.
M. BERNARD SENTEIN, tel 80.84.40.42.

CHEMAUDIN, Doubs 25320, Map 16 ⊗ ♀

LA COCOTTE, RN 73 between Dole and Besançon

Places of interest: Grottes d'Osselle (5km), le
gouffre de Poudrey, citadelle de Besançon
(7km).
Menu: 45 to 55 Frs
Restaurant: lunch 11–3pm, dinner 7–11pm.
Closed Sundays.

Speciality: choucroute.
Other points: bar, credit cards accepted,
children welcome, pets allowed, car parking.
Address: known as La Cocotte.
M. CHRISTIAN GROSPERRIN,
tel 81.58.64.70.

CHEMERY LES DEUX, Moselle 57320, Map 17 ⊗ ♀ 🏠

RELAIS MATHUIS, RD 918 between Metz and Bouzonville

Language: German
Menu: 40 to 60 Frs
Restaurant: closed Wednesdays and in
August.

Hotel: 6 rooms.
Other points: bar.
Address: Bouzonville.
MME MARIE KOCH, tel 87.64.91.73.

CHENEVIERES, Meurthe-et-Moselle 54122, Map 17 ⊗ ♀

RELAIS DES ROUTIERS, RN 59

Places of interest: Saint Dié, château de Lunéville, cristalleries de Baccarat.
Menu: 50 Frs
Restaurant: lunch 11–3pm, dinner 6–8.30pm. Closed Sundays.

Other points: bar, credit cards accepted, children welcome, à la carte menu, garden terrace, pets allowed, car parking.
Address: 10 Route Nationale.
MME AGNES REMY, tel 83.72.62.75

CHENOVE, Côte-d'Or 21300, Map 15 ⊗♍⌂☆

AU BON COIN, RN 74

Restaurant: closed Saturdays and Sundays, August.
Hotel: 13 rooms.

Other points: bar.
Address: 54 Route de Dijon.
M. MARCEL MARIN, tel 80.52.58.17.

CLAIRVAUX LES LACS, Jura 39130, Map 16 ⊗♍

LES ROUTIERS, RN 78 and RN 83

Languages: English, Italian
Restaurant: closed Sundays (out of season) and 1 to 15 September.

Other points: bar.
Address: 4 Route de Lons-le-Saulnier.
M. DENIS PERRIN, tel 84.25.85.57.

COLIGNY, Marne 51130, Map 18 ⊗♍

LE VAL DES MARAIS

Place of interest: Les caves d'Epernay (30km).
Menu: 50 Frs
Restaurant: lunch 12–2pm, dinner 7–9 pm.
Other points: bar, credit cards accepted, pets

allowed, traditional decor.
Address: 61 rue Saint Gond.
M. MICHEL LAGNIE, tel 26.52.23.15.

COLLONGES LES PREMIERES, Côte-d'Or 21110, Map 15 ⊗♍

A LA BONNE AUBERGE

Menu: 53 Frs
Restaurant: lunch 11–3pm, dinner 7–9pm. Closed Sundays and in August.
Other points: bar, credit cards accepted, pets

allowed, car parking, traditional decor.
Address: 8 rue de la Gare.
M. MICHEL GARNIER, tel 80.31.32.01.

COLOMBEY LES BELLES, Meurthe-et-Moselle 54170, Map 17 ⊗♍

AUBERGE LORRAINE, RN 74

Places of interest: Neufchateau, Donremy, Nancy, Toul.
Menu: 50 to 95 Frs
Restaurant: lunch 11.30–2.30pm, dinner 7–10pm. Closed 8 to 10 days between Christmas and New Year's day.

Other points: bar, credit cards accepted, children welcome, à la carte menu, garden terrace, car parking.
Address: 71 rue Carnot.
M. CLAUDE ARNOULD, tel 83.52.00.23.

COMBLANCHIEN, Côte-d'Or 21700, Map 15 ⊗♍⌂

AUBERGE DU GUIDON, RN 74 between Beaune and Dijon

Places of interest: Nuits Saint Georges, Beaune.
Menu: 58 Frs
Accommodation: 70 to 120 Frs
Restaurant: lunch 11.30–3pm, dinner 7–10pm. Closed Saturdays, Sundays and mid-August.

Hotel: 8 rooms: single 2, double 6.
Other points: bar, pets allowed, car parking, traditional decor.
Address: Route Nationale 74.
M. ANDRE VAUCHEZ, tel 80.62.94.39.

CONNANTRAY, Marne 51230, Map 18 ⊗♈⌂

LA ROUTIERE, RN 4

Places of interest: Nancy, Epernay.
Menu: 55 to 95 Frs
Accommodation: 54,50 to 90,50 Frs
Restaurant: lunch 11.45–3pm, dinner 6.45–11pm. Closed Sundays.

Hotel: 8 rooms: single 1, double 7.
Other points: bar, credit cards accepted, lounge area, pets allowed, car parking.
Address: Route Nationale 4.
M. MICHEL VILLAIN, tel 26.42.42.03.

CONNANTRE, Marne 51230, Map 18 ⊗♈⌂

LA GRAPPE D'OR, RN 4

Menu: 52 Frs including a drink
Accommodation: 80 to 120 Frs
Restaurant: lunch 12–2pm, dinner 7–9pm. Closed Saturday afternoons, Sundays, 15 days in August and 15 days for Christmas.
Hotel: 8 rooms: single 5, double 3. Showers,

private WCs.
Other points: bar, credit cards accepted, car parking.
Address: rue de la Gare.
M. PASCAL DUFOUR, tel 26.81.04.62.

CONSENVOYE, Meuse 55110, Map 17 ⊗♈⌂

AUBERGE LORRAINE, RD 964 between Verdun and Charleville

Places of interest: Mémorial de Verdun, champs de bataille, fortifications du cimetière militaire (vestiges du guerre 14/18).
Language: English
Menu: 53 to 95 Frs
Accommodation: 85 to 110 Frs
Restaurant: lunch 11.30–2pm, dinner 7–9pm. Closed Saturdays and 15 days in September.
Specialities: couscous, choucroute, tarte à

l'oignon, quiche lorraine.
Hotel: 6 rooms: single 2, double 4. Showers.
Other points: bar, credit cards accepted, children welcome, à la carte menu, garden terrace, pets allowed, car parking, traditional decor.
Address: 16 Grande Rue.
MME DENISE POUSSANT, tel 29.85.80.19.

CONTREXEVILLE, Vosges 88140, Map 17 ⊗♈

LE BELFORT

Restaurant: closed Saturdays and Sundays.
Other points: bar.

Address: 587 avenue de la Division Leclerc.
M. ANDRE SUNDHAUSER, tel 29.08.04.22.

COOLE, Marne 51320, Map 18 ⊗♈

LES ROUTIERS

Menu: 53 Frs
Restaurant: closed Saturday afternoons, Sundays and 15 days in July.

Other points: bar.
Address: Route Nationale 4.
M. JEAN-MARIE BRISSON, tel 26.74.34.79.

CORBIGNY, Nièvre 58800, Map 15   ⊗ ♈

LES AMIS DES ROUTIERS, RD 985

Places of interest: Parc régional de Morvan
(14km), musée Septennat à Château Chinon
(30km).
Menu: 50 Frs
Restaurant: lunch 12–3.30pm, dinner
7.30–9.30pm. Closed Saturday afternoons,

Sundays, public holidays and 15 August to 8
September.
Other points: bar, credit cards accepted, pets
allowed, car parking, traditional decor.
Address: 8 rue de Clamecy.
MME COLETTE PERINI, tel 86.20.19.77.

COSNE SUR LOIRE, Nièvre 58200, Map 15   ⊗ ♈

LA TASSEE, RN 7 to Nevers, exit south

Places of interest: Sancerre, Pouilly.
Language: English
Restaurant: lunch 12–1.30pm, dinner
8–9.30pm. Closed Sundays, public holidays and
in August.

Other points: bar, credit cards accepted,
children welcome, à la carte menu, pets
allowed, car parking.
Address: Route Nationale 7.
M. MAURICE CHET, tel 86.26.11.76.

COSNE SUR LOIRE, Nièvre 58200, Map 15   ⊗♈🏠🍲☆

LES 3 COULEURS, RN 7 between Paris and Nevers

Places of interest: Sancerre, Pouilly sur Loire,
bords de la Loire, musée de la Loire.
Menu: 50 to 120 Frs
Accommodation: 100 to 180 Frs
Restaurant: lunch 12–3pm, dinner 7–8.30pm.
Closed last week of December and first week of
January.
Specialities: coq au vin, cuisses de grenouilles
à la provençale.

Hotel: 13 rooms: single 4, double 9. Showers.
Other points: bar, credit cards accepted,
children welcome, lounge area, pets allowed,
car parking.
Address: 21 rue Saint Agnan.
MRS JEAN PIERRE MORFAUX,
tel 86.28.23.50.

COURCELLES CHAUSSY, Moselle 57530, Map 17   ⊗♈🏠

AUBERGE DE LA GARE, RN 3

Places of interest: Région Lorraine, Metz
(15km), parc Wallibie Schtroumph (15km).
Languages: German, English, Italian
Menu: 58 to 89 Frs (including coffee)
Accommodation: 80 to 140 Frs
Restaurant: lunch 12–2pm, dinner 7–10pm.
Speciality: Italian.

Hotel: 12 rooms.
Other points: bar, credit cards accepted,
garden terrace, pets allowed, car parking,
traditional decor.
Address: avenue de la Libération.
M. PIERRE PAPALIA, tel 87.64.00.22.

COURSON LES CARRIERES, Yonne 89560, Map 15   ⊗♈

LE RELAIS DE COURSON, RN 151 between Auxerre and Clamecy

Places of interest: Abbaye de la Vezelay
(30m), grottes d'Aray (25km), Avallon (35km).
Languages: English, Spanish, Portuguese
Menu: 57 to 87 Frs
Restaurant: lunch 11–3pm, dinner 6.30–12pm.

Other points: bar, credit cards accepted, à la
carte menu, lounge area, garden terrace, pets
allowed.
Address: Route Nationale 151.
M. JOSE CARVALHO, tel 86.41.52.58.

CRAVANT, Yonne 89460, Map 15   ⊗♈⌂

LES DEUX PONTS, RN 6

Restaurant.
Speciality: Portuguese.
Hotel: 10 rooms.

Other points: bar.
Address: 17 route de Paris.
MME ISABELLE NOGUERIA, tel 86.42.24.01.

CRENEY PRES TROYES, Aube 10150, Map 18   ⊗♈

LE RELAIS DU CENTRE, RC 960 between Troyes and Brienne

Places of interest: Lacs et forêt d'Orient.
Menu: 55 Frs
Restaurant: lunch 11–2.30pm, dinner 7–9pm.
Closed Saturdays.
Other points: bar, credit cards accepted,

children welcome, pets allowed, car parking,
traditional decor.
Address: 29 route de Brienne.
M. JACQUES JEANDON, tel 25.81.39.79.

CRESANCEY, Haute-Saône 70100, Map 16   ⊗♈

AUBERGE DE LA PETITE FRINGALE

Language: English
Restaurant: closed Monday mornings,
Wednesday afternoons and Thursday mornings.

Other points: bar, car parking.
Address: Route Départementale 7.
M. JEAN-PAUL LOISEL, tel 84.31.56.08.

CUSSY LES FORGES, Yonne 89420, Map 15   ⊗♈

LE RELAIS 6, RN 6 between Avallon and Dijon

Places of interest: Région du Marvan,
Vezelay, caves de vin de Bourgogne, grottes
d'Arcy (15km), vallée du Cousin, Avallon et
ses remparts.
Menu: 50 to 65 Frs
Restaurant: closed Sundays.

Specialities: couscous maison, paëlla.
Other points: bar, credit cards accepted, à la
carte menu, garden terrace, pets allowed, car
parking.
Address: Route Nationale 6.
M. HAMID ADJAOUD, tel 86.33.10.14.

DANJOUTIN, Territoire-de-Belfort 90400, Map 16   ⊗♈

LE CHALET FLEURI

Language: English
Menu: 55 Frs
Restaurant: lunch 12–2pm, dinner 7–9.30pm.
Closed Saturdays and Sundays.

Other points: bar, car parking.
Address: 2 rue de Bosmons.
M. MICHEL BEDA, tel 84.28.56.12.

DANNEMOINE, Yonne 89700, Map 15   ⊗♈⌂

A LA BONNE AUBERGE, RD 905

Places of interest: La fossedionne à Tonnerre
(5km), château de Tanlay (15km).
Menu: 50 to 65 Frs
Accommodation: 60 to 100 Frs
Restaurant: lunch 12–2pm, dinner 7.30–8.30 pm.

Hotel: 13 rooms: single 8, double 5.
Other points: bar, credit cards accepted, car
parking, traditional decor.
Address: Route Départementale 905.
MME NICOLE VERDIN, tel 86.55.54.22.

DECIZE, Nièvre 58300, Map 15 ⊗♀

LES ROUTIERS, between Mâcon and Italy

Menu: 55 Frs
Restaurant: lunch 11–3pm, dinner 6–9pm.
Closed Sundays and in August.

Other points: bar.
Address: 164 avenue de Verdun.
M. ANDRE DEMERY, tel 86.25.01.86.

DEVAY, Nièvre 58300, Map 15 ⊗♀

L'ETRIER

Language: German
Restaurant.
Other points: bar.

Address: Route Nationale.
M. JEAN-MARC BOUTET, tel 86.25.15.65.

DIJON, Côte-d'Or 21000, Map 15 ⊗♀🏠

MODERN' HOTEL

Places of interest: Dijon, la route de vins de
Bourgogne.
Languages: English, Italian
Menu: 56 Frs
Accommodation: 100 to 125 Frs
Restaurant: lunch 12–3pm, dinner 7–10pm.
Closed Sundays and 15 days in August.

Hotel: 18 rooms.
Other points: bar, credit cards accepted,
garden terrace, pets allowed, car parking.
Address: 3 rue des Ateliers, Zone d'Activités
Dijon South.
M. JEAN BLUM, tel 80.52.56.46.

DIJON, Côte-d'Or 21000, Map 15 ⊗

RELAIS DE DIJON COTE D'OR, in both directions

Languages: German, English
Restaurant.
Other points: credit cards accepted, children
welcome, à la carte menu, self-service, lounge
area, garden terrace, pets allowed, car
parking.
Address: Aire de Service de Dijon-Brognon.
Tel 80.23.30.20.

DORLISHEIM, Bas-Rhin 67120, Map 17 ⊗🏠

RESTAURANT DE LA GARE, RN 392

Menu: 70 to 90 Frs
Restaurant: lunch 12–1.30pm, dinner
7–8.30pm. Closed Saturday afternoons, Sunday
afternoons and afternoons of public holidays.
Hotel: 7 rooms: single 3, double 4. Showers.

Other points: pets allowed, car parking,
traditional decor.
Address: 4 avenue de la Gare.
M. RENE JOST, tel 88.38.14.28.

ECROUVES, Meurthe-et-Moselle 54200, Map 17 ⊗♀🏠

LE RELAIS MATHY – Les Routiers, RD 400 between Toul and Saint Mihiel

Places of interest: La cathédrale de Toul,
église d'Ecrouves, le fort de Villey le Sec
(seulement les dimanches).
Menu: 36 to 68 Frs
Accommodation: 98 Frs
Restaurant: lunch 12–2pm, dinner 7–9.30pm.

Closed Friday 3pm to Sunday 10am and 1
week between Christmas and New Year's day.
Specialities: tête de veau, coq au vin, cervelle,
ris de veau, gibier (en saison).
Hotel: 15 rooms: single 13, double 2.

Other points: bar, credit cards accepted, à la carte menu, garden terrace, pets allowed, car parking, traditional decor.

Address: 825 avenue du 15ème Génie, Toul. HOTELS MATHY, tel 83.43.04.27.

EIX-ABAUCOURT, Meuse 55400, Map 17

BAR DU COMMERCE – Chez Odile, RN 3 between Etain and Verdun

Places of interest: Le champ de bataille à Verdun, l'ossuaire de Douaumont, fort de Vaux, sites de guerre 14–18.
Language: English
Menu: 54 to 150 Frs
Restaurant: closed Sundays (out of season).
Specialities: escalope normande, moules, saumon du chef.

Other points: bar, credit cards accepted, children welcome, à la carte menu, lounge area, garden terrace, pets allowed, car parking, traditional decor.
Address: Route Nationale 3.
MME MARIE-ODILE VINCENT, tel 29.88.31.94.

ENSISHEIM, Haut-Rhin 68190, Map 17

LE PETIT SAVOYARD

Language: German
Menu: 60 Frs
Restaurant: closed Wednesdays.
Specialities: pierrade, raclette, fondues savoyardes, bourguignones et chinoises.

Other points: bar, car parking.
Address: 42 rue de la 1ère Armée.
MME MARTINE COLON, tel 89.81.70.14.

EPERNAY, Marne 51200, Map 18

LES ROUTIERS – Chez Madame Préjent, RN 3

Menu: 60 to 90 Frs
Accommodation: 100 to 160 Frs
Restaurant: closed Saturday nights and Sundays.
Hotel: 15 rooms: single 9, double 6. Showers, private WCs.

Other points: bar, children welcome, pets allowed, car parking.
Address: 13 rue Jean-Jacques Rousseau.
MME MARIE-LOUISE PREJENT, tel 26.55.23.29.

EPINAL, Vosges 88000, Map 17

LE RELAIS DE L'ABATTOIR, RN 57

Place of interest: Musée de l'imagerie.
Restaurant: dinner 7–12pm. Closed Sundays and mid-July to mid-August.

Other points: bar, credit cards accepted.
Address: 63 rue de Nancy.
M. GERARD DIDIER, tel 29.82.32.13.

EPINEAU LES VOVES, Yonne 89400, Map 15

RELAIS DES SIX BOULES, RN 6

Languages: Arabic, German
Restaurant.
Other points: bar.

Address: 2 route de Chambery.
M. AHMED BETROUNE, tel 86.91.20.45.

ETAIS LA SAUVIN, Yonne 89480, Map 15

CAFE DE LA PLACE, CD 104 towards the grain silos

Places of interest: Château de Druyes, belles fontaines, étangs de Saint Forgeau, musée de Clamecy.
Menu: 55 to 60 Frs
Restaurant: lunch 11–2pm, dinner 5–7pm. Closed Tuesdays and September.

Speciality: boeuf bourguignon.
Other points: bar, garden terrace, pets allowed, car parking, traditional decor.
Address: rue de la Gare.
M. GÉRARD DUPUIS, tel 86.47.21.46.

ETOGES, Marne 51270, Map 18   ⊗ 🍷

LE CAVEAU DE L'ANCIENNE FORGE

Restaurant: closed Wednesdays.
Other points: bar.

Address: Grande Rue.
HOTELS LA FORGE, tel 26.59.32.79.

FINS (LES), Doubs 25500, Map 16   ⊗ 🍷 🏠

HOTEL DU COMMERCE, between Morteau and Besançon

Places of interest: Saut du Doubs, nombreuses grottes, barrage de Chatelot, gouffre de Poudrey.
Language: German
Menu: 57 to 135 Frs
Accommodation: 95 to 160 Frs
Restaurant: lunch 11.30–3pm, dinner 7.30–9.30pm.

Specialities: gibier, entrecôte forestière, croûtes aux morilles, truites.
Hotel: 12 rooms, showers, baths, private WCs.
Other points: bar, children welcome, à la carte menu, garden terrace, pets allowed, car parking, traditional decor.
Address: 2 route de Besançon.
M. ALBAN LEGRAND, tel 81.67.12.29.

FONTVANNES, Aube 10190, Map 18   ⊗ 🍷 🏠

AUBERGE DE LA VANNE, RN 60 between Troyes and Sens

Places of interest: Les lacs de la forêt d'Orient et Troyes (15km).
Language: English
Menu: 55 Frs
Accommodation: 80 Frs
Restaurant: lunch 11.30–1.30pm. Closed Sundays.

Hotel: 8 rooms, showers, private WCs.
Other points: bar, à la carte menu, lounge area, pets allowed, car parking.
Address: 1 rue Léandre Denis.
M. MICHEL DUBRULLE, tel 25.70.37.60.

FRASNE, Doubs 25560, Map 16   ⊗ 🍷

L'ARC EN CIEL, RD 471 between Champagnole and Pontarlier

Places of interest: Château de Joux (17km), gouffre de Poudrey, lac de Saint Point, Salins les Bains.
Languages: German, English, Italian
Menu: 55 Frs
Restaurant: lunch 12–2pm. Closed Tuesday

afternoons.
Other points: bar, children welcome, à la carte menu, pets allowed, car parking.
Address: 98 Grand' Rue.
M. CLAUDE GUYON, tel 81.49.83.68.

FROUARD, Meurthe-et-Moselle 54390, Map 17   ⊗ 🍷 🏠

LA CHARENTAISE, on the old road to Metz

Menu: 50 Frs including a drink
Accommodation: 70 to 110 Frs
Restaurant: lunch 11.30–3pm. Closed Sundays.
Speciality: couscous sometimes.
Hotel: 8 rooms: single 4, double 4. Showers, private WCs.

Other points: bar, garden terrace, pets allowed, car parking.
Address: 29 rue de l'Embanie.
MME PIERRETTE MATIGNON, tel 83.24.36.08.

FROUARD, Meurthe-et-Moselle 54390, Map 17 ⊗ 𝟌

LA GRANDE CHOPE, RN 57

Places of interest: Metz, la vallée de la Moselle, Nancy (place Stanislas).
Language: Hungarian
Menu: 43 Frs
Restaurant: lunch 11.30–2pm. Closed Saturdays, Sundays and in August.

Other points: bar, pets allowed, car parking.
Address: 4 rue de la Gare.
MME CHRISTIANE PALLAGI, tel 93.49.05.64.

FROUARD, Meurthe-et-Moselle 54390, Map 17 ⊗ 𝟌

LE RELAIS ROUTIERS – Chez Viviane, RN 57

Language: German
Menu: 49,50 Frs
Restaurant: lunch 12–2pm, dinner 7–9pm. Closed Monday afternoons.

Other points: bar, car parking.
Address: 1 rue de la Salle.
MME VIVIANE POIROT, tel 83.49.03.52.

FUMAY, Ardennes 08170, Map 18 ⊗𝟌⌂☆

HOTEL LION, RN 51 near the station

Place of interest: Musée de l'ardoise.
Menu: 54 to 100 Frs
Accommodation: 55 to 120 Frs
Restaurant: lunch 12–2pm, dinner 6–9pm. Closed Sundays and in September.
Specialities: couscous, cassoulet.

Hotel: 7 rooms: single 3, double 4. Showers, baths, private WCs.
Other points: bar, à la carte menu, pets allowed.
Address: 41 rue de la Céramique.
MME EDITH POTIER, tel 24.41.10.27.

GERMIGNY SUR YONNE, Yonne 89600, Map 15 ⊗𝟌⌂

LE RELAIS DES ROUTIERS, RN 5

Restaurant: closed Sundays.
Hotel: 9 rooms.
Other points: bar.

Address: route de Genève.
M. CORNU, tel 86.35.06.39.

GOLBEY, Vosges 88190, Map 17 ⊗𝟌

RELAIS DU PETIT CERF, RN 166 and 460

Place of interest: Musée de l'imagerie à Epinal (2km).
Menu: 58 Frs including wine and coffee
Restaurant: lunch 11.30–2.30pm, dinner 6–8pm. Closed Sundays, public holidays and in

August.
Other points: bar, credit cards accepted, pets allowed, car parking.
Address: 63 rue du Général Leclerc.
M. CHRISTIAN KUNTZ, tel 29.34.23.25.

GUERIGNY, Nièvre 58130, Map 15 ⊗♍⌂

HOTEL DU COMMERCE, CD 977 between Nevers and Auxerre

Places of interest: Musée du vieux Guérigny, musée du Septennat à Château Chinon (60km).
Language: German
Menu: 52 to 70 Frs
Accommodation: 100 to 190 Frs
Restaurant: lunch 11.30-2pm, dinner 7-8.30pm. Closed Saturday afternoons and Sundays (out of season), and 20 December to 5 January.

Hotel: 8 rooms: single 4, double 4. Showers.
Other points: bar, credit cards accepted, children welcome, garden terrace, pets allowed, car parking, traditional decor.
Address: 2 Grande Rue.
M. GERARD PAGE, tel 86.37.32.77.

GUMBRECHTSHOFFEN, Bas-Rhin 67110, Map 17 ⊗♍

AU SOLEIL, RN 62 and RD 242 between Niederbronn and Haguenau

Places of interest: Les Vosges du Nord, châteaux, musées, distilleries, poteries.
Language: German
Menu: 32 to 100 Frs
Accommodation: 130 Frs
Restaurant: dinner 7–10pm. Closed Sunday afternoons and in August.
Specialities: gibiers, choucroutes alsaciennes,

couscous, pigeonneaux.
Hotel: 3 double rooms. Baths.
Other points: bar, à la carte menu, phone, lounge area, pets allowed, car parking, traditional decor.
Address: 30 rue Principale.
MME LILIANE PEIFER, tel 88.72.90.77.

GUMERY, Aube 10400, Map 18 ⊗♍⌂

AU RELAIS, RD 439 between Nogent sur Seine and Sens

Places of interest: Château de la Motte Tilly (2km), musée à Nogent sur Seine (8km), Provins et ses remparts (20km).
Language: English
Menu: 52 Frs
Accommodation: 80 to 120 Frs
Restaurant: lunch 11.30–2pm, dinner 7–9pm. Closed Sundays and 3 weeks in August.

Hotel: 5 rooms: single 3, double 2. Showers, baths.
Other points: bar, children welcome, garden terrace, pets allowed, car parking, traditional decor.
Address: 3 route de Sens.
MME EVELYNE VISSE, tel 25.39.16.01.

HABSHEIM, Haut-Rhin 68440, Map 17 ⊗♍

A LA VILLE DE MULHOUSE, RN 66

Languages: German, English
Restaurant.
Other points: bar.

Address: 76 rue du Général de Gaulle.
MME GABRIELLE LEHMANN,
tel 89.44.31.33.

HAGONDANGE, Moselle 57300, Map 17 ⊗♍⌂

LES ROUTIERS, RN 53

Places of interest: Metz, Annéville les Thermes, parc Bing-Bang Strouchps.
Menu: 54 Frs including wine
Accommodation: 115 to 165 Frs

Restaurant: lunch 12–2pm. Closed Saturday afternoons, Sunday afternoons and in August.
Hotel: 9 rooms: single 4, double 5. Showers, private WCs.

Other points: bar, credit cards accepted, traditional decor.

Address: 36 rue de Metz.
MME MARTINE BOGNOLO, tel 87.71.46.63.

HUTTENHEIM, Bas-Rhin 67230, Map 17

AU JARDIN DES ROSES, RN 83

Language: German
Restaurant: closed Saturdays and mid-August.
Other points: bar.

Address: Route Nationale 83, near Benfeld.
M. MAURICE SCHNEIDER, tel 88.74.41.44.

HYEVRE PAROISSE, Doubs 25110, Map 16

RELAIS LA CREMAILLERE, RN 83 exit A 36 between Baumes-les-Dames (10km) and Isle sur le Doubs

Places of interest: Clerval (15km), Montagne au pied du Jura, grotte de la Glacière, Saut du Doubs, Besançon citadelle.
Languages: German, English
Menu: 60 to 180 Frs
Accommodation: 230 to 260 Frs
Restaurant: closed Saturdays and in October.
Specialities: coq au vin, canard à l'orange,

fritures, carpes.
Hotel: 21 rooms, showers, baths, private WCs, TV, phone.
Other points: bar, credit cards accepted, children welcome, à la carte menu, garden terrace, pets allowed, car parking.
Address: at Baume-les-Dames.
M. ALFRED ZISS, tel 81.84.07.88.

IMLING SARREBOURG, Moselle 57400, Map 17

LE RELAIS DE LA FERME, RN 4 between Paris and Strasbourg

Language: German
Menu: 40 to 135 Frs
Restaurant: lunch 11.30–2.30pm, dinner 6.30–11pm. Closed Friday nights and 3 weeks after 10 August.

Other points: bar, children welcome, à la carte menu, pets allowed, car parking, traditional decor.
Address: route de Sarrebourg.
M. JEAN-LUC STEINER, tel 87.23.68.72.

IS SUR TILLE, Côte-d'Or 21120, Map 15

CAFE DU MIDI

Menu: 54 Frs
Restaurant: lunch 11.30–2.30pm.
Other points: bar, pets allowed, car parking.

Address: 2 place Villeneuve Motet.
M. PHILIPPE CHALOPET, tel 80.95.07.51.

JUZANVIGNY, Aube 10500, Map 18

CHEZ JACKY ET ROSE, RD 400

Restaurant: closed Saturdays, Sundays and August.
Hotel: 3 rooms.

Other points: bar.
Address: Brienne le Château.
M. JACQUES DEFLIN, tel 25.92.80.57

KOGENHEIM, Bas-Rhin 67230, Map 17

A L'ETOILE, RN 83 between Selestat and Benfeld

Places of interest: La Volerie des aigles, la montagne des singes, le parc d'attractions de Rust, l'Allemagne (15km).
Language: German
Menu: 34 to 85 Frs
Accommodation: 100 to 130 Frs
Restaurant: lunch 12–3pm, dinner 7–12pm. Closed Monday evenings and 3 weeks in January.

Specialities: couscous, cheval braisé.
Hotel: 9 rooms: single 5, double 4. Showers, baths, private WCs.
Other points: bar, credit cards accepted, à la carte menu, pets allowed, car parking, traditional decor.
Address: 36 route de Strasbourg.
M. ROBERT RAPP, tel 88.74.70.02.

LANGRES, Haute-Marne 52200, Map 18

RELAIS DE LA COLLINIERE, RN 19

Place of interest: Ville romaine.
Language: Portuguese
Menu: 55 Frs
Accommodation: 85 to 150 Frs
Restaurant: lunch 12–2pm, dinner 7–10pm. Closed Sundays and end December.
Speciality: couscous.

Hotel: 8 rooms: single 5, double 3. Showers, private WCs.
Other points: bar, garden terrace, pets allowed, car parking, traditional decor.
Address: faubourg de la Collinière.
MME ELISABETH GUERRA, tel 25.87.03.27.

LANGRES, Haute-Marne 52200, Map 18

LA BONNE AUBERGE, RN 74 between Chaumont and Dijon

Menu: 60 to 85 Frs
Restaurant: lunch 12–2pm, dinner 7–9.30pm. Closed Sundays and 2 weeks for Christmas and New Year's day.
Hotel: 6 rooms.

Other points: bar, à la carte menu.
Address: faubourg de la Collinière.
SNC BAUMANN AND OLIVIER,
tel 25.87.09.18.

LAVANS LES DOLE, Jura 39700, Map 16

LE PANORAMIC, RN 73 between Dôle and Besançon

Places of interest: Salines, Arc, Senan, Dôle, vallée du Doubs, forêt de Chaux.
Languages: German, Italian
Menu: 54 to 80 Frs
Accommodation: 120 to 150 Frs
Restaurant: lunch 11–2.30pm, dinner 7–10pm. Closed Sundays.

Specialities: Italian and Jurassienne.
Hotel: 9 rooms: single 2, double 7. Showers.
Other points: bar, credit cards accepted, children welcome, garden terrace, pets allowed, car parking.
Address: Route Nationale 73.
M. JEAN-LUC CONFAIS, tel 84.81.21.41.

LESMENILS, Meurthe-et-Moselle 54700, Map 17

LE ZENIUM

Places of interest: Nancy, Metz, abbaye des Remontrés, Pont à Mousson.
Languages: German, English, Italian
Menu: 45 to 170 Frs
Restaurant: lunch 12–2pm, dinner 7–10pm. Closed Saturday lunch.

Other points: bar, credit cards accepted, car parking.
Address: Tête de Saint Euchamps.
M. BERNARD STABILE – SACLOM,
tel 83.82.81.38.

LESMONT, Aube 10500, Map 18

⊗♀

LE RELAIS DES LACS, RN 60

Place of interest: Lacs de la forêt d'Orient.
Menu: 53 Frs to 110 Frs including coffee
Restaurant: lunch 11.30–2pm, dinner 7–10pm.
Closed Saturdays and for Christmas and New
Year.
Other points: bar, credit cards accepted,

children welcome, à la carte menu, garden
terrace, pets allowed, car parking, traditional
decor.
Address: Route Nationale 60.
M. JEAN-CLAUDE DENIZOT,
tel 25.92.45.35

LIGNY EN BARROIS, Meuse 55500, Map 17

⊗♀

RELAIS EUROP

Language: English
Menu: 50 Frs
Restaurant: closed Saturdays and Sundays
(except reservations).

Other points: bar, car parking.
Address: rue des Etats Unis.
M. HERVE LESEUR, tel 29.78.00.83.

LOISY PONT A MOUSSON, Meurthe-et-Moselle 54700, Map 17

⊗♀

RESTAURANT DU RELAIS DE L'OBRION, A 31

Places of interest: Luxembourg, Metz, Nancy.
Languages: German, English
Menu: 53 Frs
Restaurant.
Other points: bar, children welcome, self-

service, garden terrace, car parking.
Address: Aire de Service de l'Obrion.
MME JACQUELINE FRERES,
tel 83.81.18.89.

LONGEAU, Haute-Marne 52250, Map 18

⊗♀⌂

AUBERGE ROUTIERE – Chez Patricia, RN 74 autoroute A 31, exit Langres South

Places of interest: Langres (10km), fouilles
gallo-romaines d'Andilly (30km), nombreux
lacs.
Menu: 45 to 90 Frs
Accommodation: 75 to 130 Frs
Restaurant: closed Sunday nights (out of
season).

Speciality: cuisses de grenouilles.
Hotel: 9 rooms: single 4, double 5.
Other points: bar, credit cards accepted,
children welcome, à la carte menu, pets
allowed, traditional decor.
Address: Route Nationale 74.
MME PATRICIA GODART, tel 25.88.42.16.

LONGEAU, Haute-Marne 52250, Map 18

⊗♀⌂

CAFE DES ROUTIERS, RN 74 between Langres and Dijon (10km south of Langres)

Places of interest: Les fortifications de la ville
de Langres, lac de Villegusien, fouilles
d'Andilly, grottes de Sabinus.
Menu: 30 to 95 Frs
Accommodation: 75 to 95 Frs
Restaurant: lunch 12–2pm, dinner 7–10pm.
Closed Friday afternoons.

Speciality: terrine maison.
Hotel: 7 rooms: single 4, double 3.
Other points: bar, credit cards accepted,
children welcome, à la carte menu, pets
allowed, car parking, traditional decor.
Address: Route Nationale.
MME EDWIGE DENIS, tel 25.88.40.51.

LUSIGNY SUR BARSE, Aube 10270, Map 18 ⊗🍷🏠

AUBERGE DES PRAIRIES, RN 19

Places of interest: Lac de la forêt d'Orient, les 9 églises de Troyes.
Menu: 55 Frs
Accommodation: 80 Frs
Restaurant.
Hotel: 4 rooms: single 1, double 3. Showers, private WCs.
Other points: bar, credit cards accepted, à la carte menu, pets allowed, car parking.
Address: Route Nationale 19.
MME MONIQUE MIREUX, tel 25.41.20.32.

MAILLY LE CAMP, Aube 10230, Map 18 ⊗🍷🏠

RESTAURANT DU CENTRE, RN 77

Place of interest: Mailly centre.
Menu: 55 to 91 Frs
Accommodation: 80 to 170 Frs
Restaurant: lunch 11.30–2.30pm, dinner 5–10pm. Closed Friday afternoons and Saturday afternoons.
Speciality: andouillettes de Troyes.
Hotel: 15 rooms: single 13, double 2.
Other points: bar, credit cards accepted, garden terrace, pets allowed, car parking, traditional decor.
Address: 64 rue du Général de Gaulle.
SNC BARDIVAT-MANTZ, tel 25.37.30.08.

MAISON NEUVE – RIOZ, Haute-Saône 70190, Map 16 ⊗🍷🏠

LES ROUTIERS, RN 57 between Vesoul and Besançon

Menu: 50 to 60 Frs
Accommodation: 80 to 180 Frs
Restaurant: lunch 11.30–3pm, dinner 7–10pm. Closed Saturdays, Sundays, 3 weeks in August and 2 for Christmas.
Hotel: 8 rooms: single 5, double 3.
Other points: bar, credit cards accepted, children welcome, lounge area, garden terrace, pets allowed, car parking, traditional decor.
Address: Quenoche.
MME CHANTAL CARTIER, tel 84.91.80.54.

MAIZIERES LA GRANDE PAROISSE, Aube 10510, Map 18 ⊗🍷

LE RELAIS DE POUSSEY, RN 19

Language: English
Restaurant: closed Sundays.
Other points: bar.
Address: Industrial Zone: La Glacière.
MME SYLVAINE GAILLARD, tel 25.24.27.96.

MARBACHE, Meurthe-et-Moselle 54820, Map 17 ⊗🍷

LA MARMITE, RN 57 between Nancy and Metz

Languages: English, Spanish
Menu: 48 Frs
Restaurant: lunch 11.30–2.30pm, dinner 7–8.30pm. Closed Sundays.
Specialities: couscous, choucroute.
Other points: bar, credit cards accepted, children welcome, garden terrace, pets allowed, car parking, traditional decor.
Address: 136 rue Jean Jaurès.
M. JEAN-MICHEL REPIQUET, tel 83.24.90.04.

MESGRIGNY, Aube 10170, Map 18 ⊗🍷

LA BELLE ETOILE, RN 19 between Paris and Soisons

Place of interest: Troyes.
Language: English
Menu: 57 Frs including wine and coffee
Restaurant: closed Sundays.
Other points: bar, credit cards accepted, children welcome, lounge area, garden terrace, pets allowed, car parking, traditional decor.
Address: La Belle Etoile.
MME SYLVIE SCHMUTZ, tel 25.21.15.70.

MESSIA SUR SORNE, Jura 39570, Map 16 ⊗ 🍷

LA CHARMILLE, RN 83 exit Lons-le-Saunier towards Lyon

Places of interest: Les grottes de Baume, les cascades du Hérisson, le pont de la Pyle.
Language: English
Menu: 50 Frs
Restaurant: lunch 12–2pm. Closed Sundays.
Other points: bar, garden terrace, pets allowed, car parking, traditional decor.
Address: 570 Route de Lyon.
M. PATRICK VAUCHER, tel 84.24.65.92.

MONETEAU, Yonne 89470, Map 15 ⊗ 🍷 🏠 🍽

AU RENDEZ-VOUS DES PECHEURS, RD 84 exit Auxerre Nord

Language: Spanish
Menu: 55 to 135 Frs
Restaurant: lunch 12–3pm, dinner 7.30–10pm. Closed Sundays and August.
Speciality: poissons.
Hotel: 6 rooms.
Other points: bar, credit cards accepted, children welcome, à la carte menu, garden terrace, pets allowed, car parking, traditional decor.
Address: 14 rue d'Auxerre.
M. ROGER GAUFFILET, tel 86.40.63.32.

MONTBARD, Côte-d'Or 21500, Map 15 ⊗ 🍷 🏠

LE VOLTAIRE, RN 5 between Paris and Lyon

Menu: 45 to 60 Frs
Accommodation: 50 to 65 Frs
Restaurant: lunch 12–1.30pm, dinner 8–9.30pm. Closed Saturday nights, Sundays and mid-July to mid-August.
Hotel: 10 rooms: single 4, double 6.
Other points: bar, children welcome, pets allowed.
Address: 5 rue François Debussy.
MME PIQUET, tel 80.89.42.21.

MONTBENOIT, Doubs 25650, Map 16 ⊗ 🍷 🏠 ☆ ☆

HOTEL RESTAURANT DES VOYAGEURS

Places of interest: Abbaye de Montbenoît, distillerie à Pontarlier.
Menu: 52 to 140 Frs
Accommodation: 120 to 170 Frs
Restaurant: lunch 11.30–1.30pm, dinner 6.30–9pm. Closed Tuesday evenings except vacations.
Specialities: croûte fôrestière, jambon de montagne, saucisse de morteau.
Hotel: 5 rooms, showers.
Other points: bar, credit cards accepted, à la carte menu, pets allowed, traditional decor.
Address: place de l'Abbaye.
M. PIERRE MAGNIN-FEYSOT, tel 81.38.10.85.

MOUCHARD, Jura 39330, Map 16 ⊗ 🍷 🏠

LA TONNELLE – Relais Routiers, RN 83

Menu: 60 to 110 Frs
Accommodation: 100 to 200 Frs
Restaurant: lunch 12–1.30pm, dinner
7.30–10.30pm. Closed Saturday nights,
Sundays and in August.
Hotel: 12 rooms: single 6, double 6. Showers,
baths.

Other points: bar, credit cards accepted,
children welcome, à la carte menu, lounge area,
garden terrace, pets allowed, car parking,
traditional decor.
Address: Pagnoz.
M. BERNARD MILLER, tel 84.37.81.17.

MOULINS DES MALADES, Jura 39700, Map 16   ⊗

AU RENDEZ-VOUS DE LA MARINE, RN 73

Restaurant: closed Saturdays and in August.
Address: 73 Route Nationale.

MLLE JOSETTE BULLET, tel 84.71.32.10.

MULHOUSE, Haut-Rhin 68100, Map 17   ⊗ ♀

AUBERGE LEFEBVRE

Places of interest: Mulhouse et ses musées,
écomusée d'alsace.
Menu: 55 Frs
Restaurant: lunch 11–3pm, dinner 7–11pm.
Closed Sundays.

Other points: bar, credit cards accepted,
traditional decor.
Address: 82 rue Lefèbvre.
MME MONIQUE GUERQUIN,
tel 89.46.25.25

MYENNES, Nièvre 58440, Map 15   ⊗ ♀

LE RANCH

Menu: 50 Frs
Restaurant.
Other points: bar, car parking.

Address: 68 rue de Paris.
M. ROGER DUFOUR, tel 86.28.00.98.

NANCY, Meurthe-et-Moselle 54000, Map 17   ⊗ ♀

RELAIS VICTOR, RN 4

Places of interest: La place Stanislas, la vieille
ville.
Menu: 42 Frs
Restaurant: closed Saturdays and Sundays.

Other points: bar, pets allowed, car parking.
Address: 7 rue Victor.
CHRISTIANE AND JEAN-MARIE HECHT,
tel 83.36.53.27.

NANCY, Meurthe-et-Moselle 54000, Map 17   ⊗ ♀ 🍽

RESTAURANT DU PORT, RN 4

Places of interest: La place Stanislas, jardin
botanique, aquarium, musée.
Languages: English, German
Menu: 50 Frs
Restaurant: closed Friday nights, Saturdays,
Sundays, public holidays and in August.

Specialities: coq au vin, gibiers.
Other points: bar, pets allowed, car parking,
traditional decor.
Address: 5 rue Henri Bazin.
M. CLAUDE DOPP, tel 83.35.49.85.

NEUVY SAUTOUR, Yonne 89570, Map 15   ⊗ ♀

AU BON COIN – Chez Gérard, RN 77 between Toyes and Auxerre

Place of interest: Eglise classée.
Menu: 47 Frs
Restaurant: lunch 12–2pm, dinner 7–9pm.
Closed Saturday afternoons, Sundays and in
August.

Other points: bar, pets allowed, car parking.
Address: 29 route de Troyes.
M. GERARD CHARPIGNON, tel 86.56.35.52.

NOCLE MAULAIX (LA), Nièvre 58250, Map 15 ⊗ ?

HOTEL DE LA POSTE, RD 3

Menu: 35 to 100 Frs
Restaurant: lunch 12–1.30pm. Closed
Mondays and in September.

Other points: bar, à la carte menu.
M. MARCEL SENOTIER, tel 86.30.80.32.

NOLAY, Côte-d'Or 21340, Map 15 ⊗ ? 🏠 ☆ ☆

HOTEL DU CHEVREUIL, RN 6 and A 6 between Paris and Lyon on N6 and D73 towards Autun

Places of interest: Caves et circuit des vins de
Bourgogne, falaise de Cormot, château de
Rochepot.
Languages: English, Spanish
Menu: 170 to 290 Frs
Restaurant: closed Wednesdays (out of
season) and in December.
Specialities: écrevisses au gratin, poulet de

bresse, filet de boeuf.
Hotel: 14 rooms: single 3, double 11. Showers,
baths, private WCs, TV, phone.
Other points: bar, children welcome, à la carte
menu, lounge area, garden terrace, pets
allowed, car parking.
Address: place de l'Hôtel de Ville.
MME RACHEL SUISSA, tel 80.21.71.89.

NOUZONVILLE, Ardennes 08700, Map 18 ⊗ ? 🏠

RESTAURANT DE LA PLACE, RD 1

Places of interest: Vallées de la Meuse et de la
Semoy, Belgique (10km).
Menu: 45 Frs
Accommodation: 60 to 90 Frs
Restaurant: lunch 12–1.30pm, dinner
7.30–8.30pm. Closed Sundays.

Hotel: 6 rooms: single 2, double 4. Showers,
private WCs.
Other points: bar, pets allowed, car parking,
traditional decor.
Address: 15 place Gambetta.
MME ANNIE BOQUILLON, tel 24.53.80.43.

NOVION PORCIEN, Ardennes 08270, Map 18 ⊗ ?

LE FRANCO BELGE, RN 985

Place of interest: Rocroi.
Menu: 42 Frs
Restaurant: lunch 12–2.30pm, dinner
7–9.30pm. Closed Sunday mornings.

Other points: bar, pets allowed, car parking,
traditional decor.
Address: place de la Gare.
MLLE SIMONE BONIFACE, tel 24.38.70.06.

OGEVILLER, Meurthe-et-Moselle 54450, Map 17 ⊗ ?

LE RELAIS DE LA VERDURETTE, RN 4

Place of interest: Strasbourg.
Language: German
Menu: 50 Frs
Restaurant: closed Saturdays, Sundays and in
August.

Other points: bar, car parking.
Address: 22 route de Strasbourg.
MICHEL AND LYDIE MARTIN,
tel 83.72.24.65.

OGEVILLER, Meurthe-et-Moselle 54450, Map 17 ⊗

RELAIS D'OGEVILLER

Language: German
Restaurant.

Address: 8 route de Strasbourg.
M. CHRISTIAN PERRETTE, tel 83.72.27.82.

ORNANS, Doubs 25290, Map 16 ⊗☉⌂☆🍽

HOTEL LE PROGRES, RD 67 between Besançon and Lausanne

Places of interest: Vallée de la Loue, lacs, maison nationale de la pêche à Ornans, Trépot, musée de la fromagerie, musée de la vigne et du vin, musée Courbet, musée de l'eau et de la pêche.
Menu: 70 to 250 Frs
Accommodation: 190 to 250 Frs
Restaurant: lunch 11.30–3pm, dinner 7–12pm. Closed Sundays in January and February.
Specialities: terrine, filet de perche, escargots,

champignons, truite, terrine maison, escargots maison.
Hotel: 18 double rooms. Showers, private WCs, TV, phone.
Other points: bar, credit cards accepted, children welcome, à la carte menu, lounge area, pets allowed, car parking, traditional decor.
Address: 11 rue Jacques Gervais.
M. LOUIS PERRIOT-COMTE,
tel 81.62.16.79.

PAGNY SUR MEUSE, Meuse 55190, Map 17 ⊗☉

LA FAVORITE

Languages: German, English, Italian
Menu: 50 to 54,50 Frs including coffee
Restaurant: closed Saturday afternoons and Sundays.

Other points: bar, car parking.
Address: Route Nationale 4.
M. MICHEL BEDEL, tel 29.90.60.84.

PERTHES, Haute-Marne 52100, Map 18 ⊗☉⌂

CHEZ JEAN

Place of interest: Lac du Der
Menu: 51,70 to 66 Frs
Accommodation: 62 to 94 Frs
Restaurant: closed Saturday afternoons, Sundays and in August.
Hotel: 26 rooms.

Other points: bar, children welcome, à la carte menu, pets allowed, car parking.
Address: Route Nationale 4.
MME LAURENCE KACZMAREK,
tel 25.56.40.27.

PETIT REDERCHING, Moselle 57410, Map 17 ⊗☉

AUBERGE DE LA FROHMUHL, RN 62

Places of interest: Ligne Maginot, citadelle de Bitche (10km), nombreux musées.
Languages: German, English
Menu: 59 to 138 Frs
Restaurant: closed Mondays.

Speciality: la pierrade.
Other points: bar, credit cards accepted, garden terrace, car parking, traditional decor.
Address: 33 route de Strasbourg.
M. ANTOINE BACH FILS, tel 87.96.43.52.

PETIT REDERCHING, Moselle 57410, Map 17 ⊗☉

RESTAURANT DE LA GARE, RN 62 near the station

Places of interest: Citadelle de Bitche, Ligne Maginot, vestiges romains de Bliesbruck, faïencerie de Sarreguemines, musée et fabrique de cristal de Meisenthal.
Language: German
Menu: 50 to 85 Frs
Restaurant: lunch 12–2pm, dinner 6.30–8.30pm. Closed Saturdays and 14 July to 15 August.
Specialities: estomac de porc farci, tête de veau, baeckoffe, choucroute, poissons frais.
Other points: bar, credit cards accepted, à la carte menu, garden terrace, pets allowed, car parking.
Address: 6 rue de Strasbourg.
M. BERNARD VOGEL, tel 87.09.81.09.

PLOMBIERES LES BAINS, Vosges 88370, Map 17

LE RELAIS STRASBOURGEOIS, RN 57

Place of interest: Station thermale.
Language: English
Menu: 70 Frs
Accommodation: 90 to 170 Frs
Restaurant: lunch 12–2pm, dinner 7–8.30pm. Closed Sundays (1 October to 1 April) and in November.
Specialities: terrine maison, truite à la crème, vacherin glacé.
Hotel: 13 rooms, showers, baths, private WCs, TV, phone.
Other points: bar, credit cards accepted, à la carte menu, lounge area, garden terrace, pets allowed, car parking.
Address: 3 Place Beaumarchais.
M. ALAIN ROBERT, tel 29.66.00.70.

POIX TERRON, Ardennes 08430, Map 18

LE GODILLOT, opposite the pharmacy

Places of interest: Vallée de la Meuse, lac de Bairen (15km).
Menu: 54 Frs including a drink
Accommodation: 90 Frs
Restaurant: lunch 11.30–2pm, dinner 7.30–9pm. Closed Friday afternoons, Saturdays, Sundays and 15 days between Christmas and New Year.
Specialities: couscous, lasagnes maison.
Hotel: 6 rooms: single 3, double 3. Private WCs.
Other points: bar, credit cards accepted, car parking.
Address: 26 place de la Gare.
M. JOSE MICHEL, tel 24.35.61.46.

PONT A BINSON, Marne 51700, Map 18

CAFE RESTAURANT DE LA GARE

Place of interest: Reims (vin de champagne – 3km).
Languages: German, English
Menu: 55 Frs including coffee
Accommodation: 140 (demi-pension) to 185 Frs (pension)
Restaurant.
Hotel: 4 rooms.
Other points: bar, pets allowed, car parking.
Address: 22 rue du Général Leclerc.
MME VIVIANE DERRIEN, tel 26.58.30.41.

PONT DE PANY, Côte-d'Or 21410, Map 15

BAR DE LA POSTE, RN 5

Menu: 80 to 110 Frs
Restaurant: closed 24 December to 1 January.
Hotel: 5 rooms.
Other points: bar.
M. JACQUES VEAULIN, tel 80.23.62.70.

PONT SUR YONNE, Yonne 89140, Map 15 ⊗♉⌂

CARRE D'AS

Languages: English, Italian
Restaurant.
Hotel: 7 rooms.
Other points: bar.

Address: 29 avenue du Général Leclerc.
M. DANIEL PIRONY-ROUSSEAU,
tel 86.67.03.03.

PONTARLIER, Doubs 25300, Map 16

CAFE DE LA LIBERTE ⊗♉

Places of interest: Ville de Pontarlier, château
de Joux.
Menu: 55 Frs
Restaurant: closed Sundays and 15 August to
5 September.

Other points: bar, credit cards accepted,
children welcome.
Address: 36 rue de Salins.
MMES BESAND AND PETIT,
tel 81.39.01.68.

PONTIGNY, Yonne 89230, Map 15 ⊗♉⌂

RELAIS DE PONTIGNY, RN 77 between Auxerre and Troyes

Languages: German, English, Italian
Menu: 52 to 95 Frs
Restaurant: lunch 12–2.15pm, dinner 7–10pm.
Closed Sundays and mid-December to mid-
January.
Hotel: 8 rooms.

Other points: bar, children welcome, à la carte
menu.
Address: 9 rue Paul Desjardin.
MME CAROLE LEDUCQ, tel 86.47.54.48.

POUILLY EN AUXOIS, Côte-d'Or 21490, Map 15 ⊗

RELAIS DE L'AUXOIS, A 6 between Paris and Lyon

Language: English
Restaurant.
Other points: credit cards accepted, children
welcome, à la carte menu, self-service, garden
terrace, pets allowed, car parking.

Address: Aire de Service du Chien Blanc.
Tel 80.90.74.25.

POUILLY EN AUXOIS, Côte-d'Or 21490, Map 15 ⊗

RELAIS DE L'AUXOIS, A 6 between Lyon and Paris

Language: English
Restaurant.
Other points: credit cards accepted, children
welcome, self-service, garden terrace, pets

allowed, car parking.
Address: Aire de Service des Lochères.
Tel 80.90.83.28.

PREMERY, Nièvre 58700, Map 15 ⊗♉

LE ROUTIER, RD 977 between Clamecy and Nevers

Place of interest: La Bourgogne.
Languages: German, English
Menu: 50 to 70 Frs
Restaurant: lunch 11.30–4pm, dinner 7–9pm.
Closed Sunday afternoons.
Other points: bar, credit cards accepted, children welcome, self-service, lounge area, garden terrace, pets allowed, car parking, traditional decor.
Address: 8 rue de Lurcy.
M. JEAN-JACQUES LEMARIE, tel 86.37.97.59.

PREZ SOUS LAFAUCHE, Haute-Marne 52700, Map 18 ⊗ 🍸

LES 3 VALLEES between Chaumont and Nancy

Menu: 60 to 150 Frs
Restaurant: lunch 11–2pm, dinner 7–11pm.
Closed Saturday nights, Sunday nights and in August.
Other points: bar, credit cards accepted, children welcome, à la carte menu, car parking, traditional decor.
MME ELIANE TROMMENSCHLAGER, tel 25.31.57.84

PROSNES, Marne 51400, Map 18 ⊗ 🍸

RELAIS CONSTANTINE, RD 31, A4 exit Reims towards Sainte Menehould

Places of interest: Caves et vignobles champenois, musée, cimetières des vestiges de la guerre 14–18, cathédrale de Reims, le moulin de Valmy.
Menu: 50 to 100 Frs
Restaurant: lunch 12–1.30pm, dinner 7–9pm.
Closed Saturdays, Sundays and 15 to 31 August.
Speciality: tête de veau.
Other points: bar, credit cards accepted, à la carte menu, garden terrace, pets allowed, car parking.
Address: known as Constantine, Route Nationale.
M. RENE ROSELET, tel 26.61.70.70.

RACHECOURT SUR MARNE, Haute-Marne 52170, Map 18 ⊗🍸🏠

L'AURORE, RN 67

Menu: 50 to 90 Frs
Accommodation: 70 to 200 Frs
Restaurant: dinner 7–10pm.
Hotel: 4 rooms: single 1, double 3. Showers, private WCs.
Other points: bar, credit cards accepted, à la carte menu, garden terrace, car parking.
Address: avenue de Belgique.
M. MARIUS NARAT, tel 25.04.41.58

REGUISHEIM, Haut-Rhin 68890, Map 17 ⊗🍸🏠

RESTAURANT A L'ANGE, RD 201

Place of interest: Meyenheim.
Language: German
Menu: 40 to 60 Frs
Restaurant: lunch 12–1.30pm, dinner 7–9.30pm. Closed Saturdays, Sundays and in August.
Hotel: 5 rooms.
Other points: credit cards accepted, à la carte menu, pets allowed, car parking, traditional decor.
Address: 90 Grand Rue.
M. RAYMOND BERTRAND, tel 89.61.12.66.

REIMS, Marne 51400, Map 18 ⊗

RELAIS REIMS and CHAMPAGNE, A 4 in both directions

Languages: German, English
Restaurant.
Other points: credit cards accepted, children welcome, à la carte menu, self-service, garden

terrace, pets allowed, car parking.
Address: Aire de service de Reims.
Tel 26.03.93.57.

REVIN, Ardennes 08500, Map 18

CHEZ ALEX, RN 388
Restaurant.
Hotel: 4 rooms.
Other points: bar.

Address: 6 rue Voltaire.
MME JOSEPHA MAHUT, tel 24.40.12.91.

RIVIERES DE CORPS (LA), Aube 10300, Map 18

LA QUEUE DE LA POELE, RN 60 between Troyes and Sens

Places of interest: Troyes (4km), forêt d'Orient, cathédrale et musée de Lévy, Dieuville (parc d'attractions Wigloland).
Menu: 55 to 110 Frs
Restaurant: lunch 11.30–2pm, dinner 7–10pm. Closed Sunday nights and 3 weeks in August.

Speciality: andouillette de Troyes.
Other points: bar, credit cards accepted, children welcome, garden terrace, pets allowed, car parking.
Address: rue Lafontaine.
M. GABY BARBIER, tel 25.74.47.94.

ROCROI, Ardennes 08230, Map 18

HOTEL DE LA GARE, RN 51 and 377

Place of interest: Vallée de la Meuse (15km).
Menu: 50 to 100 Frs
Accommodation: 100 to 200 Frs
Restaurant: lunch 12–2pm, dinner 7–9pm.
Hotel: 10 rooms: single 1, double 9. Showers, baths, private WCs.

Other points: bar, à la carte menu, car parking, traditional decor.
Address: 1 avenue du Général Moreau.
HOTELS MINUCCI, tel 24.54.10.32.

RONCHAMP, Haute-Saône 70250, Map 16

LE RELAIS DE LA POMME D'OR, RN 19 between Belfort and Vesoul

Places of interest: La chapelle le Corbusier, musées, plans d'eau.
Menu: 48 to 190 Frs
Accommodation: 100 to 165 Frs
Restaurant: lunch 12–2.30pm, dinner 7–10.30pm.
Hotel: 30 rooms: single 14, double 16. Showers, baths, private WCs, TV, phone.

Other points: bar, credit cards accepted, children welcome, à la carte menu, pets allowed, car parking.
Address: rue le Corbusier.
MME LUCETTE CENCI, tel 84.20.62.12.

ROUVROIS SUR MEUSE, Meuse 55300, Map 17

AUBERGE DU CHAUDRON FLEURI

Language: English
Menu: 53 to 100 Frs
Accommodation: 110 to 230 Frs

Restaurant: closed Friday afternoons (out of season) and in February.
Specialities: patés lorrains, terrine maison,

truite à la lorraine.
Hotel: 5 rooms.
Other points: bar, car parking.

Address: rue Principale.
HOTELS DU CHAUDRON FLEURI,
tel 29.90.13.43.

ROYE, Haute-Saône 70200, Map 16 ⊗

LE RELAIS DES ROUTIERS, RN 19 between Paris and Belfort

Places of interest: Ronchamp, chapelle le
Corbusier, les Vosges Saînaises.
Menu: 40 to 50 Frs
Restaurant: lunch 12–1.30pm. Closed
Sundays.

Other points: garden terrace, pets allowed, car
parking.
Address: 50 rue de la Verrerie.
MME HUGUETTE KUHN, tel 84.30.06.48.

RUPT SUR MOSELLE, Vosges 88360, Map 17 ⊗ ♀

L'ETAPE, RN 66

Place of interest: Mulhouse.
Language: German
Menu: 45 Frs
Restaurant: lunch 11–1.45pm, dinner
6–8.45pm. Closed Sunday afternoons.

Other points: bar, credit cards accepted, pets
allowed, car parking.
Address: known as Les Meix, Route Nationale
66.
MME CATHERINE SPATZ, tel 29.24.35.17.

RYE, Jura 39230, Map 16 ⊗ ♀

CHEZ LUCETTE, RD 468

Menu: 52 Frs
Restaurant: lunch 11.30–2pm. Closed
Thursday afternoons and first 2 weeks of
August.

Other points: bar.
MME LUCETTE CAMBAZARD,
tel 84.48.61.60.

SAINT AVOLD, Moselle 57740, Map 17 ⊗

RELAIS DE LORRAINE, A 4, in both directions

Languages: German, English
Restaurant.
Other points: credit cards accepted, children
welcome, à la carte menu, self-service, lounge

area, garden terrace, pets allowed, car
parking.
Address: Aire de Service de Saint-Avold.
Tel 87.92.23.89.

SAINT DENIS LES SENS, Yonne 89100, Map 15 ⊗ ♀

LES CERISIERS, RN 360, A 6 exit Sens

Places of interest: Cathédrale, musées, jardins.
Language: English
Menu: 54 Frs
Restaurant: lunch 11–2pm, dinner 7–9pm.
Closed weekends (except reservations, 30
persons min) and in August.

Other points: bar, children welcome, garden
terrace, pets allowed, car parking.
Address: 1 rue de Paris.
M. MICHEL FERRIERE, tel 86.65.28.52.

SAINT HIPPOLYTE, Doubs 25190, Map 16 ⊗♈⌂

LE GRAND CLOS, RD 437

Places of interest: Belfort, Pontarlier, Besançon, château (30km), saut du Doubs, grottes (40km).
Language: German
Menu: 45 to 80 Frs
Accommodation: 95 to 130 Frs
Restaurant: closed Saturdays.

Speciality: jambon de montagne.
Hotel: 6 rooms: single 4, double 2. Showers, private WCs.
Other points: bar, credit cards accepted, à la carte menu, garden terrace, pets allowed, car parking, traditional decor.
MME MARTINE LEPEME, tel 81.96.51.12.

SAINT LOUP SUR SEMOUSE, Haute-Saône 70800, Map 16 ⊗♈⌂

HOTEL DE LA TERRASSE, RD 64

Restaurant: closed Sundays and 1 to 15 August.
Hotel: 4 rooms.

Other points: bar.
Address: rue de la Gare.
M. JEAN BALLOT, tel 84.49.02.20.

SAINT MARC SUR SEINE, Côte-d'Or 21450, Map 15 ⊗♈⌂

HOTEL DU SOLEIL D'OR, RN 71

Language: English
Restaurant: closed Saturdays and 22 December to 2 January.

Hotel: 7 rooms.
Other points: bar.
MME GENEVIEVE GIRARD, tel 80.93.21.42.

SAINT MIHIEL, Meuse 55300, Map 17 ⊗♈⌂

LES ROUTIERS, RD 964, on the road to Verdun

Places of interest: Verdun, les côtes de la Meuse.
Language: English
Menu: 49 Frs
Restaurant: lunch 12–3pm, dinner 7–9pm. Closed Saturdays, Sundays and in August.

Speciality: couscous.
Hotel: 8 rooms: single 4, double 4. Showers.
Other points: bar, credit cards accepted, children welcome, garden terrace, pets allowed.
Address: 19 rue de Verdun.
M. CLAUDE ROUSSELOT, tel 29.89.00.44.

SAINT PHAL, Aube 10130, Map 18 ⊗♈

RESTAURANT DU COMMERCE, RN 77 between Auxerre and Troyes

Places of interest: La forêt d'Othe, le lac de la forêt d'Orient, Troyes (20km).
Language: German
Menu: 52 to 135 Frs
Restaurant: lunch 11–1.30pm, dinner 7–8.45pm. Closed Monday afternoons and August.

Specialities: ris de veau, terrines maison.
Other points: bar, credit cards accepted, children welcome, pets allowed, car parking, traditional decor.
M. DANIEL GODEFROY, tel 25.42.16.39.

SAINT PIERRE LE MOUTIER, Nièvre 58240, Map 15 ⊗♈

RELAIS SAINT IMBERT, RN 7 between Moulins and Clermont

Places of interest: Arborétom de Boleine, châteaux.
Language: German

Menu: 55 to 70 Frs
Restaurant: lunch 12–2.30pm, dinner 7–10.30pm. Closed Saturday afternoons,

Sundays, 15 days in June and 15 in December.
Specialities: boeuf stroganoff, poissons, choucroute, potée.
Other points: bar, credit cards accepted, children welcome, à la carte menu, pets allowed, car parking, traditional decor.
Address: Route Nationale 7, Saint Imbert.
MLLE PIA FRESSLE, tel 86.38.61.65.

SAINT PIERREMONT, Vosges 88700, Map 17

LE RELAIS VOSGIEN, RD 414 between Luneville and Baccarat

Places of interest: Lunéville, cristallerie Baccarat, sources et étangs.
Language: German
Menu: 60 to 200 Frs
Accommodation: 170 to 330 Frs
Restaurant: lunch 12–2pm, dinner 7–9pm. Closed Monday evenings.
Hotel: 14 double rooms. Showers, baths, private WCs, TV, phone.
Other points: bar, credit cards accepted, children welcome, à la carte menu, lounge area, garden terrace, pets allowed, car parking, traditional decor.
Address: Rambervilliers.
MME CHRISTIANE PRÉVOST, tel 29.65.02.46.

SAINT SAUVEUR, Haute-Saône 70300, Map 16

CHEZ MAXIM, RN 57 between Nancy and Besançon

Places of interest: Luxeuil (basilique, maison du cardinal, tour de Bailly, conservatoire de la dentelle, distilleries de kirsch à Fougerolles).
Languages: German, English
Menu: 46,50 Frs to 86 Frs
Accommodation: 74 to 110 Frs
Restaurant: lunch 12–2.30pm, dinner 7.30–10.30pm. Closed Sunday nights and in February.
Specialities: jambon de Luxeuil, kirsch de Fougerolles.
Hotel: 8 rooms: single 6, double 2. Showers, baths, private WCs.
Other points: bar, credit cards accepted, children welcome, garden terrace, pets allowed, car parking, traditional decor.
Address: 10 avenue Georges Clémenceau.
MME COLETTE LACK, tel 84.40.02.91.

SAINTE MARGUERITE, Vosges 88100, Map 17

LE RELAIS DES AMIS, RN 59 to tunnel of Sainte Marie Mines

Places of interest: Région d'Alsace (à 20 minutes).
Menu: 80 to 140 Frs
Restaurant: lunch 12–2pm, dinner 7–9pm. Closed Sundays (in winter).
Hotel: 16 rooms: single 10, double 6. Showers.
Other points: bar, garden terrace, pets allowed, car parking.
Address: 486 rue d'Alsace.
M. FRANCOIS BERNAT, tel 29.56.17.23.

SALINS LES BAINS, Jura 39110, Map 16

RESTAURANT DES SPORTS

Restaurant: closed Wednesday afternoons and in September.
Other points: bar.
Address: 107 avenue de la République.
MME DENISE REVERCHON, tel 84.73.11.18.

SARREGUEMINES, Moselle 57200, Map 17

LES ROUTIERS, RN 74 in town centre

Place of interest: Musée de faïencerie.
Language: German
Menu: 30 to 50 Frs
Accommodation: 50 to 120 Frs
Restaurant: lunch 12–3pm, dinner 7–12pm.
Closed Sundays and in July or August.

Speciality: choucroute garnie.
Hotel: 11 rooms: single 1, double 10. Showers, baths.
Other points: children welcome, car parking.
Address: 19 rue du Bac.
M. CAMILLE FASEL, tel 87.98.15.39.

SAULIEU, Côte-d'Or 21210, Map 15 ⊗ ♀ ⌂

AUX POIDS LOURDS, RN 6

Place of interest: Lac de Settons (25km).
Menu: 51 Frs
Accommodation: 65 to 90 Frs
Restaurant: lunch 12–2pm. Closed Saturday afternoons, Sundays and in August.

Hotel: 7 rooms: single 5, double 3.
Other points: bar, credit cards accepted, pets allowed, car parking, traditional decor.
Address: 12 rue Courtépée.
MME MICHELE GODET, tel 81.64.19.83.

SENAN, Yonne 89710, Map 15 ⊗ ♀

HOTEL DE LA CROIX BLANCHE, RD 955

Restaurant: closed Sunday afternoons.
Other points: bar.
Address: 16 rue d'Aillant.

M. JEAN-CLAUDE LECOURT,
tel 86.63.41.31.

SOMMESSOUS, Marne 51320, Map 18 ⊗ ♀

LE MIRABELLIER

Languages: German, English
Menu: 53 Frs
Restaurant.

Other points: bar, self-service, car parking.
Address: Aire de Service de Sommessous.
HOTELS SG2R, tel 26.70.17.04.

SOUGY SUR LOIRE, Nièvre 58300, Map 15 ⊗ ♀

LE SNACK, RN 81 between Décize (7km) and Nevers (27km)

Places of interest: Décize, Nevers.
Language: English
Menu: 55 (including wine and coffee) to 80 Frs
Restaurant: closed Sunday afternoons.
Other points: bar, credit cards accepted,

children welcome, à la carte menu, garden terrace, pets allowed, car parking, traditional decor.
Address: Route Nationale 81, La Mouille.
M. DANIEL CHEVALIER, tel 86.50.13.88.

SOULAINES DHUYS, Aube 10200, Map 18 ⊗ ♀

LE RELAIS DES ROUTIERS, RD 960 between Troyes and Nancy

Places of interest: Lac du Der (15km), port nautique de Dienville (20km).
Menu: 45 to 70 Frs
Restaurant: lunch 12–2.30pm, dinner 7–11pm. Closed Sundays.

Other points: bar, credit cards accepted, car parking.
Address: Route Départementale 960.
MME YVETTE DEMONGEOT,
tel 25.92.76.10.

SPINCOURT, Meuse 55230, Map 17 ⊗ ♀ ⌂

HOTEL RESTAURANT DE LA GARE

Place of interest: Verdun (25km).
Languages: German, English, Spanish, Italian
Menu: 60 Frs
Accommodation: 170 Frs
Restaurant: closed Tuesdays.

Speciality: Italian.
Hotel: 4 rooms, showers.
Other points: bar, pets allowed, car parking,
traditional decor.
M. BRUNO CAMPOLMI, tel 29.85.96.93.

STENAY, Meuse 55700, Map 17   ⊗ ♑ 🏠

BAR DES SANGLIERS – La Mangeoire, RD 947 near Reims

Place of interest: Musée de la Bière.
Language: German
Menu: 58 to 150 Frs
Accommodation: 120 to 150 Frs
Restaurant: lunch 11.30–2pm, dinner
7.30–9pm. Closed Saturdays and in August.

Hotel: 4 rooms: single 1, double 3. Showers,
baths, private WCs.
Other points: bar, credit cards accepted, à la
carte menu, pets allowed, car parking.
Address: 1 rue Carnot.
M. DANIEL DEMACON, tel 29.80.60.06.

STRASBOURG, Bas-Rhin 67000, Map 17   ⊗ ♑ 🏠

AU RHIN FRANCAIS, RN 4 near the border, opposite the frontier bridge.

Place of interest: Cathédrale de Strasbourg.
Menu: 60 Frs
Accommodation: 140 Frs
Restaurant: closed Saturdays and Sundays.
Specialities: baeckoffe, couscous, boullabaisse.
Hotel: 10 rooms, showers, baths, private WCs.

Other points: bar, credit cards accepted,
children welcome, à la carte menu, lounge area,
car parking, traditional decor.
Address: 83 route du Rhin.
M. MARCEL WENDLING, tel 88.61.29.00.

STRASBOURG MEINAU, Bas-Rhin 67100, Map 17   ⊗

BRASSERIE DES BATELIERS, RN 4

Places of interest: Pont couvert, Petite France.
Languages: German, Spanish
Menu: 40 to 120 Frs
Restaurant: lunch 11.30–2.30pm, dinner
7–10pm. Closed Saturdays after 3pm, Sundays
and 3 weeks between July and October.
Other points: credit cards accepted, à la carte

menu, garden terrace, pets allowed, car parking,
traditional decor.
Address: 33 rue de la Plaine de Bouchers, ZI
Meinau.
M. JEAN-CLAUDE PICCINELLI,
tel 88.39.19.50.

SUIPPES, Marne 51600, Map 18   ⊗ ♑

AU BON COIN, RN 77 and 31 between Sedan and Chalons sur Marne

Language: Italian
Menu: 59 to 90 Frs
Restaurant: dinner 7–9pm.
Speciality: Italian.
Other points: bar, credit cards accepted,

garden terrace, pets allowed, car parking,
traditional decor.
Address: 25 rue de la Libération.
SDF TILOCA, tel 26.70.05.84.

TALMAY, Côte-d'Or 21270, Map 15   ⊗ ♑

CAFE DE LA PLACE

Restaurant: closed August.
Other points: bar.

MME MONIQUE TRUDIN, tel 80.36.13.24.

THAON LES VOSGES, Vosges 88150, Map 17   ⊗♍🏠

RELAIS ROUTIERS 60 10, RN 57

Places of interest: Epinal, musée de l'imagerie
à Epinal (9km).
Menu: 50 to 70 Frs
Accommodation: 110 Frs
Restaurant: lunch 11.45–1.30pm, dinner
7–8.30pm. Closed Saturday lunch and Sundays.

Speciality: tête de veau.
Hotel: 4 rooms, showers, private WCs, TV.
Other points: bar, credit cards accepted,
children welcome, pets allowed, car parking.
Address: 200 rue de Lorraine.
M. ROBERT GEHIN, tel 29.39.21.67.

TOUR DU MEIX (LA), Jura 39270, Map 16   ⊗♍🥘

AUBERGE DU PONT DE LA PYLE, RD 470 between Lons le Saunier and St Claude via Orgelet

Places of interest: Lac de Vouglano (800m),
cascades du Hérisson (12km), grottes
d'Osselles et de Moidon, barrage de Vouglans.
Languages: English, German
Menu: 55 to 150 Frs
Restaurant: lunch 12–3pm, dinner 7–10pm.
Closed Wednesdays and in October.
Specialities: filets de perches au beurre, cuisses

de grenouilles.
Other points: bar, credit cards accepted,
children welcome, à la carte menu, garden
terrace, pets allowed, car parking, traditional
decor.
Address: Route Nationale 470.
M. JACQUES BERGER, tel 84.25.41.92.

TREMBLOIS LES ROCROI, Ardennes 08150, Map 18   ⊗♍

RELAIS ROUTIERS DU PIQUET, RN 43

Places of interest: Vallée de la Meuse, lac des
Vieilles Forges, Rocroi.
Languages: Spanish, Portuguese
Menu: 52 Frs
Restaurant: lunch 11.30–2.30pm, dinner
7–9pm. Closed Saturdays and Sundays, and

1 week between Christmas and New Year's
day.
Other points: bar, credit cards accepted, car
parking.
Address: Le Piquet.
M. GERARD CLERICE, tel 24.35.13.86.

TRESNAY, Nièvre 58240, Map 15   ⊗♍

LA SCIERIE, RN 7 between St Pierre le Moutier and Moulins

Language: English
Menu: 54 Frs
Restaurant: lunch 12–2.30pm, dinner
7.30–11.30pm. Closed Saturdays, Sundays and
in August.

Other points: bar, credit cards accepted, à la
carte menu, self-service, lounge area, car
parking.
Address: Route Nationale 7.
M. MARTIAL PETTINGER, tel 86.38.62.14.

TRONSANGES, Nièvre 58400, Map 15   ⊗♍

L'AUBERGE DU SOLEIL LEVANT, RN 7

Menu: 46 to 65 Frs
Restaurant: lunch 12–2pm. Closed Sundays
and in September.
Other points: bar, children welcome, pets

allowed.
Address: Route Nationale 7, Barbeloup.
MME RENEE REICHHARD, tel 86.37.84.02.

TRONSANGES, Nièvre 58400, Map 15

DE LA CROIX DU PAPE, RN 7

Restaurant.
Other points: bar, car parking.

Address: Barbeloup.
MME AGNES DUMAINE, tel 86.37.84.03.

UCKANGE, Moselle 57270, Map 17

LE PRESSOIR, RD 952

Restaurant: closed Saturdays, Sundays, August and 15 days at Christmas.
Other points: bar.

Address: 22 rue Jeanne d'Arc.
M. SILVIO PICCIN, tel 82.58.20.38.

UNIENVILLE, Aube 10140, Map 18

CHEZ CHRISTIANE ET MARCEL, RD 46

Menu: 50 Frs including a drink and coffee
Restaurant: lunch 11.30–1.30pm, dinner 7–8pm.

Other points: bar, pets allowed, car parking.
MME CHRISTIANE SAGET, tel 25.92.70.80.

VELAINE EN HAYE, Meurthe-et-Moselle 54840, Map 17

RESTAURANT DU PARC

Places of interest: Cathédrale de Toul.
Menu: 60 to 80 Frs
Restaurant: lunch 11.30–2pm. Closed Saturdays and Sundays.
Other points: bar, credit cards accepted, à la carte menu, self-service, pets allowed, car parking.
Address: 6 allée des Erables.
M. PATRICK HEBACKER, tel 83.23.28.48.

VENDENHEIM, Bas-Rhin 67550, Map 17

LE RELAIS DE LA MAISON ROUGE, RN 63

Places of interest: Maison alsacienne, cathédrale de Strasbourg.
Language: German
Menu: 55 to 125 Frs
Restaurant: closed Tuesday afternoons, Wednesdays and 1 week in February.
Specialities: foie gras, tripes, épaule de marcassin spaëtzle, ragoût de chevreuil, rognons de veau, coquelet au riesling, choucroute.
Other points: credit cards accepted, children welcome, à la carte menu, garden terrace, pets allowed, traditional decor.
Address: 2 route de Brumath.
MME GERMAINE MICHIELINI-CHAST, tel 88.69.51.79.

VENOY, Yonne 89290, Map 15

L'ARCHE DE VENOY 1, A 6

Places of interest: Auxerre (11km), vignobles de Chablis (15km), Vezelay (40km).
Language: English
Menu: 55 to 80 Frs
Accommodation: 255 to 295 Frs
Restaurant: lunch 10–6pm, dinner 6–9 pm.
Hotel: 74 rooms: single 52, double 22.
Showers, baths, private WCs, TV, phone.
Other points: credit cards accepted, children welcome, self-service, garden terrace, pets allowed, car parking.
Address: Aire de Grosse Pierre.
Tel 86.40.31.71.

VENOY, Yonne 89290, Map 15 ⊗ ♈ 🏠 ☆ ☆

L'ARCHE DE VENOY 2, A 6

Places of interest: Cathédrale d'Auxerre (11km), Vezelay (40km), vignobles de Chablis (15km).
Language: English
Menu: 57 Frs
Accommodation: 255 to 295 Frs
Restaurant: lunch 10–6pm, dinner 6–8pm.
Speciality: jambon braisé à l'os.

Hotel: 74 rooms: single 52, double 22. Showers, baths, private WCs, TV, phone.
Other points: bar, credit cards accepted, children welcome, à la carte menu, self-service, lounge area, garden terrace, pets allowed, car parking.
Address: Aire du Soleil Levant.
Tel 86.40.35.52.

VERDUN, Meuse 55100, Map 17 ⊗ ♈ 🏠

A LA BONNE AUBERGE, RN 3 between SNCF and freight stations

Places of interest: Champs de bataille.
Languages: German, English
Menu: 49,90 a to 75 Frs
Accommodation: 65 to 91 Frs
Restaurant.
Hotel: 7 rooms: single 3, double 4.

Other points: bar, à la carte menu, pets allowed, traditional decor.
Address: 11 avenue Garibaldi.
MME YOLANDE GAIOTTI-MORANO, tel 29.86.05.16.

VERDUN, Meuse 55100, Map 17 ⊗

L'ARCHE DE VERDUN, A 4, 250km Paris and 240km Strasbourg, in both directions.

Place of interest: Verdun (15km).
Restaurant.
Other points: credit cards accepted, children welcome, à la carte menu, self-

service, garden terrace, pets allowed, car parking.
Address: Aire de Verdun Saint-Nicolas.
M. SERGE MONCEAU, tel 29.86.41.18.

VERMENTON, Yonne 89270, Map 15 ⊗ ♈ 🏠

LE NOUVEAU RELAIS, RN 6 between Paris and Lyon

Places of interest: Avallon, Auxerre.
Menu: 90 Frs
Restaurant: closed Sundays and mid-December to mid-January.
Specialities: boeuf bourgignon, coq au vin, escaloppe milannaise.

Hotel: 12 rooms.
Other points: bar, à la carte menu, pets allowed, car parking, traditional decor.
Address: 74 Route Nationale 6.
M. PIERRE JEAN, tel 86.81.51.51.

VILLENEUVE AU CHEMIN, Aube 10130, Map 18 ⊗ ♈

LE PETIT SAINT JEAN, RN 77 between Troyes and Auxerre

Language: Arabic
Menu: 60 Frs
Restaurant.
Speciality: couscous.
Other points: bar, credit cards accepted,

children welcome, à la carte menu, garden terrace, pets allowed, car parking.
Address: Route Nationale 77.
M. NAFAA NAIT MOHAND, tel 25.42.10.51.

VILLENEUVE L'ARCHEVEQUE, Yonne 89190, Map 15 ⊗ ♈ 🏠

L'ESCALE 60, RN 60 between Sens and Troyes

Place of interest: Cathédrale de Sens (25km).
Language: English
Menu: 53 Frs
Accommodation: 110 to 170 Frs
Restaurant: lunch 11.30–1.30pm, dinner
7–9pm. Closed Saturdays and Sundays.
Specialities: escalope normande, coq au vin,
rognon de génisse maison.

Hotel: 10 rooms: single 7, double 3. Showers.
Other points: bar, credit cards accepted, à la
carte menu, garden terrace, pets allowed, car
parking.
Address: 10 route de Sens.
M. DOMINIQUE BOIRE, tel 86.86.74.42.

VILLEVALLIER, Yonne 89330, Map 15   ⊗ 🍽 🏠

RELAIS 89, RN 6

Place of interest: Vallée de l'Yonne.
Menu: 54 Frs
Restaurant: closed Saturdays and Sundays.
Hotel: 6 rooms: single 2, double 4.
Other points: bar, credit cards accepted,

children welcome, à la carte menu, garden
terrace, pets allowed, car parking.
Address: 9 rue de la République.
MME YVETTE PETIT, tel 86.91.11.17.

VILLIERS LOUIS, Yonne 89760, Map 15   ⊗ 🍽

LE TALLEYRAND, RN 60

Language: English
Menu: 53 to 95 Frs
Restaurant: lunch 10.30–3.30pm, dinner
6.30–10pm.

Other points: bar, car parking.
Address: Route Nationale 60, Le Petit Villiers.
M. MICHEL VANWYMEERSCH,
tel 86.88.24.02.

VITTEAUX, Côte-d'Or 21350, Map 15   ⊗ 🍽

RELAIS DE LA ROUTE BLANCHE, RN 5

Places of interest: Dijon, Semur en Auxois.
Menu: 50 Frs
Restaurant: lunch 12–3pm, dinner 7–9pm.
Closed Sundays and mid-August to mid-
September.

Specialities: boeuf bourguignon, jambon persillé.
Other points: bar, credit cards accepted, car
parking, traditional decor.
Address: rue de Verdun
M. ROGER LE GALL, tel 80.49.60.13.

VITTONVILLE, Meurthe-et-Moselle 54700, Map 17   ⊗ 🍽

L'AIGLE D'OR, RN 57 between Metz and Nancy

Places of interest: Buttes de Mousson (château
historique), lac de Madine.
Languages: Dutch, Italian
Menu: 50 to 75 Frs
Restaurant: closed Saturdays after 10am and
Sundays.

Other points: bar, credit cards accepted,
children welcome, à la carte menu, self-service,
lounge area, garden terrace, pets allowed, car
parking.
Address: Route Nationale 57, Pont à Mousson.
ELIANE AND ERIC LANZI, tel 83.81.04.08.

WARCQ, Ardennes 08000, Map 18   ⊗ 🍽 🏠

RELAIS ROUTIERS DES 4 VENTS

Languages: German, English
Menu: 51 to 80 Frs
Accommodation: 60 to 80 Frs
Restaurant: lunch 11.30–2pm, dinner 7–10.30pm.
Closed Saturday afternoons and Sundays.

Hotel: 11 rooms.
Other points: bar, car parking.
Address: 132 boulevard L. Pierquin.
MME JACKIE LARNO, tel 24.56.12.34.

WASSELONNE, Bas-Rhin 67310, Map 17

AU ROCHER, RN 4 between Saverne and Strasbourg

Places of interest: Haut Koemisbourg
(château), cathédrale de Strasbourg, Mont Saint
Odile, Saverne.
Languages: German, English
Menu: 60 to 100 Frs
Accommodation: 100 to 250 Frs
Restaurant: lunch 11.30–2.30pm, dinner
7–9pm. Closed Sundays.

Specialities: choucroute paysanne, cuisses de
grenouilles à la provençale, boeuf bourguignon.
Hotel: 8 rooms, showers, baths, private WCs.
Other points: bar, credit cards accepted,
children welcome, à la carte menu, pets
allowed, car parking, traditional decor.
Address: 18 route de Strasbourg.
M. ANDRE HECKER, tel 88.87.06.72.

WITRY LES REIMS, Marne 51420, Map 18

RELAIS 51-08, RN 51 between Charleville-Mézière and Reims

Place of interest: Reims (3km).
Menu: 55 to 150 Frs
Accommodation: 100 Frs
Restaurant: lunch 12–2.30pm, dinner
7–10.30pm. Closed Saturdays after 3pm and
Sundays.
Hotel: 4 rooms: single 1, double 3. Showers.

Other points: bar, credit cards accepted,
children welcome, à la carte menu, garden
terrace, pets allowed, car parking, traditional
decor.
Address: 62 avenue de Reims.
M. ROBERT VAN HOUTTE, tel 26.97.08.30.

WITTELSHEIM GRAFFENWALD, Haut-Rhin 68310, Map 17

HOTEL DES VOSGES, RN 83

Languages: German, Italian
Menu: 45 to 65 Frs
Accommodation: 120 to 150 Frs
Restaurant: lunch 12–2.30pm, dinner 7–9pm.
Closed Sundays.
Specialities: choucroute, carpes.
Hotel: 13 rooms: single 5, double 8. Showers,

baths, private WCs.
Other points: bar, credit cards accepted,
children welcome, car parking, traditional
decor.
Address: 137 rue de Reiningue.
M. DORIS RIEDLE, tel 89.55.10.20.

WOIPPY, Moselle 57140, Map 17

LE CHARDON LORRAIN, RN 412

Places of interest: Metz, Saint Quentin.
Language: German
Menu: 50 Frs
Accommodation: 70 to 75 Frs
Restaurant: lunch 12–2pm, dinner 7–9pm.
Closed Wednesday afternoons and 19
December to 7 January.

Hotel: 3 rooms: single 2, double 1. Showers,
baths.
Other points: bar, credit cards accepted,
lounge area, garden terrace, pets allowed, car
parking.
Address: 58 rue de Metz.
MME FRANCOISE CECCO, tel 87.30.46.61.

XONRUPT LONGEMER, Vosges 88400, Map 17 ⊗♉⌂

LA PIERRE CHARLEMAGNE – Chez Dédé

Languages: German, English
Menu: 45 to 70 Frs
Accommodation: 100 to 140 Frs
Restaurant: lunch 12–2.30pm, dinner 7–10pm.
Closed Mondays (out of season), first 2 weeks
of June and first week of October.
Specialities: choucroute garnie, quiche
lorraine, truite.

Hotel: 6 rooms: single 3, double 3.
Other points: bar, credit cards accepted,
children welcome, à la carte menu, pets
allowed, car parking, traditional decor.
Address: Le Saut des Cuves.
M. ANDRE CAEL, tel 29.63.03.86.

YUTZ, Moselle 57110, Map 17 ⊗♉

CHEZ CHANTAL ET NOEL, RN 153

Place of interest: Trêves.
Menu: 56 Frs
Restaurant: lunch 11.30–3pm, dinner 7–10pm.
Closed Saturdays and Sundays.
Other points: bar, credit cards accepted,

children welcome, à la carte menu. pets
allowed, car parking.
Address: 140 Route Nationale.
M. NOEL RUBEILLON, tel 82.56.00.28.

The Loire

ABSIE (L'), Deux-Sèvres 79240, Map 7   ⊗ �

RESTAURANT DE LA POSTE

Restaurant: closed Sundays.
Other points: bar.

Address: 21 rue de la Poste.
M. EUGENE BIGNON, tel 49.95.90.21.

AIGURANDE, Indre 36140, Map 6   ⊗ � ☆ ☆

LE RELAIS DE LA MARCHE

Places of interest: Barrage d'Eguzon, vallée
noire, château de Georges Sand.
Languages: English, Spanish
Menu: 55 to 190 Frs
Accommodation: 120 to 210 Frs
Restaurant: lunch 11–2pm, dinner 7–9.30pm.
Closed Saturdays.
Specialities: coq au vin, potée.

Hotel: 7 rooms: single 6, double 1. Showers,
private WCs, TV, phone.
Other points: bar, credit cards accepted,
children welcome, à la carte menu, garden
terrace, pets allowed, car parking.
Address: place du Champ de Foire.
M. JEAN-PIERRE CHAMBON,
tel 54.06.31.58.

AIRVAULT, Deux-Sèvres 79600, Map 7   ⊗ �

LES CHENES VERTS, RD 938 between Parthenay and Thouars

Places of interest: Airvault: église, musée,
barrage.
Menu: 47,50 to 89 Frs including wine and
coffee
Accommodation: 70 to 150 Frs
Restaurant: lunch 12–2pm, dinner 7–9pm.
Closed Saturdays and 15 September to 15
October.

Hotel: 10 rooms, showers.
Other points: bar, credit cards accepted,
children welcome, à la carte menu, garden
terrace, pets allowed, lounge area, car parking,
traditional decor.
Address: La Maucarrière.
M. ALAIN ROUSSEAU, tel 49.49.71.11.

AIX D'ANGILLON (LES), Cher 18220, Map 6   ⊗ �

LE PARISIEN, near information centre

Places of interest: Château de Menetou Salon
(9km), château de Maupas (7km), Bourges
(20km).
Menu: 49 to 72 Frs
Accommodation: 90 to 140 Frs
Restaurant: lunch 12–2pm, dinner 7.30–8.30
pm. Closed Sundays and in August.

Hotel: 7 rooms: single 4, double 3.
Other points: bar, pets allowed, car parking,
traditional decor.
Address: 20 place du Général de Gaulle.
M. JACQUES BLANCHET, tel 48.64.43.62.

ALLOGNY, Cher 18110, Map 6   ⊗ ⍻

CAFE RESTAURANT DE LA MAIRIE, RD 944 between Salbris and Bourges

Places of interest: Cathédrale de Bourges,
poterie.
Language: English
Menu: 55 Frs
Restaurant: lunch 12–2pm, dinner 7.30–10pm.
Closed Thursdays.

Specialities: gibiers (in season).
Other points: bar, credit cards accepted,
children welcome, à la carte menu, self-service,
garden terrace, pets allowed, car parking.
Address: place de la Mairie.
M. NOEL HELLEGOUARCH, tel 48.64.00.71.

AMBOISE, Indre-et-Loire 37400, Map 6 ⊗ ♍ ⌂

LE CHANTECLERC, RD 152 between Tours and Blois

Places of interest: Château d'Amboise, musée
de la poste, Pagode de Chanteloup.
Menu: 48 Frs
Accommodation: 80 to 120 Frs
Restaurant: lunch 12–2pm, dinner 7.30–9pm.
Closed Sundays out of season.

Hotel: 4 rooms: single 1, double 3.
Other points: bar, credit cards accepted,
garden terrace, pets allowed, car parking.
Address: 34 avenue de Tours.
M. ERIC BOITELLE, tel 47.57.11.94.

ANGLIERS, Vienne 86330, Map 7 ⊗ ♍

AU MILLE PATTES, RN 147 between Angers and Poitiers

Places of interest: Chinon (30km), Saumur
(30km).
Languages: English, Spanish, Portuguese
Menu: 52 Frs including wine and coffee
Restaurant.
Specialities: saumon, sauce Galuche.

Other points: bar, credit cards accepted,
children welcome, à la carte menu, garden
terrace, pets allowed, car parking.
Address: Route Nationale 147.
MME ANNICK ELMON, tel 49.22.48.92.

ARDENTES, Indre 36120, Map 6 ⊗ ♍

LE RELAIS DE CLAVIERES

Place of interest: Château de Georges Sand.
Restaurant.
Accommodation: 75 to 100 Frs
Hotel: 4 rooms: single 3, double 1. Showers.

Other points: bar, garden terrace, pets
allowed, car parking.
Address: route de Montluçon Clavières.
MME PASCALE PORTRAIT, tel 54.26.98.46.

ARDENTES, Indre 36120, Map 6 ⊗ ♍

CAFE DES SPORTS, between Châteauroux and La Chatre

Places of interest: Château de Georges Sand à
Nohant (15km), château du Magnet à Mers sur
Indre (15km).
Menu: 50 to 60 Frs
Restaurant: lunch 12–2pm, dinner 7–8.30pm.
Closed Saturday nights, Sundays (except bar)
and 1 to 15 August.

Other points: bar, credit cards accepted,
children welcome, car parking, traditional
decor.
Address: 21 avenue de Verdun.
MME CECILE PASCAUD, tel 54.36.21.19.

ARGENT SUR SAULDRE, Cher 18410, Map 6 ⊗ ♍

AUBERGE DES BRUYERES, RD 940

Place of interest: Musée des métiers.
Restaurant: lunch 12–2pm, dinner 7–10pm.
Other points: bar, à la carte menu, pets
allowed, traditional decor.

Address: 10 rue Nationale.
M. JEAN-YVES MUELLE, tel 48.73.60.20.

ARGENTON SUR CREUSE, Indre 36200, Map 6 ⊗ ♍ ⌂ ⊂

LE RELAIS, RN 20

Places of interest: Etangs de la Brenne, vallée de la Creuse, site archéologique.
Languages: English, Spanish
Menu: 62 to 100 Frs
Accommodation: 90 to 140 Frs
Restaurant: lunch 12–2pm, dinner 7–8.30pm. Closed Sundays and 15 December to 15 January.
Specialities: coq au vin, coquilles de crabes, andouillettes grillées.

Hotel: 6 rooms: single 4, double 2. Showers, baths, private WCs.
Other points: bar, children welcome, à la carte menu, lounge area, garden terrace, pets allowed, car parking, traditional decor.
Address: 7 rue du Président Fruchon Saint Marcel.
MME MAURICETTE CALMEL, tel 54.24.01.77.

ARTHENAY, Loiret 45410, Map 6

LE RELAIS D'ARTHENAY, RN 20 Paris to Orléans

Places of interest: Arthenay, Orléans, châteaux de la Loire, Cléry: tombeau de Louis XI.
Languages: English, Spanish
Menu: 52 to 155 Frs
Accommodation: 110 to 250 Frs
Restaurant: lunch 11.30–2pm, dinner 7.30–10.30pm.

Hotel: 34 rooms: single 17, double 17. Showers, baths, private WCs, TV, phone.
Other points: bar, credit cards accepted, children welcome, à la carte menu, lounge area, garden terrace, pets allowed, car parking.
Address: Route Nationale 20.
MLLE FATIMA KRIBI, tel 38.80.40.78.

ASCOUX, Loiret 45300, Map 6

AUBERGE SAINT ELOI, RN 721

Accommodation: 130 Frs
Restaurant: closed Sundays.
Hotel: 10 single rooms.
Other points: bar, credit cards accepted, car

parking, traditional decor.
Address: 1 rue de Pithiviers.
ROBILLARD-DAROUX, tel 38.33.00.20.

ATHEE SUR CHER, Indre-et-Loire 37270, Map 6

L'ESCALE, RN 76 between Tours and Vierzon

Places of interest: Chanteloup: châteaux, églises, pagode (15km).
Languages: German, English
Menu: 50 Frs including coffee
Restaurant: lunch 11.30–2.30pm, dinner 7–9.30pm. Closed Sundays, 1 weekend in February and 15 days in August.

Speciality: galette de pommes de terre.
Other points: bar, credit cards accepted, children welcome, garden terrace, pets allowed, car parking.
Address: Les Ruelles.
M. GERARD RAMAZEILLES, tel 47.50.67.29.

AUBIERS (LES), Deux-Sèvres 79250, Map 7

HOTEL DU CHEVAL BLANC

Restaurant: lunch 12–2pm. Closed Saturdays, Sundays and in August.
Hotel: 2 rooms.

Other points: bar.
Address: 9 place Saint Mélaine.
MME MARCELLE SAUER, tel 49.65.60.51.

AUBIGNY SUR NERE, Cher 18700, Map 6 ⊗♓⌂

LES ROUTIERS, RN 940 between Gien and Vierzon

Places of interest: Châteaux et vignobles de Sancerre.
Menu: 47 Frs
Accommodation: 80 to 104 Frs
Restaurant: lunch 11–1.30pm, dinner 7.30–9.30pm. Closed Saturday afternoons, Sundays, public holidays, in August and 1 week at Christmas.

Specialities: gibiers: sanglier, chevreuil (in season).
Hotel: 9 double rooms. Showers.
Other points: bar, credit cards accepted, pets allowed, car parking, traditional decor.
Address: 17 avenue Charles Lefèbvre.
M. BERNARD OLLIER, tel 48.58.01.42.

AUMONE (L'), Indre 36170, Map 6 ⊗♓⌂

LES ROUTIERS, RN 20, 20km from Argenton towards Limoges

Places of interest: Châteaux, étang, lacs.
Menu: 45 to 75 Frs
Accommodation: 80 to 120 Frs
Restaurant: lunch 11.30–4pm, dinner 7–11pm. Closed Sundays and 19 to 28 September.
Specialities: pâté aux cèpes, cuisses de canard confites.

Hotel: 6 rooms: single 4, double 2. Showers.
Other points: bar, credit cards accepted, children welcome, à la carte menu, lounge area, pets allowed, car parking, traditional decor.
Address: Route Nationale 20
M. PIERRE BOUSSELY, tel 54.47.55.11.

AUNEAU, Eure-et-Loir 28700, Map 6 ⊗♓⌂

AUX TROIS MARCHES, A 11 exit Ablis/A 10 exit Allainville

Place of interest: Château.
Menu: 52 Frs including wine and coffee
Accommodation: 100 to 160 Frs
Restaurant: lunch 11.30–3pm, dinner 7–9pm. Closed Sundays, public holidays and in August.
Hotel: 8 rooms: single 1, double 7.

Other points: bar, credit cards accepted, children welcome, pets allowed, car parking, traditional decor.
Address: 2 rue Emile Labiche.
REGINE AND CHRISTIAN SETTAOUI-GASNIER, tel 37.31.70.49.

AUSSAC, Charente 16560, Map 7 ⊗♓

LA BELLE CANTINIERE, RN 10, 20km north of Angoulême

Menu: 50 Frs
Restaurant: closed Saturdays and Sundays.
Specialities: fruits de mer.
Other points: bar, credit cards accepted,

garden terrace, pets allowed, car parking, traditional decor.
Address: Route Nationale 10.
M. FERNAND JUDES, tel 45.20.66.89.

AZAY LE FERRON, Indre 36290, Map 6 ⊗♓

L'UNION

Places of interest: Château d'Azay le Ferron, parc de la Haute Touche.
Menu: 50 to 110 Frs
Restaurant: dinner 8–9pm. Closed Monday afternoons.
Specialities: fruits de mer, gibiers.

Other points: bar, credit cards accepted, children welcome, à la carte menu, car parking, traditional decor.
Address: place de l'Eglise.
M. THIERRY AUDOIN, tel 54.39.20.88.

AZAY LE RIDEAU, Indre-et-Loire 37190, Map 6

RESTAURANT DE LA GARE, RD 57

Places of interest: Châteaux de la Loire.
Language: English
Menu: 46 to 70 Frs
Restaurant: lunch 12–2.30pm, dinner 7–9.30.
Closed Sundays.

Other points: bar, credit cards accepted, garden terrace, pets allowed, car parking, traditional decor.
Address: 59 avenue de la Gare.
M. PATRICK VITEL, tel 47.45.40.60.

BARBEZIEUX, Charente 16360, Map 7

LA CAMBROUSSE, RN 10 Paris to Bordeaux

Menu: 53 Frs
Accommodation: 90 to 110 Frs
Restaurant: lunch 12–2pm, dinner 7–11pm. Closed Saturday afternoons and Sundays.

Hotel: 13 rooms: single 10, double 3. Showers, baths, private WCs.
Other points: bar, car parking, traditional decor.
Address: La Tâtre, Route Nationale 10.
M. JEAN-CLAUDE PICHON, tel 45.78.52.83.

BARBEZIEUX SAINT HILAIRE, Charente 16120, Map 7

RELAIS DE LA BILLETTE, RN 10, 20 km south of Angoulême/10 km north of Barbezieux

Places of interest: Château de Barbezieux, hôtel de ville d'Angoulême.
Language: Spanish
Menu: 60 to 100 Frs.
Restaurant: closed Sundays and 1 week in August.

Specialities: confit de canard, escalope à la Charentaise, magret de canard.
Other points: bar, pets allowed, car parking.
Address: Ladiville.
MME DANIELLE HOUDUSSE, tel 45.78.57.09.

BARMAINVILLE, Eure-et-Loir 28310, Map 6

RELAIS DES BOISSEAUX, RN 20 Paris to Orléans

Menu: 54 Frs
Restaurant: lunch 12–2pm, dinner 7–11pm. Closed Saturdays, Sundays and in August.

Other points: pets allowed, car parking, traditional decor.
Address: La Poste de Boisseaux.
MME NADINE BAUGER, tel 38.39.61.20.

BAZOCHE GOUET (LA), Eure-et-Loir 28330, Map 6

LA BONNE AUBERGE, RD 927 Chartres to Le Mans

Menu: 50 Frs
Restaurant: closed 15 days in February and 15 in July.

Other points: bar, children welcome.
Address: 54 avenue du Général Leclerc.
M. JEAN-PAUL THIERRY, tel 37.49.21.61.

BAZOCHES EN DUNOIS, Eure-et-Loir 28140, Map 6

AU BON ACCUEIL, RN 827 and RD 27

Places of interest: Châteaux de la Loire, cathédrale de Chartres, Orléans.
Menu: 48 to 180 Frs
Restaurant: lunch 11–3pm, dinner 8–10pm.
Specialities: truite à l'oignon, potée beauceronne, rognons au vin rouge, pot au feu

sauce normande, tarte à la rhubarbe.
Other points: bar, children welcome, pets allowed, car parking, traditional decor.
Address: 7 rue de l'Eglise.
MME MARIE-CLAUDE BOUCHER, tel 37.22.08.30.

BEAUNE LA ROLANDE, Loiret 45340, Map 6 ⊗🍸🏠

HOTEL DE LA GARE between Orléans and Paris

Places of interest: Montargis, Pithiviers, Nemours, Gien.
Menu: 55 to 145 Frs including wine and coffee
Accommodation: 170 to 230 Frs
Restaurant: lunch 12–3pm, dinner 7–10pm. Closed Tuesdays.

Hotel: 10 rooms: single 6, double 4.
Other points: bar, credit cards accepted, children welcome, à la carte menu, garden terrace, pets allowed, car parking, traditional decor.
Address: 25 gare d'Auxy.
M. THIERRY DEVOUCOUX, tel 38.96.70.44.

BEAUVOIR SUR NIORT, Deux-Sèvres 79360, Map 7 ⊗🍸

L'ETAPE, RN 150 between St Jean d'Angély and Niort

Places of interest: Zoo de Chizé (10km), moulin de Rimbaud (1km), églises (10km).
Language: a little English
Menu: 48 to 70 Frs including wine and coffee

Restaurant: lunch 12–2pm, dinner 7–9pm. Closed Sunday afternoons.
Other points: bar, à la carte menu, garden terrace, pets allowed, car parking.
Address: 7 place de l'Hôtel de Ville.
MME ANNICK DUVERNE, tel 49.09.70.17.

BEURLAY, Charente-Maritime 17250, Map 7 ⊗🍸

LE RELAIS D'ARY, RN 137 between Rochefort and Saintes

Place of interest: Château de la Rochecourbon.
Language: Spanish
Menu: 30 to 60 Frs
Restaurant: lunch 10–3pm, dinner, 7–12pm. Closed Sundays.

Other points: bar, credit cards accepted, à la carte menu, garden terrace, car parking, traditional decor.
Address: 1 route de Rochefort.
M. YVES MARIAUD, tel 46.95.01.39.

BINAS, Loir-et-Cher 41240, Map 6 ⊗🍸🏠

LE SAINT CHRISTOPHE, RN 157 Orléans to Le Mans

Places of interest: Châteaux de la Loire.
Menu: 51 to 75 Frs
Accommodation: 110 to 160 Frs
Restaurant: lunch 11.30–1.45pm, dinner 7.30–9pm. Closed Friday nights and Sundays.

Hotel: 6 rooms, showers, private WCs.
Other points: bar, credit cards accepted, à la carte menu, garden terrace, pets allowed, car parking, traditional decor.
Address: 17 place Saint-Maurice.
M. PHILIPPE DUVERNET, tel 54.82.40.26.

BLERE, Indre-et-Loire 37150, Map 6 ⊗🍸

LE RELAIS, RN 76

Places of interest: Châteaux de la Loire, musée du Poids Lourds, abbaye de Pontlevoy.
Menu: 55 Frs
Restaurant: lunch 12–2pm, dinner 7–10pm.
Other points: bar, credit cards accepted,

children welcome, à la carte menu, garden terrace, pets allowed, car parking.
Address: 48 rue de Tours.
MME PAULETTE ROSSIGNOL, tel 47.57.92.31.

BLOIS, Loir-et-Cher 41000 ⊗🍸

BAR DE LA CITE, RD 951, town centre, towards Vendôme.

Places of interest: Châteaux de la Loire: Blois, Chambord (17km), Cheverny (23km), la ville de Blois.
Menu: 50 Frs including wine
Restaurant: lunch 12–2pm, dinner 7.30–9pm. Closed Saturdays and Sundays.

Other points: bar, children welcome, lounge area, garden terrace, pets allowed, car parking.
Address: 55 avenue de Vendôme.
M. DIDIER MOREAU, tel 54.43.48.54.

BLOIS, Loir-et-Cher 41000, Map 6 ⊗

L'ARCHE DE BLOIS, A 10

Language: English
Restaurant: lunch 11–4pm, dinner 6–12pm.
Other points: credit cards accepted, children welcome, à la carte menu, self-service, garden

terrace, pets allowed, car parking.
Address: Aire de Blois-Villerbon towards Bordeaux and Paris autoroute.
M. VINCENT STAELENS, tel 54.46.81.71.

BORDS, Charente-Maritime 17430, Map 7 ⊗🍸

CAFE DU CENTRE, RN 137 La Rochelle to Bordeaux

Menu: 48 Frs
Other points: bar, pets allowed, traditional decor.

Address: place de l'Eglise.
M. MARTIAL PERROCHEAU, tel 46.83.84.31.

BOULAY LES BARRES, Loiret 45140, Map 6 ⊗🍸🏠

AUBERGE DE LA ROUTE, RN 155

Restaurant: closed Saturdays, August.
Hotel: 5 rooms.
Other points: bar.

Address: 21 route d'Orléans.
M. JACKY GASNOT, tel 38.75.34.90.

BOURGES, Cher 18000, Map 6 ⊗🍸🏠

LES AILES, RN 151 towards Châteauroux

Places of interest: Bourges: la vieille ville, cathédrale, palais Jacques Coeurs.
Language: English
Menu: 46 to 75 Frs
Accommodation: 100 to 170 Frs
Restaurant: lunch 12–2pm, dinner 7.30–10pm. Closed Saturday nights, Sundays, 15 days in

August and 8 days at Christmas.
Hotel: 16 rooms: single 9, double 7.
Other points: bar, credit cards accepted, à la carte menu, pets allowed, car parking.
Address: 147 avenue Marcel Haegelen.
HOTELS LES AILES, tel 48.21.57.86.

BOURGES, Cher 18000, Map 6 ⊗

RELAIS DU BERRY, A 71 in both directions

Restaurant.
Other points: credit cards accepted, à la carte menu, children welcome, garden terrace, pets allowed, car parking.

Address: Aire de Service de Farges-Allichamps.

BOUVILLE, Eure-et-Loir 28800, Map 6 ⊗🍸

RELAIS ROUTIER DU BOIS DE FEUGERES, RN 10 between Chartres and Châteaudun

Place of interest: Cathédrale de Chartres.
Languages: English, German
Menu: 52 to 66 Frs. Closed Saturday nights and Sundays.
Restaurant.

Other points: bar, credit cards accepted, children welcome, à la carte menu, pets allowed, car parking, traditional decor.
Address: 26 Route Nationale.
M. ALAIN LAURENT, tel 37.96.33.01.

BRECHES, Indre-et-Loire 37330, Map 6 ⊗ ♀

RESTAURANT ROUTIERS, RD 766 between Bois (75km) and Angers (80km)

Places of interest: Châteaux de la Loire.
Menu: 53 Frs including wine.
Restaurant: closed Saturdays, Sundays and 3 weeks in August.

Other points: bar, credit cards accepted, pets allowed, car parking, traditional decor.
Address: known as Le Bel Air.
MME ANITA VAILLANT, tel 47.24.13.03.

BRIARE, Loiret 45250, Map 6 ⊗ ♀ ⌂

LE RELAIS, RN 7

Menu: 55 to 65 Frs
Accommodation: 75 to 85 Frs
Restaurant: closed Saturday nights and Sundays.
Hotel: 9 rooms: single 2, double 7. Showers.

Other points: bar, children welcome, pets allowed, car parking, traditional decor.
Address: Gare de Chatillon sur Loire.
M. ERIC BOURGOIN, tel 38.31.44.42.

BRION PRES THOUET, Deux-Sèvres 79290, Map 7 ⊗ ♀

LE RELAIS DE BRION, RD 938, Niort to Saumur

Places of interest: Saumur (25km), Montreuil Bellay (7km), Thouars.
Language: English.
Menu: 50 to 85 Frs
Accommodation: 90 to 150 Frs
Restaurant: lunch 11.30–2pm, dinner 7–9pm. Closed Sundays, public holidays and 3 weeks in August.

Hotel: 2 rooms: single 1, double 1.
Other points: bar, credit cards accepted, children welcome, à la carte menu, self-service, garden terrace, pets allowed, car parking, traditional decor.
Address: 39 rue Principale.
M. ALAIN BRUNELEAU, tel 49.67.73.34.

BRIOUX SUR BOUTONNE, Deux-Sèvres 79170, Map 7 ⊗ ♀

AUBERGE DU CHEVAL BLANC, RD 950 Poitiers to Saintes.

Places of interest: Le Futuroscope (Poitiers), mines d'argent (Melle), zoo (Chizé).
Languages: German, English
Menu: 52 to 126 Frs
Restaurant: lunch 11.30–2pm, dinner 7–8.30pm. Closed Sunday nights and end January.

Other points: bar, credit cards accepted, children welcome, à la carte menu, pets allowed, car parking, traditional decor.
Address: 23 place du Champ de Foire.
MME CATHERINE RICHARD, tel 49.07.50.52.

BROU, Eure-et-Loir 28160, Map 6 ⊗ ♀ ⌂

HOTEL DE LA GARE – Le Relais de l'Arc-en-Ciel

Accommodation: 100 to 140 Frs
Restaurant: lunch 11–2pm. Closed Sundays.
Hotel: 8 rooms. Showers.
Other points: bar, credit cards accepted, children welcome, lounge area, pets allowed, car parking, traditional decor.
Address: 76 avenue du Général de Gaulle.
M. ALAIN DUPARC, tel 32.44.60.38.

BUZANCAIS, Indre 36500, Map 6   ⊗ ♀ 🏠

LE RELAIS DES ROUTIERS, RN 143 between Tours and Châteauroux

Places of interest: Etangs de la Brenne, réserve Haute Touche (animaux), châteaux.
Menu: 50 Frs
Accommodation: 80 Frs
Restaurant: lunch 12–1.15pm, dinner 7–9pm. Closed Sundays and 15 days in August.
Hotel: 9 rooms: single 5, double 4. Showers.
Other points: bar, garden terrace, pets allowed, car parking, traditional decor.
Address: 19 rue des Hervaux.
MME REGINE IMBERT, tel 54.84.07.37.

CELLE SAINT AVANT (LA), Indre-et-Loire 37160, Map 6   ⊗ ♀ 🏠

LA CARAVANE, RN 10 between Poitiers and Tours

Places of interest: Châteaux de la Loire, Futuroscope (Poitiers).
Menu: 55 to 65 Frs including wine
Accommodation: 60 to 150 Frs
Restaurant: lunch 11.30–3pm, dinner 7–11pm.
Hotel: 8 rooms: single 4, double 4.
Other points: bar, credit cards accepted, children welcome, pets allowed, car parking, traditional decor.
Address: Route Nationale 10.
M. JACKY BAUDOUIN, tel 47.65.07.82.

CELON, Indre 36200, Map 6   ⊗ ♀

LA BROUETTE, RN 20

Restaurant: closed Sundays.
Other points: bar.
MME YVETTE DUFOUR, tel 54.25.32.08.

CHADURIE, Charente 16250, Map 7   ⊗ ♀

LE RELAIS DE LA TOUR, RD 674 between Libourne and Angoulême

Place of interest: Abbaye Puyperoux.
Menu: 50 Frs including wine and coffee
Restaurant: lunch 11–3pm, dinner 7–10pm. Closed Saturday afternoons.
Other points: bar, children welcome, garden terrace, pets allowed, car parking, traditional decor.
Address: known as Bois Rond.
MME MARIE-ROSE DESCHAMPS, tel 45.24.82.11.

CHAMPAGNE MOUTON, Charente 16350, Map 7   ⊗ ♀ 🏠 ☆

HOTEL PLAISANCE, RN 740 between Ruffec and Confolens

Places of interest: Confolens, vallée de l'Argent, Nanteuil en Vallée.
Menu: 60 to 150 Frs
Accommodation: 150 to 200 Frs
Restaurant: lunch 12–2pm, dinner 7–9pm.
Specialities: fruits de mer, langoustines à l'américaine, magret de canard.
Hotel: 15 rooms: single 9, double 6. Showers, baths, private WCs.
Other points: bar, credit cards accepted, children welcome, à la carte menu, lounge area, garden terrace, pets allowed, car parking.
Address: place du Château.
MME DENISE DELHOUME, tel 45.31.80.52.

CHAMPROND EN GATINE, Eure-et-Loir 28240, Map 6   ⊗ �

RELAIS DE CHAMPROND, RN 23

Restaurant: closed Sundays and last 2 weeks
of August.
Other points: bar.

Address: 5 Grande Rue.
M. MICHEL JONNIER, tel 37.49.82.16.

CHAPELLE SAINT LAURENT (LA), Deux-Sèvres 79430, Map 7   ⊗ ♀

CAFE DES SPORTS, RN 748

Places of interest: Les marais poitevins
(50km), le moulin des Mothes (4km).
Menu: 46 Frs
Restaurant: lunch 12–3pm, dinner 7.30–10pm.
Other points: bar, credit cards accepted,

children welcome, pets allowed, car parking,
traditional decor.
Address: 6 route de Bressuire.
MME LOUISETTE GUERIN, tel 49.72.05.64.

CHAPELLE SAINT SEPULCRE (LA), Loiret 45210, Map 6   ⊗ ♀

LA POTENCE, RN 60

Restaurant: closed Saturdays, Sundays and 15
days in June.
Other points: bar.

Address: Route Nationale 60.
MME LILIANE VISIER, tel 38.92.03.10.

CHAPELLE SUR LOIRE (LA), Indre-et-Loire 37140, Map 6   ⊗ ♀ ⌂

LE RELAIS DE LA MAIRIE, RN 152 between Tours and Saumur

Places of interest: Châteaux de la Loire.
Menu: 50 to 95 Frs
Restaurant: lunch 12–2pm.
Specialities: coq au vin, rillon, rillette, friture
de Loire.
Hotel: 12 rooms.

Other points: bar, children welcome, à la carte
menu, garden terrace, pets allowed, car
parking.
Address: place Albert Ruelle.
M. JACQUES JOYEAU, tel 47.97.34.07.

CHAPELLE SUR LOIRE (LA), Indre-et-Loire 37140, Map 6   ⊗ ♀

LE ZEBRE A CARREAUX, RN 152

Languages: German, English, Flemish
Menu: 45 Frs
Restaurant.

Other points: bar, car parking.
Address: Le Bourg.
M. RAYMOND NOEL, tel 47.97.45.50.

CHARENTON DU CHER, Cher 18210, Map 6   ⊗ ♀

A LA BONNE TABLE, RN 151

Restaurant: closed Tuesday evenings and in
August.
Other points: bar, pets allowed, car parking.

Address: 36 rue Nationale.
MME ANTOINETTE FREGE, tel 48.60.72.73.

CHARROUX, Vienne 86250, Map 7   ⊗ ♀ ⌂ 🍽

LA CROIX BLANCHE (RELAIS) between Niort and Limoges

Place of interest: La Tour de Charlemagne.
Menu: 50 to 88 Frs
Restaurant.
Accommodation: 80 to 95 Frs
Hotel: 8 single rooms. Showers.

Other points: bar, credit cards accepted, children welcome, garden terrace, pets allowed, car parking, traditional decor.
Address: route de Limoges.
MME FLORENCE BAYON, tel 49.87.61.81.

CHARSONVILLE, Loiret 45130, Map 6 ⊗♀

LES ROUTIERS, RN 157 between Orléans and Le Mans

Places of interest: Châteaux de la Loire.
Menu: 43 Frs
Restaurant: lunch 11.45–2.15pm. Closed Sundays, Monday afternoons and in August.

Other points: bar, credit cards accepted, garden terrace, pets allowed, car parking.
Address: 15 rue de la Libération.
MME PATRICK BILLARD, tel 38.74.23.00.

CHARTRES, Eure-et-Loir 28000, Map 6 ⊗♀🍽

RESTAURANT LE PALMIER, RN 10

Place of interest: Cathédrale de Chartres.
Menu: 45 to 98 Frs
Restaurant: lunch 11.30–3pm, dinner 7–10pm.
Specialities: couscous, paëlla, grillades.

Other points: bar, credit cards accepted, à la carte menu, traditional decor.
Address: 20 rue Saint Maurice.
M. BOUSSAD NAAR, tel 37.21.13.89.

CHARTRES, Eure-et-Loir 28000, Map 6 ⊗♀🏠🍽☆☆

RELAIS BEAUCERON, A 11 and RN 10 between Chartres and Tours

Places of interest: Cathédrale de Chartres, moulin du bois de Feugère, église Meslay le Grenet, bords du Loir, châteaux de la Loire et de Châteaudun.
Languages: English, Spanish
Menu: 69 to 135 Frs. Menus for groups available.
Accommodation: 190 to 220 Frs
Restaurant: lunch 11.45–2.30pm, dinner 6.45–10.30pm. Closed Saturday nights and Sundays (out of season).
Specialities: velouté d'escargots à la fondue de poireaux, roulade de lapin farcie aux champignons des bois, salade de caille, oeufs à la Chartres, côte de boeuf au gris meunier.
Hotel: 30 rooms: single 22, double 8. Showers, baths, private WCs, phone.
Other points: bar, credit cards accepted, children welcome, à la carte menu, lounge area, garden terrace, pets allowed, car parking, traditional decor.
Address: Route Nationale 10, Mignières.
M. LICHET, tel 37.26.46.21.

CHATEAU GAILLARD SANTILLY, Eure-et-Loir 28310, Map 6 ⊗♀

AU ROUTIER GAILLARD CHEZ LILI, RN 20

Restaurant: closed Saturday nights and Sundays.
Other points: bar.

Address: 1 rue Charles Péguy.
MME LILIANE BOIDROU, tel 37.90.07.03.

CHATEAU GAILLARD SANTILLY, Eure-et-Loir 28310, Map 6 ⊗♀

LE RELAIS 20, RN 20

Menu: 54 Frs
Restaurant: closed Sundays.
Speciality: couscous.

Other points: bar.
Address: 33 rue Charles Péguy
MME DAHMANI FRERES, tel 37.90.07.33.

CHATEAU LA VALLIERE, Indre-et-Loire 37330, Map 6   ⊗ ♀ ⌂ ☆ ☆

LE GRAND CERF, RD 959 Tour/Laval between Le Lude and Château la Vallière

Places of interest: Châteaux du Lude, lac de
Rille, zoo, la Flèche.
Language: English
Menu: 54 to 280 Frs
Accommodation: 130 to 240 Frs
Restaurant: lunch 2–2pm, dinner 7–9pm.
Closed Saturdays (in winter), Sunday
nights and from 25 October to 15
November.

Specialities: rillette de la Sarthe, ris de veau,
aiguillette de canard.
Hotel: 24 double rooms. Showers, private
WCs, phone.
Other points: bar, credit cards accepted,
children welcome, à la carte menu, garden
terrace, pets allowed, car parking.
Address: La Porerie.
M. JEAN MEUNIER, tel 47.24.11.06.

CHATEAUBERNARD, Charente 16100, Map 7   ⊗ ♀

PENSION DU CAMP, between Cognac and Bordeaux

Place of interest: Cognac.
Language: English
Menu: 50 to 75 Frs
Accommodation: 100 to 160 Frs
Restaurant: dinner 7–11pm. Closed Friday
afternoons, Saturdays and Sundays.
Specialities: couscous, cassoulet, choucroutte
(Thursdays only).

Hotel: 3 double rooms. Showers.
Other points: bar, credit cards accepted,
children welcome, garden terrace, car
parking.
Address: Route de Barbezieux.
M. JEAN-LOUIS BRUNO, tel 45.82.09.47.

CHATEAUNEUF SUR LOIRE, Loiret 45110, Map 6   ⊗ ♀ ⌂ ⥅

HOTEL DE LA PLACE, RN 60 between Orléans and Montargis, Châteauneuf sur Loire exit

Places of interest: Vallée des rois, église
carolingienne, monastère Saint Benoît, château
de Sully sur Loire, Gien.
Menu: 50 to 120 Frs
Accommodation: 100 to 170 Frs
Restaurant: lunch 12–2pm, dinner 8–9.30pm.
Closed Fridays (out of season) and from 15
January to 15 February.
Speciality: Fricassé de pintade aux aubergines.

Hotel: 12 rooms: single 8, double 4. Showers,
baths, private WCs, phone.
Other points: bar, credit cards accepted,
children welcome, garden terrace, pets allowed,
car parking, traditional decor.
Address: Le Bourg, Germiny des Près.
JACKY AND CHRISTIANE MAILLARD,
tel 38.58.20.14.

CHATEAUROUX, Indre 36000, Map 6   ⊗ ♀

BAR DE L'AVENUE, RN 20

Language: English
Restaurant: closed Sundays.
Other points: bar.

Address: 1 avenue de la Manufacture.
M. LAURENT GUILLOT, tel 54.34.09.27.

CHATEAUROUX, Indre 36000, Map 6   ⊗ ♀ ⌂ ☆

LE RALLYE, RN 20

Restaurant.
Accommodation: 68 to 120 Frs
Hotel: 8 rooms: single 2, double 6. Closed
Sundays and public holidays.

Other points: bar, pets allowed.
Address: 9 rue Bourdillon.
MME FRANCOISE JASMIN, tel 54.34.37.41.

CHATELLERAULT, Vienne 86100, Map 7 ⊗

RELAIS DE CHATELLERAULT ANTRAN, A 10 between Paris and Bordeaux.

Menu: 59 Frs
Restaurant: lunch 11–4pm, dinner 6–12pm.
Other points: credit cards accepted, self-service,
garden terrace, pets allowed, car parking.
Address: Aire d'Antran.
Tel 49.02.72.04.

CHATILLON SUR INDRE, Indre 36700, Map 6 ⊗ ♈ 🏠

LE RELAIS DU MAIL, RN 143

Place of interest: Château d'Azay le Ferron
(20km).
Menu: 48 Frs
Accommodation: 90 to 190 Frs
Restaurant: lunch 12–2pm, dinner 7–9pm.
Closed 10 days at All Saints holiday.
Hotel: 5 rooms, baths.
Other points: bar, pets allowed, car parking,
traditional decor.
Address: boulevard du Général Leclerc.
MME HUGUETTE SORET, tel 54.38.71.21.

CHATRES SUR CHER, Loir-et-Cher 41320, Map 6 ⊗ ♈

LES ROUTIERS, RN 76 between Tours and Vierzon.

Menu: 55 Frs
Restaurant: lunch 12–2pm. Closed Sundays
and second 2 weeks of August.
Other points: bar, credit cards accepted,
children welcome, pets allowed, car parking,
traditional decor.
Address: 60 rue du 11 Novembre.
MME GERARD COUTAUD, tel 54.98.01.93.

CHAUNAY LE BOURG, Vienne 86510, Map 7 ⊗ ♈ 🏠 ☆

LE COMMERCE, RN 10 between Bordeaux and Paris

Places of interest: La Rochelle, Royan, Ile de
Ré, Ile d'Oléron.
Menu: 55 to 110 Frs
Accommodation: 80 to 165 Frs
Restaurant: lunch 11.30–3pm, dinner 7–11.30pm.
Hotel: 8 rooms: single 1, double 7. Showers,
baths, private WCs.
Other points: bar, credit cards accepted,
children welcome, à la carte menu, self-service,
garden terrace, pets allowed, car parking,
traditional decor.
MME NELLY SALLES, tel 49.59.02.71.

CHAUVIGNY, Vienne 86300, Map 7 ⊗ ♈

RESTAURANT DU MARCHE, RN 151 between Poitiers and Châteauroux

Places of interest: Chauvigny (cité médiévale),
cimetière mérovingien.
Menu: 45 to 57 Frs
Restaurant: lunch 12–2pm, dinner 7.30–9pm.
Closed Thursdays and 15 September to 15
October.
Other points: bar, credit cards accepted,
garden terrace, pets allowed, car parking.
Address: 8 place du Marché.
M. JOEL TORSAT, tel 49.46.32.34.

CHICHE, Deux-Sèvres 79350, Map 7 ⊗ ♈

CHEZ JACQUES, RN 149

Menu: 40 to 55 Frs
Restaurant: closed Wednesday afternoons, 15 days in August and between Christmas and New Year's day.

Other points: bar, pets allowed, car parking.
Address: 27 place Saint Martin.
M. JACQUES VINCENT, tel 49.72.40.51.

CHINON, Indre-et-Loire 37500, Map 6

LE RELAIS DE LA FORET, RD 751 between Tours and Chinon, towards Saumur

Places of interest: Château de Chinon, caves.
Menu: 55 Frs including wine and coffee
Restaurant: lunch 11–3pm, dinner 6–10.30pm. Closed Saturdays, Sundays, from 25 July to 15 August and for 15 days at Christmas.

Other points: bar, children welcome, garden terrace, pets allowed, car parking, traditional decor.
Address: Route de Tours, Les Plaines de Vaux.
M. MARCO MILLET, tel 47.93.19.08.

CIVRAY, Vienne 86400, Map 7

LE RELAIS DES USINES, between Niort and Limoges

Places of interest: Eglise de Civray, Saint Nicolas, Charroux.
Menu: 48 Frs
Restaurant: dinner 7–8.30pm. Closed Saturday afternoons and Sundays.

Other points: bar, children welcome, pets allowed, car parking, traditional decor.
Address: 19 rue Norbert Portejoie.
MME BRIGITTE NICOULAUD, tel 49.87.04.33.

CIVRAY DE TOURAINE, Indre-et-Loire 37150, Map 6

LE MARECHAL, RN 76 between Tours and Vierzon

Places of interest: Châteaux de Chenonceaux (2km), Ambroise (10km), Loches (25km).
Menu: 50 to 62 Frs
Restaurant: lunch 12–2pm, dinner 7–10pm. Closed Saturday afternoons, Sundays, public holidays and from 15 August to 15 September.

Other points: bar, credit cards accepted, children welcome, à la carte menu, garden terrace, pets allowed, car parking, traditional decor.
Address: 1 rue de Bléré.
M. JEAN JABVENEAU, tel 47.23.92.16.

CLERAC, Charente-Maritime 17270, Map 7

LES BANANIERS, CD 158 between Bédenac and Montguyon

Menu: 50 Frs
Accommodation: 80 to 110 Frs
Restaurant: lunch 12–1.30pm, dinner 7–9pm. Closed Saturdays.
Hotel: 5 rooms: single 4, double 1.

Other points: bar, garden terrace, car parking, traditional decor.
Address: Les Bananiers.
MME DANIELLE ARCAY, tel 46.04.13.17.

CLION SUR INDRE, Indre 36700, Map 6

AUBERGE DU PIE DE BOURGES

Restaurant: lunch 11–1.30pm, dinner 7–9pm.
Hotel: 7 rooms.
Other points: bar.

Address: 31 rue Nationale.
MME NICOLE CHAMTON, tel 54.38.60.90.

COMBRES, Eure-et-Loir 28480, Map 6 ⊗♀🏠

HOTEL DE LA CROIX BLANCHE, CD 15

Menu: 47 to 60 Frs
Accommodation: 105 Frs
Restaurant: lunch 12–1.30pm, dinner 7–9pm.
Hotel: 7 rooms: single 3, double 4.

Other points: bar, pets allowed, car parking.
Address: La Croix Blanche.
MME CHRISTIANE VAUX, tel 37.29.59.54.

CONFOLENS, Charente 16500, Map 7 ⊗♀

RELAIS DES CIGOGNES, CD 951 between Gueret and Angoulême

Place of interest: Ouradour sur Glane.
Menu: 56 Frs including wine and coffee
Restaurant: lunch 11–3pm, dinner 6–10pm.
Closed Monday afternoons.

Other points: bar, credit cards accepted, pets allowed, car parking, traditional decor.
Address: Brillac.
M. SAID YASSA, tel 45.89.45.90.

CORME ROYAL, Charente-Maritime 17600, Map 7 ⊗♀🏠

LES TILLEULS

Menu: 49 to 120 Frs
Accommodation: 120 to 140 Frs
Specialities: escargots à la charentaise.
Hotel: 7 rooms.

Other points: bar, à la carte menu.
Address: 1 rue du Grand Pré Le Bourg.
MME ARLETTE MARSAY, tel 46.94.72.48.

CORMENON, Loir-et-Cher 41170 , Map 6 ⊗♀

AUBERGE DU PARC, RD 921

Places of interest: Mondoubleau, étang, vallée du Loir.
Menu: 48 to 75 Frs
Restaurant: closed Sundays and second 2 weeks of August.

Other points: bar, credit cards accepted, children welcome, car parking.
Address: 86 rue de la Poterie.
M. ANDRE TOUFFU, tel 54.80.92.04.

CORMERY, Indre-et-Loire 37310, Map 6 ⊗♀

AUBERGE DE LA CHAUMIERE, RN 143

Places of interest: Tours, Loches, Châteauroux, châteaux de la Loire.
Menu: 47 to 69 Frs
Accommodation: 70 to 140 Frs
Restaurant: lunch 11.55–2.30pm, dinner 7–8.30pm. Closed Wednesday afternoons and in August.

Specialities: fruits de mer, coquillages farcis.
Hotel: 3 rooms: single 1, double 2.
Other points: bar, credit cards accepted, children welcome, garden terrace, pets allowed, car parking.
Address: 1 avenue de la Gare, Tauxigny.
M. DOMINIQUE GORON, tel 47.43.40.26.

COULOMBIERS, Vienne 86600, Map 7 ⊗♀

LE RELAIS DE LA PAZIOTERIE, RN 11 between Poitiers and Saintes

Restaurant.
Other points: bar.
Address: Lusignan.

MME YVONNE BARRUSSEAU,
tel 49.60.90.59.

COURTENAY, Loiret 45320, Map 6

LE RELAIS DES SPORTS, RD 60

Languages: German, English
Menu: 52 Frs
Accommodation: 70 to 120 Frs
Restaurant: lunch 12–2pm, dinner
7.30–9.30pm. Closed Sunday nights and from
15 August to 15 September.

Hotel: 6 rooms: single 4, double 2. Showers.
Other points: bar, credit cards accepted, pets
allowed, traditional decor.
Address: 38 rue de Villeneuve.
M. GERARD MARTIN, tel 38.97.32.37.

COURVILLE, Eure-et-Loir 28190, Map 6

L'ESCALE ROUTIERE, RN 23

Menu: 52 to 61 Frs
Restaurant: closed Saturdays 6.30pm,
Sundays, and in December.
Other points: bar, credit cards accepted, pets

allowed, car parking, traditional decor.
Address: 1 rue de la Libération.
HOTELS LES CHATELETS, tel 37.23.21.75.

COZES, Charente-Maritime 17120, Map 7

STATION SERVICE SHELL

Address: Route de Royan, Grezac.
M. JACQUES GADIOU, tel 46.90.84.12.

CREVANT-MONTIERCHAUME, Indre 36130, Map 6

AU CHEZ SOI, RN 151 between Châteauroux and Bourges

Menu: 45 Frs including a drink and coffee
Restaurant: lunch 11–3pm. Closed Saturdays,
Sundays and August.
Other points: children welcome, pets allowed.

Address: Route Nationale 151.
MME YVONNE BELOUIN-FERRE,
tel 54.26.00.19.

CROIX CHAPEAU, Charente-Maritime 17220, Map 7

CAFE DE PARIS, between La Rochelle and St Jean d'Angély, 15km from La Rochelle

Languages: English, Spanish
Menu: 50 Frs
Restaurant: closed Sundays.
Other points: bar, credit cards accepted,

children welcome, self-service, garden terrace,
pets allowed, car parking, traditional decor.
Address: 60 avenue de la Libération.
M. DANIEL MINEUR, tel 46.35.81.20.

DARVOY, Loiret 45150, Map 6

LES ROUTIERS, RD 951 approximately 18km from Orléans, towards Gien

Places of interest: La Sologne (10km),
châteaux de la Loire (rayon de 80km),
cathédrale d'Orléans, parc floral.
Menu: 50 Frs
Restaurant: lunch 12–2pm. Closed Saturday
afternoons, Sundays and in August.

Other points: bar, pets allowed, car parking,
traditional decor.
Address: 4 route d'Orléans, known as La
Place.
MME JULIE VINGERDER, tel 38.59.71.00.

DEOLS, Indre 36130, Map 6

⊗🍸

LE RELAIS DE L'INTER

Languages: English, Spanish, Arabic
Menu: 49,50 to 98,50 Frs
Restaurant: lunch 10.30–3.30pm, dinner 6.30–11.30pm.
Specialities: couscous, grillade.
Other points: bar, credit cards accepted, children welcome, à la carte menu, garden terrace, pets allowed, car parking.
Address: Route d'Issoudun.
M. BOUBEKEUR ABDERRAHMANE, tel 54.27.20.07.

DEOLS, Indre 36130, Map 6

⊗🍸

RESTAURANT L'ESCALE, RN 20 between Paris and Limoges

Restaurant: lunch 11.30–2.30pm, dinner 7–10.30pm.
Other points: bar, credit cards accepted, à la carte menu, pets allowed, car parking.
Address: Route Nationale 20.
M. DIDIER NOIRET, tel 54.22.03.77.

DIGNY, Eure-et-Loir 28250, Map 6

⊗🍸

AUBERGE DE LA VALLEE, RD 928 between La Loupe and Dreux

Places of interest: Cathédrale de Chartres (28km), la Ferté Vidaure, château et musée (25km), musée de la miniature (12km).
Menu: 55 to 120 Frs
Restaurant: closed 15 days in February and 15 days in August.
Specialities: couscous, paëlla, pizza.
Other points: bar, children welcome, à la carte menu, garden terrace, pets allowed, car parking, traditional decor.
Address: 35 rue du Maréchal Leclerc.
M. CLAUDE DOLE, tel 37.29.01.04.

DRACHE, Indre-et-Loire 37800, Map 6

⊗🍸

RESTAURANT DE LA PIERRE PERCEE, RN 10 between Châtellerault and Sainte Maure

Places of interest: Musée et château de Sainte Maure, Monument de la Pierre Percée.
Languages: German, English
Menu: 59 Frs including wine and coffee
Restaurant: lunch 11–3pm, dinner 6–11pm. Closed Saturdays and first 2 weeks of August.
Other points: bar, credit cards accepted, children welcome, garden terrace, pets allowed, car parking, traditional decor.
Address: Route Nationale 10.
MME NADIA KITTEL, tel 47.65.08.64.

DREUX, Eure-et-Loir 28100, Map 6

⊗🍸

CAFE DE LA POSTE, RN 12 and 154

Restaurant.
Other points: bar.
Address: 2 rue du Général de Gaulle.
MME THERESE SEDAINE, tel 37.42.12.00.

DREUX, Eure-et-Loir 28100, Map 6

⊗🍸

LE MARCEAU, RN 12 and 154 between Chartres and Le Man

Places of interest: Chappelle royale, vieux beffroi.
Menu: 51,50 Frs
Restaurant: lunch 12–2pm. Closed Sundays and in August.
Other points: bar, credit cards accepted, garden terrace, pets allowed, car parking.
Address: 40–2 avenue du Général Marceau.
M. JEAN-PIERRE PARENT, tel 37.46.05.57..

ENNORDRES, Cher 18380, Map 6   ⊗ 🍷

LE RELAIS DES ROUTIERS, RN 30

Restaurant: closed Saturdays.
Other points: bar.
Address: Route Départementale 30.

MME GEORGETTE CHAMPION,
tel 48.58.06.36.

EPANNES, Deux-Sèvres 79270, Map 7   ⊗ 🍷 🏠

LE RELAIS SUISSE OCEAN, RN 11

Places of interest: La Rochelle, marais
poitevins (10km).
Menu: 52 to 130 Frs
Accommodation: 95 to 140 Frs
Restaurant: lunch 11.30–2.30pm, dinner
7.30–9pm. Closed Saturday nights, Sundays
and beginning of September.

Specialities: fruits de mer, poissons.
Hotel: 10 double rooms.
Other points: bar, children welcome, à la carte
menu, pets allowed, car parking, traditional
decor.
M. JACKY GUILLOTEAU, tel 49.04.80.01.

ETAGNAC, Charente 16150, Map 7   ⊗ 🍷 🏠

RELAIS D'ETAGNAC, RN 141/948

Language: English
Restaurant.
Hotel: 10 rooms.

Other points: bar.
M. LOUIS LABROUSSE, tel 45.89.21.38.

FERRIERE (LA), Deux-Sèvres 79390, Map 7   ⊗ 🍷

AU BON ACCUEIL, RN 149 between Poitiers and Nantes

Places of interest: Futuroscope de Poitiers, Jaunay.
Language: English
Menu: 51 to 58 Frs
Restaurant: lunch 12–2pm, dinner 7.30–9pm.
Closed Thursday evenings, 15 days in January
and 3 weeks at the end of August.

Other points: bar, credit cards accepted, pets
allowed, car parking.
Address: 10 avenue de Poitiers.
MMES BILHEU-BERGER, tel 49.63.03.01.

FLEURE, Vienne 86340, Map 7   ⊗ 🍷

AUX AMIS DE LA ROUTE, RN 147 between Poitiers and Limoges

Place of interest: Futuroscope de Poitiers.
Menu: 50 to 80 Frs
Restaurant: lunch 12–2.30pm, dinner 7–10pm.
Other points: bar, credit cards accepted,

children welcome, à la carte menu, pets
allowed, car parking, traditional decor.
MME MICHELE GUIONNET,
tel 49.42.60.25.

FONDETTES, Indre-et-Loire 37230, Map 6   ⊗ 🍷

LE BEAU MANOIR, RN 152 between Angers and Nantes

Places of interest: Châteaux de la Loire
(10–30km).
Menu: 51 Frs
Restaurant: lunch 12–2pm, dinner 7–9.30pm.
Closed Saturday afternoons, Sundays and first 2
weeks of May.

Other points: bar, credit cards accepted,
children welcome, garden terrace, pets allowed,
car parking, traditional decor.
Address: 6 quai de la Guignière.
MME EDITH BOURREAU, tel 47.42.01.02.

FONTAINE LE COMTE, Vienne 86240, Map 7 ⊗♥

AUBERGE DE LA GARENNE, RN 11 and A 10, exit Poitiers South, exit Niort

Place of interest: Futuroscope (10km).
Menu: 58 to 120 Frs
Restaurant: lunch 11.30–2pm, dinner 7–10pm.
Closed Sundays, public holidays and in August.
Other points: bar, credit cards accepted,

children welcome, à la carte menu, garden
terrace, pets allowed, car parking, traditional
decor.
Address: allée des Cerfs.
MME MICHELLE GUERIN, tel 49.57.01.22.

FONTAINE SIMON, Eure-et-Loir 28240, Map 6 ⊗♥🏠

AU BON COIN, RD 2 and 25

Restaurant: lunch 12–2pm, dinner 7–8.30pm.
Closed Fridays and in August.
Hotel: 10 rooms, showers, private WCs.
Other points: bar, credit cards accepted, pets

allowed, car parking, traditional decor.
Address: 1 rue de la Mairie, La Loupe.
MME SERGINE DURAND, tel 37.81.84.98.

FONTENAY SUR LOING, Loiret 45210, Map 6 ⊗♥

LES 100 BORNES, RN 7 between Montargis and Dordives

Menu: 53 to 90 Frs
Restaurant: lunch 11.45–3pm, dinner 7–12pm.
Closed 15 days in August.
Other points: bar, credit cards accepted, pets

allowed, car parking.
Address: Route Nationale 7.
M. GUY MARTIN, tel 38.95.82.06.

FORGES, Charente-Maritime 17290, Map 7 ⊗♥

CHEZ NENE, RN 137 between La Rochelle and Angoulême

Places of interest: La Rochelle (20km), poterie
d'art, dolmènes (10km), Surgères (10km).
Language: English
Menu: 50 Frs including wine
Restaurant: lunch 12–2.30pm, dinner
7.30–9pm. Closed Sundays.

Other points: bar, credit cards accepted,
garden terrace, pets allowed, car parking,
traditional decor.
Address: Puydrouard.
M. RENE BOURIEAU, tel 46.35.07.83.

FOSSE, Loir-et-Cher 41330, Map 6 ⊗♥

BAR DE L'ESPERANCE, RN 153 between Vendôme and Le Mans

Menu: 53 Frs
Restaurant: lunch 11.30–2.30pm, dinner
7–9.30pm. Closed Saturdays and Sundays.
Other points: bar, credit cards accepted,

children welcome.
Address: 7 rue de Saint Sulpice.
MME BRIGITTE CHAUVIN-SALA,
tel 54.20.01.77.

FRETEVAL, Loir-et-Cher 41160, Map 6 ⊗♥

LE PLESSIS, RN 10 between Vendôme (20km) and Châteaudun (24km)

Places of interest: Vendôme, vallée du Loir.
Languages: German, English, Spanish
Menu: 54 to 90 Frs

Restaurant: lunch 12–2pm, dinner 7–10pm.
Closed Saturdays and between Christmas and
New Year's day.

Other points: bar, credit cards accepted, pets allowed, car parking, traditional decor.
Address: Route Nationale 10.

MME ISABELLE THEBAULT, tel 54.82.64.28.

GIDY, Loiret 45520, Map 6   ⊗

LA PORTE DU VAL DE LOIRE, A 10 in both directions

Places of interest: Vallée de la Loire et ses châteaux.
Menu: 59 Frs
Restaurant.
Other points: credit cards accepted, children

welcome, self-service, lounge area, pets allowed, car parking.
Address: Aire de Gidy.
Tel 38.73.31.02.

GIEN, Loiret 45500, Map 6   ⊗ 🍷

CAFE DU NORD, RN 140 and CD 952.

Language: English.
Restaurant: closed Sundays and first 2 weeks of August.

Other points: bar.
Address: 51 place de la Victoire.
MME SUZANNE BOTINEAU, tel 38 67 32 98.

GIEN, Loiret 45500, Map 6   ⊗ 🍷 🏠

LE RELAIS NORMAND, opposite the pottery.

Places of interest: Musée de la faïencerie, musée de la chasse.
Menu: 49 Frs
Accommodation: 100 to 150 Frs
Restaurant: lunch 12–2pm, dinner 7.30–9pm. Closed Saturdays and Sundays.

Hotel: 12 rooms: single 8, double 4. Showers.
Other points: bar, children welcome, garden terrace, pets allowed, car parking.
Address: 64 place de la Victoire.
M. PIERRE MONTCEAU, tel 38.67.28.56.

GIEVRES, Loir-et-Cher 41130, Map 6   ⊗ 🍷

RELAIS NORAY, RN 76 near Châteauroux (2km).

Place of interest: Château de Selles sur Cher.
Menu: 50 Frs
Restaurant: lunch 11–2pm, dinner 7.30–10.30pm. Closed Saturday nights and Sundays.

Other points: bar, garden terrace, pets allowed, car parking, traditional decor.
Address: route de Vierzon.
M. CHRISTIAN LITHIER, tel 54.98.64.00.

HUISSEAU EN BEAUCE, Loir-et-Cher 41310, Map 6   ⊗ 🍷

LES PLATANES, RN 10 between Vendôme and Tours.

Place of interest: Vallée du Loir.
Menu: 55 Frs
Restaurant: lunch 12–3pm, dinner 7–10.30pm. Closed Saturday nights and Sundays, public holidays and first week of September.

Other points: bar, credit cards accepted, children welcome, pets allowed, car parking.
Address: Route Nationale 10.
M. HUBERT BRETON, tel 54.82.81.46.

ISDES, Loiret 45620, Map 6   ⊗ 🍷 🏠

HOTEL DU DAUPHIN, RD 83 between La Motte Beuvron and Sully.

Places of interest: Château de Sully, musée de la chasse à Gien, Pont Canal à Briare, château de Chambord, maison de Jeanne d'Arc à Orléans.
Menu: 55 to 120 Frs
Accommodation: 60 to 120 Frs
Restaurant: lunch 11.30–2pm, dinner

7–8.30pm. Closed Monday afternoons.
Hotel: 11 rooms: single 9, double 2. Showers.
Other points: bar, children welcome, garden terrace, pets allowed, car parking, traditional decor.
Address: 11 grande Rue.
M. LUCIEN LAURENT, tel 38.29.10.29.

ISSOUDUN, Indre 36100, Map 6 ⊗ ♀ ⌂

LE RELAIS D'ISSOUDUNOIS, RN 151 between Châteauroux (27km) and Bourges (27km).

Places of interest: Issoudun, Bourges.
Language: English.
Menu: 50 to 129 Frs including wine.
Accommodation: 160 Frs
Restaurant: lunch 11.45–2.30pm, dinner 7–10.30pm.
Hotel: 16 double rooms. Showers, baths,

private WCs, phone.
Other points: bar, credit cards accepted, children welcome, à la carte menu, garden terrace, car parking.
Address: 8 route de Bourges.
M. HERVE, tel 54.03.04.05.

ISSOUDUN, Indre 36100, Map 6 ⊗ ♀ ⌂

LE RELAIS DE LA CROIX ROUGE, RN 151.

Languages: English, German, Italian, Turkish.
Restaurant: closed Saturdays, Sundays, mid-August.

Hotel: 5 rooms.
Address: 14 faubourg de la Croix Rouge.
M. CLAUDE GROSYEUX, tel 54.21.04.91.

JARNAC, Charente 16200, Map 7 ⊗ ♀

LES ROUTIERS, RN 141

Menu: 50 Frs
Restaurant: lunch 12–2pm, dinner 7–10pm. Closed Sundays (except reservations).

Other points: bar, children welcome.
Address: 77 rue Pasteur.
MME MARYSE BOUFFINIE, tel 45.81.02.40.

JARNAC, Charente 16200, Map 7 ⊗ ♀

RELAIS DES VIGNES, RN 141 between Cognac and Royan.

Place of interest: Distillerie de cognac (20km).
Menu: 48 to 51,50 Frs
Restaurant: lunch 11.30–3pm, dinner 7.30–10pm. Closed Sundays and from 15 August to 15 September.

Other points: bar, credit cards accepted, pets allowed, car parking.
Address: Route Nationale 141, Bourras.
MME MONIQUE DELAVOIE, tel 45.35.81.62.

LADON, Loiret 45270, Map 6 ⊗ ♀ ⌂

LE RELAIS DE LADON, RN 60 between Montargis and Orléans.

Place of interest: Moulin à vent.
Menu: 48 to 85 Frs
Accommodation: 54 to 99 Frs
Restaurant: closed Sundays, from 28 June to 19 July and for 15 days after Christmas.

Hotel: 7 double rooms. Showers.
Other points: bar, garden terrace, pets allowed, car parking.
Address: 400 avenue du 24 Novembre.
M. PIERRE GUILLAUMIN, tel 38.95.51.32.

LANDES, Charente-Maritime 17380, Map 7 ⊗🍴🍷

LES AMIS DE LA ROUTE, RN 139.

Language: English.
Menu: 50 to 70 Frs
Restaurant.
Specialities: grillades, tournedos.

Other points: bar, car parking.
Address: rue Aunis Sainaunge, Le Bourg.
M. JACKY GODEMAN, tel 46.59.73.12.

LAONS, Eure-et-Loir 28270, Map 6 ⊗🍷

L'EOLE

Menu: 45 Frs
Restaurant: closed Sundays.
Address: place du Carrefour.

MME CHRISTINE EMILIE JEUDON,
tel 37.38.10.21.

LENCLOITRE, Vienne 86140, Map 7 ⊗🍷

AU 14 ANNE ANDRE, D 725 and D 757 between Chatellerault and Nantes.

Places of interest: Futuroscope (10km), les marais poitevins, châteaux de la Loire, Azay le Rideau, Villandry, Chinon, Saumur.
Menu: 47 to 55 Frs
Restaurant: lunch 11–3pm, dinner 7–11 pm.

Closed Sundays.
Other points: bar, credit cards accepted, lounge area, pets allowed, car parking.
Address: 2 place du Champ de Foire.
M. ANDRE PERNELLE, tel 49.90.71.29.

LISSAY LOCHY, Cher 18340, Map 6 ⊗🍷

AUBERGE DES MAISONS ROUGES, at crossroads of RD 28 and 73

Place of interest: Bourges.
Menu: from 50 Frs
Restaurant: closed December.
Other points: bar, credit cards accepted, à la

carte menu, garden terrace, pets allowed, car parking, traditional decor.
Address: Les Maisons Rouges.
M. ROBERT LEGER, tel 48.64.76.07.

LOGE (LA), Loir-et-Cher 41300, Map 6 ⊗🍷🏠🛏☆

RELAIS DE LA LOGE, RN 20 near Vierzon (13km)

Language: English.
Menu: 75 to 120 Frs
Restaurant.
Specialities: gibiers (in season).
Hotel: 30 rooms: single 15, double 15.

Showers, private WCs.
Other points: bar, credit cards accepted, car parking.
Address: Route Nationale 20.
M. GUY PAILLAUD, tel 54.83.37.20.

LOGRON, Eure-et-Loir 28200, Map 6 ⊗🍷

AUBERGE SAINT NICOLAS, between Orléans and Alençon.

Menu: 48 to 90 Frs
Restaurant: lunch 11.30–1pm, dinner 7–10pm.
Closed Monday afternoons and 15 days at Christmas.

Other points: bar, children welcome, à la carte menu, car parking.
Address: 2 rue des Buissonnots.
M. BRUNO HUBERT, tel 37.98.98.02.

LORRIS, Loiret 45260, Map 6 ⊗ ϒ

AUBERGE DE LA CROIX ROUGE, RD 961

Restaurant: closed Sunday afternoons.
Other points: bar, children welcome, à la carte menu.

Address: 28 rue Guillaume.
MME LISIANE BERLIN, tel 38.92.47.03.

LORRIS, Loiret 45260, Map 6 ⊗ ϒ

LA CHAUMIERE, road towards Montargis/Bellegarde/Gien

Places of interest: Châteaux de la Loire.
Restaurant: lunch 12–2pm. Closed September.
Other points: bar, credit cards accepted, children welcome, à la carte menu, pets

allowed, car parking, traditional decor.
Address: 97 Grand-Rue.
MME HUGUETTE SMETHURST, tel 38.92.30.67.

LOULAY, Charente-Maritime 17330, Map 7 ⊗ ϒ ⌂

CHEZ JO, RN 150 exit Niort

Places of interest: La Rochelle (40km), les marais poitevins, forêt domaniale de Chizé, musée de la néolithique, châteaux.
Menu: 55 to 65 Frs
Accommodation: 100 to 145 Frs
Restaurant: lunch 12–2pm, dinner 7–8.30pm. Closed Saturday nights and Sunday nights (out of season).

Hotel: 5 rooms: single 1, double 4. Showers, private WCs.
Other points: bar, children welcome, garden terrace, pets allowed, car parking, traditional decor.
Address: 10 place du Général de Gaulle.
M. GEORGES MAHDID, tel 46.33.80.59.

LUNERY, Cher 18400, Map 6 ⊗ ϒ

LE BAR DU CENTRE, RD 27 between Bourges and Châteauneuf sur Cher

Place of interest: Bourges (20km).
Menu: 50 to 95 Frs, including wine, coffee.
Restaurant: lunch 12–2.30pm, dinner 7–10pm. Closed Tuesdays, 15 days in February and 15 days in September.
Specialities: Pâté aux pommes de terre, magret

de canard.
Other points: bar, children welcome, à la carte menu, pets allowed, car parking, traditional decor.
Address: 1 place Jacques Georges.
M. MICHEL PORCHERON, tel 48.68.98.71.

LUSSAC LES CHATEAUX, Vienne 86320, Map 7 ⊗ ϒ

LE CHENE VERT, RN 147 between Poitiers and Limoges

Places of interest: Vallée de la Vienne, les grottes préhistoriques.
Languages: English, Spanish, Italian
Menu: 46 Frs
Restaurant: closed Sundays.
Other points: bar, credit cards accepted, à la

carte menu, garden terrace, pets allowed, car parking, traditional decor.
Address: 14 avenue Léon Pineau.
MME ALEXANDRINE DOS REIS MARTINS, tel 49.48.40.30.

LUTZ EN DUNOIS, Eure-et-Loir 28200, Map 6 ⊗ ϒ ⌂

LA RENCONTRE, D 955 between Orléans and Alençon

Places of interest: Châteaudun (château, grottes, moulins à vent), vallée du Loir.
Menu: 50 Frs
Accommodation: 60 Frs
Restaurant: lunch 11–3pm, dinner 7–9.30pm. Closed Saturday nights, Sundays and from February to early March.

Hotel: 5 rooms: single 4, double 1. Showers, baths.
Other points: bar, credit cards accepted, garden terrace, pets allowed, car parking, traditional decor.
M. FRANCIS BERRIER, tel 37.45.18.08.

MAINVILLIERS, Eure-et-Loir 28300, Map 6 ⊗

L'ARCHE DE CHARTRES NORD, A 11

Place of interest: Cathédrale de Chartres.
Language: English
Menu: from 59 Frs
Restaurant: lunch 11–4pm, dinner 6–12pm.
Specialities: jambon braisé à l'os.
Other points: credit cards accepted, children

welcome, à la carte menu, self-service, garden terrace, pets allowed, car parking.
Address: Aire de Gasville, between Le Mans and Rennes.
M. JEAN-JACQUES BIGOT, tel 37.31.62.42.

MAINVILLIERS, Eure-et-Loir 28300, Map 6 ⊗

L'ARCHE DE CHARTRES SUD, A 11

Place of interest: Cathédrale de Chartres.
Menu: from 59 Frs
Restaurant.
Specialities: jambon braisé aux épinards.
Other points: credit cards accepted, children

welcome, self-service, garden terrace, pets allowed, car parking.
Address: Aire de Bois Paris, between Nantes and Paris.
M. PATRICK LAFUENTE, tel 37.31.62.41.

MANTHELAN, Indre-et-Loire 37240, Map 6 ⊗☐

LE RELAIS DE LA CROIX VERTE

Language: English
Restaurant.
Other points: bar, car parking.

Address: 25 rue Nationale.
MME CHRISTIANE MARTIN,
tel 47.92.80.16.

MARANS, Charente-Maritime 17230, Map 7 ⊗☐⌂

LE POINT DU JOUR – Chez Sylviane et Joël, RN 137 between La Rochelle and Bordeaux

Places of interest: Marais poitevins, La Rochelle.
Menu: 52 to 75 Frs
Restaurant: lunch 11–4.30pm, dinner 7-11.30pm. Closed Sundays (out of season).
Hotel: 5 rooms.

Other points: bar, credit cards accepted, children welcome, pets allowed, car parking, traditional decor.
Address: 2 rue des Moulins.
MME SYLVIANE GERARD, tel 46.01.14.54.

MAROLLES, Eure-et-Loir 28260, Map 6 ⊗☐⌣

AU RELAIS DE MAROLLES, RN 12

Menu: 55 to 85 Frs
Restaurant: closed Saturdays, Sundays (except for groups) and first 2 weeks of August.
Specialities: escaloppe normande, omelette aux

pleurottes, grillades.
Other points: bar, car parking.
Address: 44 rue Georges Bréant.
MME VIVIANE BEAUVAIS, tel 37.43.20.50.

MARVILLE MOUTIERS BRULE, Eure-et-Loir 28500, Map 6   ⊗ ♉

LE RELAIS, between Chartres and Dreux

Place of interest: Cathédrale de Chartres
(27km), chapelle royale de Dreux (4km).
Menu: 50 Frs
Restaurant: closed Monday afternoons and
Sundays.

Other points: bar, car parking.
MME RAYMONDE LESCH, tel 37.38.36.20.

MERY SUR CHER, Cher 18100, Map 6   ⊗ ♉ 🏠

LE RELAIS BERRY SOLOGNE, RN 76

Places of interest: Châteaux de la Loire.
Restaurant: closed Saturdays and Sundays.
Hotel: 10 rooms, showers, baths.
Other points: bar, credit cards accepted,

garden terrace, pets allowed, car parking.
Address: route de Tours.
M. CLAUDE CARRE, tel 48.75.20.34.

MEZIERES EN BRENNE, Indre 36290, Map 6   ⊗ ♉ 🏠

RESTAURANT DES SPORTS

Menu: 90 to 220 Frs
Restaurant.
Hotel: 6 rooms: single 3, double 3. Showers.
Other points: bar, garden terrace, pets allowed,

car parking, traditional decor.
Address: 11 rue de l'Ouest.
M. CHRISTIAN CHARPENTIER,
tel 54.38.11.62.

MIGNERES, Loiret 45490, Map 6   ⊗ ♉ 🏠

LE RELAIS DE MIGNERES, RD 94 between Auxy and Montargis

Menu: 53 to 100 Frs including wine and coffee
Accommodation: 80 to 120 Frs
Restaurant: lunch 11–2pm, dinner
7.30–9.30pm. Closed Sundays.
Hotel: 7 rooms: single 4, double 3. Showers.

Other points: bar, children welcome, lounge
area, pets allowed, car parking, traditional
decor.
Address: 3 rue de la Gare.
M. ROMAIN COUSIN, tel 38.87.85.57.

MONNAIE, Indre-et-Loire 37380, Map 6   ⊗

GRILL DE TOURAINE, A 10, both directions

Places of interest: Châteaux de la Loire.
Languages: English, Spanish, Dutch
Menu: 80 to 120 Frs
Restaurant: lunch 11–3pm, dinner 7–10pm.
Specialities: rillons, andouillette au vouvray.

Other points: credit cards accepted, children
welcome, à la carte menu, garden terrace, pets
allowed, car parking.
Address: Aire de la Longue Vue.
Tel 47.56.44.94.

MONNAIE, Indre-et-Loire 37380, Map 6   ⊗

L'ARCHE DE TOURS, A 10

Places of interest: Châteaux de la Loire, Tours.
Menu: 59 Frs
Restaurant: lunch 11–4pm, dinner 5–11pm.
Other points: credit cards accepted, children
welcome, self-service, garden terrace, pets

allowed, car parking.
Address: Aire de Tours Val de Loire, between
Bordeaux and Paris.
M. CHRISTOPHE OZENNE, tel 47.56.15.49.

MONTARGIS, Loiret 45200, Map 6   ⊗🍷🏠

LE PARIS-MONTARGIS

Language: English
Restaurant: closed Sundays.
Hotel: 10 rooms.

Other points: bar.
Address: 221 rue Emile Mangin.
M. DARBIER, tel 38.85.63.04.

MONTBAZON, Indre-et-Loire 37250, Map 6   ⊗🍷🏠

LA GRANGE BARBIER, RN 10 exit south of Montbazon, towards Poitiers

Places of interest: Châteaux de la Loire.
Menu: 52 to 105 Frs
Accommodation: 100 to 150 Frs
Restaurant: lunch 12–2pm, dinner 7–9.30pm. Closed Sunday nights and second 2 weeks of July.

Hotel: 5 rooms: single 3, double 2. Showers.
Other points: bar, credit cards accepted, children welcome, garden terrace, pets allowed, car parking.
Address: Route Nationale 10.
M. WILLIAM LABORDE, tel 47.26.01.69.

MONTILS (LES), Loir-et-Cher 41120, Map 6   ⊗🍷

LES DEUX ROUES, RN 764 between Blois and Montrichard

Places of interest: Tour et vieux porche aux Montils.
Restaurant: lunch 11.30–2pm, dinner 7.30–8.30pm. Closed Sundays.

Other points: bar, car parking, traditional decor.
Address: 28 rue de Bel Air.
M. JEAN-PIERRE LEVAUX, tel 54.44.02.40.

MONTLIEU LA GARDE, Charente-Maritime 17210, Map 7   ⊗🍷

AU RENDEZ-VOUS DES ROUTIERS, RN 10

Restaurant: closed Saturday and Sunday nights.

Other points: bar.
M. ROBERT LAVILLE, tel 46.04.44.24.

MONTMOREAU, Charente 16190, Map 7   ⊗🍷🏠

LES ROUTIERS, RN 674 between Angoulème and Libourne

Place of interest: Aubeterre.
Restaurant.
Speciality: coq au vin.
Hotel: 6 rooms: single 1, double 5. Showers.

Other points: bar, garden terrace, pets allowed, car parking.
Address: 14 avenue de l'Angoumois.
MME ERNESTINE FERRIER, tel 46.60.21.17

MORNAY SUR ALLIER, Cher 18600, Map 6   ⊗🍷🏠

L'ETAPE DU RIVAGE, RN 76 between Bourges and Moulin

Places of interest: Parc animalier de Saint Augustin, parc floral et château d'Apremont sur Allier, bords de l'Allier.
Menu: 50 Frs
Accommodation: 80 to 140 Frs
Restaurant: closed Saturdays, Sundays and in August.

Hotel: 4 rooms: single 1, double 3. Showers, private WCs.
Other points: bar, credit cards accepted, children welcome, lounge area, pets allowed, car parking, traditional decor.
Address: Le Rivage.
M. CHRISTIAN MORET, tel 48.74.59.17.

MORNAY SUR ALLIER, Cher 18600, Map 6   ⊗ ⟈ 🏠

LE RELAIS DE LA ROUTE, RN 76

Places of interest: Apremont (15km), parc de
Saint Augustin (7km).
Languages: German, English
Menu: 52 to 90 Frs
Accommodation: 60 to 90 Frs
Restaurant: closed Saturday 3pm to Monday
1am.

Hotel: 5 rooms: single 2, double 3. Private
WCs.
Other points: bar, credit cards accepted, car
parking.
Address: Route Nationale 76.
MME JACQUELINE CHEVROT,
tel 48.74.53.54.

MOULISMES, Vienne 86500, Map 7   ⊗ ⟈ 🏠 ☆

LA TABLE OUVERTE, RN 147 between Poitiers and Limoges

Places of interest: Vallées de la Gartempe et
de la Vienne, futuroscope à Poitiers, Oradour
sur Glane.
Menu: 47,50 to 105 Frs
Accommodation: 105 to 195 Frs
Restaurant: lunch 12–2.30pm, dinner
7.30–9.30pm. Closed Saturday afternoons and
Sundays after lunch (except in August).

Hotel: 7 rooms: single 3, double 4. Showers,
baths, private WCs, phone.
Other points: bar, credit cards accepted, à la
carte menu, pets allowed, car parking,
traditional decor.
Address: Route Nationale 147.
HOTELS GRANSAGNE-BAUDET,
tel 49.91.90.68.

NAINTRE, Vienne 86530, Map 7   ⊗ ⟈

LA HALTE, RN 10, exit south Chatellerault take autoroute Aquitaine

Languages: English, Arabic, Spanish, German
Restaurant: closed Saturdays, Sundays.
Other points: bar.

Address: Route Nationale 10.
MME HENNI HOUAS, tel 49.90.09.69.

NERE, Charente-Maritime 17510, Map 7   ⊗ ⟈

LES ROUTIERS

Menu: 45 Frs
Restaurant: closed Sundays.
Other points: bar.

Address: route d'Aulnay.
MME MONIQUE METOIS, tel 46.33.00.30.

NEUVY, Loir-et-Cher 41250, Map 6   ⊗ ⟈ 🏠 ⌣

LA CHEMINEE, RD 923 between Paris and Angoulême

Places of interest: Chambord (10km),
Cheverny (15km), Blois (20km), Villesavin
(10km).
Languages: English, Spanish, Portuguese
Menu: 55 to 140 Frs including wine and coffee
Accommodation: 170 to 260 Frs
Restaurant: lunch 12–2pm, dinner 7–9pm.
Closed Wednesdays and 15 days in September.
Specialities: escargots, salade de gésier,
feuilleté de chèvre, rognons de veau, filet de

canard, darne de saumon, coquille Saint
Jacques, cuisses de grenouilles.
Hotel: 9 rooms: single 4, double 5. Open
7am–9pm.
Other points: bar, credit cards accepted,
children welcome, à la carte menu, lounge area,
garden terrace, pets allowed, car parking,
traditional decor.
Address: Le Bourg.
M. PHILIPPE MASCLET, tel 54.46.42.70.

NEUVY SAINT SEPULCHRE, Indre 36230, Map 6 ⊗♈🏠

LA CHARRETTE, RD 927 between La Châtre and Montluçon

Places of interest: Château de Georges Sand (15km), château Nohan Vic, basilique.
Languages: Italian, Yugoslav, Polish, Russian
Menu: 120 to 170 Frs
Restaurant: dinner 7–10pm.
Specialities: coq au vin, boeuf bourguignon, blanquette de veau (by arrangement).

Hotel: 7 rooms: single 4, double 3. Showers, baths, phone.
Other points: bar, children welcome, à la carte menu, lounge area, car parking, traditional decor.
Address: 21 place du Champ de Foire.
M. NICOLAS PAVLICEVIC, tel 54.30.84.77.

NIORT, Deux-Sèvres 79000, Map 7 ⊗♈

LE BON ACCUEIL, RN 150 between Niort and Bordeaux

Places of interest: Marais poitevins (15km), zoo et forêt de Chizé (20km).
Menu: 52,50 to 68 Frs
Restaurant: lunch 12–2pm, dinner 7.30–10pm. Closed Sundays and in August.

Other points: bar, credit cards accepted, car parking.
Address: 424 avenue St Jean d'Angély.
MME THÉRÈSE DENIBAUD,
tel 49.79.27.60.

NOGENT LE PHAYE, Eure-et-Loir 28630, Map 6 ⊗♈

LE RELAIS DU MOULIN ROUGE, RN 10 exit Chartres towards Paris

Menu: 53 Frs
Restaurant: lunch 11.30–2.30pm, dinner 7–9.45 pm. Closed Saturdays, Sundays and in August.
Other points: bar, credit cards accepted, pets

allowed, car parking, traditional decor.
Address: Le Moulin Rouge, Route Nationale 10.
M. CHRISTIAN BRU, tel 37.31.62.68.

NOGENT LE ROTROU, Eure-et-Loir 28400, Map 6 ⊗

STATION SERVICE TOTAL – Alliane Auto, RN 23

Language: German
Restaurant.
Other points: credit cards accepted, lounge

area, car parking.
Address: route du Mans.
MME DANIELLE BLOTTIN, tel 37.52.90.02.

NOHANT EN GOUT, Cher 18390, Map 6 ⊗♈

RELAIS DU BERRY, RN 151 between Charité sur Loire and Auxerre

Places of interest: Bourges et ses environs.
Languages: German, English, Spanish
Menu: 50 to 110 Frs
Restaurant: lunch 11–3.30pm, dinner 7–11pm. Closed Mondays from 3pm and for 15 days in February.
Specialities: benichonne et feuilleté de riz de veau.

Other points: bar, credit cards accepted, children welcome, à la carte menu, garden terrace, pets allowed, car parking, traditional decor.
Address: Route Nationale 151.
HOTELS LIGOT, tel 48.30.42.90.

NOYANT GARE, Indre-et-Loire 37800, Map 6 ⊗♈

LE PETIT ROUTIER – Chez Mimi, RD 760 between Ste Maure de Touraine and Chinon

Places of interest: Chinon, Azay le Rideau et son château (44km), Maillé.
Language: English
Menu: 50 Frs including wine and coffee
Restaurant: lunch 11.30–2pm, dinner 6.30–9pm. Closed Saturday afternoons and Sundays.

Other points: bar, credit cards accepted, children welcome, garden terrace, pets allowed, car parking, traditional decor.
Address: route de Chinon.
MME ANNICK GIRET, tel 47.65.82.26.

ORLEANS, Loiret 45100, Map 6 ⊗♉⌂

AUX QUATRE MARCHES, RN 20 and RD 951

Place of interest: Bords du Loiret.
Menu: 46 to 50 Frs
Restaurant: closed Saturday nights, Sundays and in August.

Hotel: 5 rooms.
Other points: bar, pets allowed.
Address: 163 avenue de Saint Mesmin.
M. PIERRE GUYOT, tel 38.66.31.12.

PELLEVOISIN, Indre 36180, Map 6 ⊗♉⌂

LE RELAIS DES ROUTIERS – Chez Babette et Joël, RD 11between Valancay and Pellevoisin

Places of interest: Châteaux de Valençay (30km) et d'Argy (6km).
Language: English
Menu: 50 Frs
Accommodation: 135 Frs
Restaurant: lunch 12–2pm, dinner 7.30–9.30pm. Closed second 2 weeks of September.

Specialities: salade au chèvre chaud, confits de canard, coq au vin.
Hotel: 4 rooms, showers, baths, phone.
Other points: bar, credit cards accepted, garden terrace, car parking, traditional decor.
Address: 30 rue Jean Giraudoux.
MME ELISABETH PETIT, tel 54.39.03.78.

PERRUSSON, Indre-et-Loire 37600, Map 6 ⊗♉⌂

LES ROUTIERS, RN 143 between Tours and Châteauroux

Restaurant: lunch 12–3pm, dinner 7–10pm. Closed Sunday nights and in August.
Hotel: 8 rooms: single 4, double 4. Showers, baths.

Other points: bar, children welcome, à la carte menu, pets allowed, car parking.
Address: 3 rue de l'Indre.
M. KLEBER LANCHAIS, tel 47.59.04.34.

PEZOU, Loir-et-Cher 41100, Map 6 ⊗♉⌂

RELAIS D'ARGENTEUIL, RN 10

Menu: 58 Frs
Accommodation: 83 to 166 Frs
Restaurant: lunch 11.30–2pm, dinner 6.30–10.30pm. Closed Saturdays after 11am, Sundays, August and end of December.
Hotel: 6 rooms: single 2, double 4. Showers.

Other points: bar, credit cards accepted, children welcome, pets allowed, car parking, traditional decor.
Address: known as Fontaine.
M. PIERRE HAUVILLE, tel 54.23.42.47.

PITHIVIERS, Loiret 45300, Map 6 ⊗♉

LA PORTE DE BEAUCE, RN 152

Places of interest: Musée du transport, château fort, circuit touristique dans un petit train à vapeur.
Languages: English, Polish
Restaurant: lunch 12–2pm. Closed Mondays and in September.

Specialities: grillades.
Other points: bar, credit cards accepted, à la carte menu, garden terrace, pets allowed, car parking, traditional decor.
Address: 6 Mail Ouest.
M. CHRISTIAN COLLARD, tel 38.30.02.52.

POITIERS, Vienne 86000, Map 7

LES DOUVES, RN 10

Languages: English, German
Menu: 55 to 150 Frs
Accommodation: 80 to 140 Frs
Restaurant: lunch 12–3pm, dinner 7–11pm. Closed Sunday nights.
Specialities: coq au vin, poissons en papillotte, gibiers.

Hotel: 5 rooms: single 3, double 2. Showers.
Other points: bar, credit cards accepted, children welcome, pets allowed, car parking, traditional decor.
Address: 2 avenue de la Libération.
MME YVONNE GREMILLON, tel 49.37.80.04.

POMPAIRE, Deux-Sèvres 79200, Map 7

LA CLE DES CHAMPS, in commercial centre

Place of interest: Parthenay (cité médiévale).
Menu: 50 to 99 Frs
Restaurant: lunch 11–4pm. Closed Sundays (except groups).
Specialities: cuisses de grenouilles, anguille provençale, plateau de fruits de mer.

Other points: bar, credit cards accepted, children welcome, à la carte menu, pets allowed, car parking.
Address: route de Saint Maixent.
MME YOLANDE DUBIN, tel 49.95.20.75.

PONT CHRETIEN CHABENET (LE), Indre 36800, Map 6

LE RELAIS DE LA BOUZANNE, RN 727 between Argenton sur Creuse and Le Blanc

Places of interest: Pont de Bais (1km), château de Chabenet, Argenton sur Creuse (3km).
Menu: 48 to 120 Frs including wine
Restaurant: lunch 12–3pm, dinner 7–10pm. Closed Wednesdays after 3pm.

Other points: bar, children welcome, à la carte menu, garden terrace, pets allowed, car parking, traditional decor.
Address: 15 rue Principale.
M. JEAN-MARC DAVID, tel 54.25.81.54.

PRESSAC, Vienne 86460, Map 7

LE RELAIS ROUTIER, RN 148 between Niort and Poitiers

Places of interest: Futuroscope (60km), circuits de la Vienne et du Vigeant, vallée du Clain.
Menu: 50 Frs including wine and coffee
Restaurant: lunch 10–4pm, dinner 7–12pm. Closed Saturdays and second 2 weeks of August.

Specialities: farcis poitevins.
Other points: bar, credit cards accepted, children welcome, garden terrace, pets allowed, car parking, traditional decor.
Address: place de l'Eglise.
MME FRANCINE BOUYER, tel 49.48.56.99.

PRUNAY LE GILLON, Eure-et-Loir 28360, Map 6

LA GERBE D'OR, RN 154 between Chartres and Orléans

Place of interest: Cathédrale de Chartres.
Menu: 55 to 110 Frs
Restaurant.
Other points: bar, credit cards accepted, children welcome, à la carte menu, garden

terrace, pets allowed, car parking, traditional decor.
Address: 10 rue du Pavillon.
M. HENRI GOSSET, tel 37.25.72.38.

RASSATS (LES) PAR BRIE, Charente 16590, Map 7   ⊗ 𝖸

L'AUBERGE DES ROUTIERS, RN 141 between Limoges and Angoulême

Place of interest: Les Charentes.
Menu: 52 Frs
Restaurant: closed Sundays and in August.
Specialities: charentaises.

Other points: bar, credit cards accepted, à la carte menu, lounge area, pets allowed, car parking, traditional decor.
DORE ET FILS, tel 45.65.90.24.

REFFANNES, Deux-Sèvres 79420, Map 7   ⊗ 𝖸

LE CHEVAL BLANC, RD 938

Restaurant: closed Saturdays
Other points: bar, pets allowed, car parking.

Address: avenue de la Grande Auberge, Le Bourg.
M. DIDIER CHEVALIER, tel 49 70 25 18.

RHODES, Indre 36170, Map 6   ⊗ 𝖸

RELAIS ROUTIERS DE RHODES, RN 20 between Limoges and Châteauroux

Places of interest: Sites gallo-romains (29km), lac Eguzon (20km), vallée de la Creuse.
Menu: 53 Frs
Restaurant: closed Saturdays, Sundays and in August.

Other points: bar, pets allowed, car parking, traditional decor.
Address: Mouhet.
M. JEAN-PIERRE PEREZ, tel 54.47.65.26.

ROCHECORBON, Indre-et-Loire 37210, Map 6   ⊗ 𝖸 🏠

RELAIS DE PATYS, RN 152

Places of interest: Nombreuses caves, châteaux de la Loire.
Languages: English, Spanish
Menu: 45 to 56 Frs
Accommodation: 95 to 130 Frs
Restaurant: lunch 12–2pm, dinner 7–9pm.

Closed Sundays and in August.
Hotel: 4 rooms: single 2, double 2.
Other points: bar, children welcome, à la carte menu, pets allowed, car parking.
Address: 1 rue de Patys.
M. JEAN-MARC NOURRY, tel 47.52.61.75.

ROCHELLE (LA), Charente-Maritime 17000, Map 7   ⊗ 𝖸 🏠

L'OCEANIC, between l'Ile de Ré and La Pallice

Places of interest: La Rochelle: vieille ville, port de plaisance, musées.
Menu: 50 to 80 Frs
Accommodation: 80 to 120 Frs
Restaurant: lunch 11.30–2pm, dinner 7.30–10pm. Closed Saturdays and Sundays.
Specialities: couscous, paëlla, cassoulet, choucroute.

Hotel: 5 rooms: single 1, double 4. Showers, private WCs.
Other points: bar, credit cards accepted, garden terrace, pets allowed, car parking, traditional decor.
Address: place du Marché de la Pallice.
M. PHILIPPE ALZIN, tel 46.42.62.37.

ROCHELLE (LA), Charente-Maritime 17000, Map 7   ⊗ ♈ 🏠 ☆

LA COTE VERTE, between La Rochelle and l'Ile de Ré

Places of interest: La Rochelle, Ile de Ré.
Languages: English, Portuguese
Menu: 50 Frs including wine
Restaurant: lunch 11.30–2.30pm, dinner
7.30–9.30pm. Closed Sunday afternoons.

Hotel: 10 rooms: single 6, double 4. Showers.
Other points: bar, credit cards accepted,
garden terrace, pets allowed, car parking.
Address: 26 boulevard du Maréchal Lyautey.
MME MURIEL PARENTE, tel 46.43.00.27.

ROCHELLE (LA), Charente-Maritime 17000, Map 7   ⊗ ♈

LE DELMAS BAR

Places of interest: Ile d'Oléron, Aix, Ré,
marais poitevins.
Restaurant.
Other points: bar, garden terrace, pets allowed,
car parking.

Address: 32 boulevard Emile Delmas.
MME JEANINE FRANCSON,
tel 46.42.60.23.

ROCHELLE (LA), Charente-Maritime 17000, Map 7   ⊗ ♈ 🏠

LE GOELAND

Places of interest: Pont de la Rochelle, Ile de
Ré, musée maritime, musée des automates.
Languages: English, Spanish
Menu: 46 Frs
Accommodation: 150 to 250 Frs
Restaurant.
Hotel: 6 double rooms. Showers, baths, TV,
phone.

Other points: bar, credit cards accepted,
children welcome, garden terrace, pets allowed,
car parking, traditional decor.
Address: 15 rue du Docteur Bigois, Place du
Marché.
M. JACQUES DURANDEAU, tel 46.42.05.29.

ROCHELLE (LA), Charente-Maritime 17000, Map 7   ⊗ ♈

LES EMBRUNS, Port de la Pallice, head of the bay

Place of interest: Port de la Pallice.
Languages: English
Menu: 48 to 120 Frs
Restaurant: lunch 11.30–3pm, dinner 7–9pm.
Closed Saturdays and Sundays.
Specialities: plateau de fruits de mer, couscous,
paëlla, choucroute (every Friday night).

Other points: bar, credit cards accepted,
children welcome, self-service, pets allowed,
car parking, traditional decor.
Address: 413 avenue Jean Guiton.
RENE AND FABIENNE POULTIER,
tel 46.42.61.88.

ROCHELLE PALLICE (LA), Charente-Maritime 17000, Map 7   ⊗ ♈

CHEZ ANNIE

Restaurant: closed Sundays.
Other points: bar.

Address: rue de l'Ile de Ré.
MME ANNIE BERNELAS, tel 46.42.53.61.

ROMORANTIN LANTHENAY, Loir-et-Cher 41200, Map 6   ⊗ ♈ 🏠 ☆

LES AUBIERS, RN 722 and 765 town centre

Places of interest: Châteaux de Chambord, Romorantin, Lassay, Blois.
Menu: 54 to 180 Frs
Accommodation: 150 to 200 Frs
Restaurant: lunch 12–2pm, dinner 7.30–9pm.
Hotel: 19 rooms: single 14, double 5. Showers, baths, private WCs, TV, phone.
Other points: bar, credit cards accepted, children welcome, à la carte menu, car parking, traditional decor.
Address: 1 avenue de Blois.
MME BOIVIN, tel 54.76.05.59.

ROMORANTIN LANTHENAY, Loire-et-Cher 41200, Map 6   ⊗ ♈

RELAIS DE L'AVENIR, RN 722 and 765

Menu: 49 to 58 Frs
Restaurant: lunch 11.45–2.30pm. Closed Saturdays and Sundays and 15 days in August.
Other points: bar, pets allowed, traditional decor.
Address: 44 avenue de Villefranche.
MME JOCELYNE BRETON, tel 54.76.14.28.

ROUILLAC, Charente 16170, Map 7   ⊗ ♈ ⌂

LA BOULE D'OR, RN 939 between Angoulême and La Rochelle

Places of interest: Château de Liguière (5km), Cognac (25km), Angoulême (25km), Saintes (50km).
Languages: German, English
Menu: 53 to 80 Frs including wine and coffee
Accommodation: 100 to 140 Frs
Restaurant: lunch 11.30–3pm, dinner 6.30–10pm. Closed Sundays and 15 days in August.
Hotel: 8 rooms: single 5, double 3. Showers.
Other points: bar, credit cards accepted, children welcome, à la carte menu, pets allowed, car parking, traditional decor.
Address: 56 rue du Général de Gaulle.
MME ELISABETH LHERMITE, tel 45.96.50.45.

ROUILLE, Vienne 86480, Map 7   ⊗ ♈ ⌂

CHEZ MARYSE, RD 950 between Poitiers and Royan

Places of interest: Les ruines gallo-romaines, futuroscope à Poitiers.
Menu: 60 Frs
Accommodation: 100 Frs
Restaurant: lunch 12–2pm, dinner 7–9pm. Closed Sundays and 18 December to 4 January.
Hotel: 6 single rooms, showers.
Other points: bar, credit cards accepted, garden terrace, pets allowed, car parking.
Address: Le Grand Breuil.
MME MARYSE TELLIER, tel 49.43.93.75.

ROUMAZIERES, Charente 16370, Map 7   ⊗ ♈

LES ROUTIERS, RN 141 between Limoges and Angoulême

Places of interest: Chassenon (ruines gallo-romaines), Rochecouart, La Rochefoucault, Confolens.
Menu: 48 Frs including wine
Restaurant: closed Saturdays, Sundays and 3 weeks in August.
Other points: bar, credit cards accepted, children welcome, pets allowed, car parking, traditional decor.
Address: 122 Route Nationale.
MME THERESE DEVESNE, tel 45.71.10.88.

ROUMAZIERES, Charente 16370, Map 7   ⊗ ♈

LES ROUTIERS, RN 141 between Limoges and Angoulêmes

Menu: 50 to 60 Frs
Restaurant: lunch 11–2pm, dinner 7–9pm.
Closed Sundays.
Other points: bar, credit cards accepted, pets
allowed, traditional decor.
Address: La Croix Rouge.
M. ANDRE TROUSSIEUX, tel 45.71.11.73.

ROUMAZIERES LOUBERT, Charente 16270, Map 7 ⊗🏠

LES ROUTIERS, RD 951

Places of interest: Confolens, Bellac, château
de Nieul (8km), La Rochefoucauld (26km).
Menu: 55 to 85 Frs
Accommodation: 90 to 110 Frs
Restaurant: lunch 11–3pm, dinner 7–11pm.
Closed Saturdays and Sundays.

Hotel: 7 rooms, private WCs.
Other points: children welcome, garden
terrace, pets allowed, car parking, traditional
decor.
Address: Les 3 Chênes.
M. RAYMOND BISSERIER, tel 45.77.71.83.

ROYAN, Charente-Maritime 17200, Map 7 ⊗♈

L'ESPERANCE

Place of interest: Royan.
Restaurant.
Menu: 60 to 80 Frs
Specialities: soupe de poissons, fruits de mer.

Other points: bar, credit cards accepted, à la
carte menu, pets allowed, car parking.
Address: 72 avenue Eléonore d'Aquitaine.
M. GIL ALEXANDRE, tel 46.05.01.02.

ROYAN, Charente-Maritime 17200, Map 7 ⊗♈🏠

LE SYMPATIC, as you enter Royan from Bordeaux

Places of interest: Musée, parc zoologique, forêts.
Menu: 53 to 70 Frs
Accommodation: 140 to 200 Frs
Restaurant: lunch 12–2pm, dinner 7–9pm.
Closed Sundays out of season.
Hotel: 15 rooms: single 5, double 10. Showers,
private WCs.

Other points: bar, credit cards accepted,
children welcome, garden terrace, pets allowed,
car parking, traditional decor.
Address: 30 avenue de la Libération.
M. YVES BOINARD, tel 46.05.67.21.

ROZIERES EN BEAUCE, Loiret 45130, Map 6 ⊗♈🏠

LA BAGATELLE, RN 157 between Orléans and Le Mans

Places of interest: Orléans, châteaux de la
Loire.
Menu: 50 to 70 Frs
Accommodation: 120 to 150 Frs
Restaurant: lunch 11–3pm, dinner 6.30–11pm.
Closed Saturdays.

Hotel: 4 rooms: single 2, double 2. Showers,
private WCs.
Other points: bar, credit cards accepted,
children welcome, pets allowed, car parking.
Address: 1 rue Bagatelle.
MME SYLVIE BIHEL, tel 38.74.22.03.

RUFFEC, Charente 16700, Map 7 ⊗♈

LE LANDAIS, RN 10 at exit for Ruffec towards Angoulême

Places of interest: Angoulême (40km),
futuroscope (70km).
Menu: 50 to 75 Frs

Restaurant: lunch 12–2.30pm, dinner 7–9pm.
Closed Sundays and 15 days in December.
Other points: bar, credit cards accepted,

children welcome, à la carte menu, garden terrace, pets allowed, car parking, traditional decor.

Address: 34 avenue Célestin Sieur. M. JEAN-MICHEL LAPEGUE, tel 45.31.04.16.

RUFFEC, Charente 16700, Map 7   ⊗ ♀

LES ROUTIERS, RN 10, SNCF station at Ruffec

Menu: 48 Frs
Restaurant: lunch 11–3pm, dinner 7–11pm. Closed Sundays and 2 weeks in August.
Other points: bar, credit cards accepted, pets

allowed, traditional decor.
Address: 15 boulevard de Verdun.
MME MARIE-HELENE CHINIER, tel 45.31.18.09.

RUFFEC, Charente 16700, Map 7   ⊗ ♀

PARIS IRUN – Chez Branger, RN 10 between Poitiers and Angoulême

Places of interest: Circuit des vallées.
Menu: 60 Frs
Restaurant: lunch 12–2pm. Closed Sundays and in August.

Other points: pets allowed, car parking.
Address: Les Adjots.
M. JACKY SOMMIER, tel 45.31.02.44.

RUFFEC LE CHATEAU, Indre 36300, Map 6   ⊗ ♀ ⌂

CHEZ P'TIT JEAN, RN 151 between Poitiers and Châteauroux

Place of interest: Parc de la Brenne.
Menu: 48 to 85 Frs
Accommodation: 85 Frs
Restaurant: lunch 11.30–2pm, dinner 7–10pm. Closed Friday nights and 15 days in September.
Hotel: 4 single rooms.

Other points: bar, credit cards accepted, children welcome, pets allowed, car parking, traditional decor.
Address: Le Bourg, Route Nationale 151.
MME MICHELINE MARANDON, tel 54.37.70.05.

SAINT AGNANT DES MARAIS, Charente-Maritime 17620, Map 7   ⊗ ♀

AU RENDEZ-VOUS DES AMIS

Places of interest: Corderie royale, Rochefort, zoo de la Palmyre.
Language: German
Restaurant: closed Saturdays.
Other points: bar, credit cards accepted,

children welcome, à la carte menu, pets allowed, car parking.
Address: avenue du Canal de la Bridoire.
M. ALAIN NEVEUR, tel 46.83.30.36.

SAINT AIGNAN LE JAILLARD, Loiret 45600, Map 6   ⊗ ♀

LE SAINT AIGNAN, RD 952 between Sully and Gien

Places of interest: Châteaux de Gien, Chambort et Sully, la Solgone, faïencerie de Gien, parcours et élevage de truites.
Menu: 50 to 110 Frs
Restaurant: lunch 12–3pm, dinner 7–10pm. Closed Wednesdays, mid-February and mid-August.

Specialities: coq au vin, couscous, choucroute, grillades.
Other points: bar, children welcome, garden terrace, pets allowed, car parking, traditional decor.
Address: 78 rue Nationale.
MME CLAUDINE GASNIER, tel 38.36.38.21.

SAINT ARNOULT DES BOIS, Eure-et-Loir 28190, Map 6 ⊗ 🍷 🏠

TY KORN

Restaurant: closed August.
Hotel: 5 rooms.
Other points: bar.

Address: 40 Grande Rue.
M. DANIEL LE CAM, tel 37.22.53.17.

SAINT AUBIN DES BOIS, Eure-et-Loir 28300, Map 6 ⊗ 🍷

LA MORICERIE, RN 23

Restaurant.
Other points: bar.
Address: Route Nationale 23.

M. DOMINIQUE LIBERATORE,
tel 37.32.99.25.

SAINT AUGUSTIN SUR MER, Charente-Maritime 17570, Map 7 ⊗ 🍷

LA MARINA, between Royan and la Tremblade

Places of interest: Royan, zoo de la Palmyre,
Ile d'Oléron.
Languages: English, Spanish
Menu: 55 to 110 Frs including wine and coffee
Restaurant: lunch 11.30–2pm, dinner
6.30–10pm. Closed 3 weeks in October.

Other points: bar, credit cards accepted,
children welcome, à la carte menu, garden
terrace, pets allowed, car parking.
Address: Centre Commercial.
M. JACKY DUSSAILLANT, tel 46.23.28.22.

SAINT BENOIT DU SAULT, Indre 36170, Map 6 ⊗ 🍷 🏠

HOTEL DU COMMERCE – Chez Marinette, RN 20 between Argenton sur Creuse and Le Blanc

Places of interest: Les cités médiévales de
Saint Benoît et Gargillesse, barrage d'Eguzon.
Menu: 50 to 70 Frs
Accommodation: 90 to 150 Frs
Restaurant: lunch 12–2pm, dinner
7.30–9.30pm.
Specialities: coq au vin, paëlla.

Hotel: 9 rooms: single 7, double 2.
Other points: bar, credit cards accepted,
children welcome, garden terrace, pets allowed,
car parking, traditional decor.
Address: place de l'Enchère.
MME MARINETTE THEVENOT,
tel 54.47.54.70.

SAINT EUGENE, Charente-Maritime 17520, Map 7 ⊗ 🍷 🍽

LES DEUX CHARENTES, RD 731 between Barbezieux and Royan

Places of interest: Distilleries à Brie et
Archiac, dolmène à Saint Fort, Cognac, Jarnac.
Menu: 50 to 140 Frs
Restaurant: lunch 11–2.30pm, dinner
7.15–9pm. Closed Wednesday afternoons and
mid-February.
Other points: bar, credit cards accepted,

children welcome, à la carte menu, garden
terrace, pets allowed, car parking, traditional
decor.
Address: La Maison de Bois.
MME MARCELLE BLANCHARD,
tel 46.49.13.28.

SAINT FLORENT SUR CHER, Cher 18400, Map 6 ⊗ 🍷

L'IMPREVU, RD 28

Restaurant: closed Sunday afternoons and in August.
Other points: bar.

Address: 60 rue Jean Jaurès.
M. BERNARD RUELLAN, tel 48.55.12.00.

SAINT GAULTIER, Indre 36800, Map 6   ⊗ �

LE COMMERCE, RN 151

Restaurant: closed Thursdays.
Other points: bar.

MME MARIE PILORGET, tel 54.47.14.81.

SAINT GENIX DE SAINTONGE, Charente-Maritime 17240, Map 7

LE RELAIS DE SAINTONGE, RN 137 and A 10 between Saintes and Bordeaux – exit 26 on A 10

Places of interest: Saintes (30km), Cognac (30km), Royan (35km), Jonzac les Thermes (10km).
Languages: German, English, Spanish
Menu: 58 to 130 Frs including wine and coffee
Accommodation: 95 to 120 Frs
Restaurant: lunch 12–2pm, dinner 7–11pm. Closed Saturdays, 2 weeks at Christmas and 3 weeks in August.

Specialities: escargots à la charentaise.
Hotel: 10 rooms: single 7, double 3.
Other points: bar, credit cards accepted, à la carte menu, lounge area, garden terrace, pets allowed, car parking, traditional decor.
Address: Route Nationale 137.
MME ANNETTE EVEN, tel 46.49.80.53.

SAINT GEORGES SUR EURE, Eure-et-Loir 28190, Map 6   ⊗ ♀ 🏠

AU RENDEZ-VOUS DES PECHEURS, RN 23 between Chartres and Le Mans

Places of interest: Cathédrale de Chartres (8km), étangs des voiliers.
Menu: 47 Frs
Accommodation: 130 to 170 Frs
Restaurant: lunch 12–2pm, dinner 7–8.30pm. Closed Sundays.

Hotel: 9 rooms, showers, baths, private WCs.
Other points: bar, credit cards accepted, children welcome, pets allowed, car parking.
Address: 9 rue Raymond Bataille.
HENRI AND MONIQUE HUBERT, tel 37.26.81.90.

SAINT HILAIRE LA GRAVELLE, Loir-et-Cher 41160, Map 6   ⊗ ♀

AUBERGE DU LOIR, RD 19 between Orléans and Le Mans

Language: English
Menu: 55 Frs
Accommodation: 180 Frs
Restaurant: lunch 12–2pm, dinner 7–10pm. Closed Wednesdays and in September.
Hotel: 2 single rooms. Showers, private WCs.

Other points: bar, credit cards accepted, children welcome, à la carte menu, garden terrace, pets allowed, car parking, traditional decor.
Address: 10 rue Léon Cibié.
M. SYLVAIN PIERDOS, tel 54.82.65.00.

SAINT JEAN D'ANGELY, Charente-Maritime 17400, Map 7   ⊗ ♀ 🏠

CHEZ VEVETTE, CD 950 between Saint Jean d'Angely and Poitiers

Menu: 60 Frs
Accommodation: 80 to 120 Frs
Restaurant: closed Friday nights, Saturday nights, Sundays and from 15 August to 1 September.

Hotel: 5 rooms: single 4, double 1.
Address: Les Eglises d'Argenteuil.
M. JOEL PILLOT, tel 46.59.94.21.

SAINT LEGER, Charente-Maritime 17800, Map 7 ⊗ ☿

L'ARCHE DE SAINT LEGER, A 10 in both directions

Places of interest: Cognac (40km), Royan (30km), La Rochelle (80km), Saintes.
Languages: German, English, Spanish
Menu: 59 Frs
Restaurant: lunch 10.30–3pm, dinner 6–11pm.
Speciality: jambon braisé.

Other points: bar, credit cards accepted, children welcome, self-service, garden terrace, pets allowed, car parking, traditional decor.
Address: Aire de Saint-Léger.
Tel 46.91.95.30.

SAINT MARTIN DE RE, Charente-Maritime 17410, Map 7 ⊗

EL PANCHO, Saint Martin, left at Intermarché

Places of interest: Remparts de Saint Martin (1km), phare des baleines, abbaye, la flotte (5km), la cristallerie à visiter sur les lieux.
Menu: 55 Frs
Restaurant: lunch 12–1.45 pm, dinner 7–10pm. Closed Sundays and in early October.
Speciality: pizza.

Other points: credit cards accepted, à la carte menu, pets allowed, car parking, traditional decor.
Address: route de la Flotte, Venelle de la Cristallerie.
MME BRIGITTE RAGUENAUD, tel 46.09.02.05.

SAINT MAUR, Indre 36250, Map 6 ⊗ ☿

LA BUVETTE DES TERRES NOIRES, RN 20 between Châteauroux and Limoges

Places of interest: Valencay, parc de la Brenne, Nohanc.
Language: English
Menu: 55 to 80 Frs including wine
Restaurant: lunch 11.45–2.15 pm, dinner 6.45–10pm. Closed Sundays and second 2 weeks of January.

Other points: credit cards accepted, children welcome, à la carte menu, garden terrace, pets allowed, car parking, traditional decor.
Address: Route Nationale 20.
M. FRANCK STEVENOT, tel 54.27.00.64.

SAINT MAURICE SUR FESSARD, Loiret 45700, Map 6 ⊗ ☿

LE RELAIS DE SAINT MAURICE, RN 60 between Orléans and Sens

Menu: 55 Frs
Restaurant: lunch 12–2pm, dinner 5.30–9.30pm. Closed Sundays.
Other points: bar, credit cards accepted, à la

carte menu, garden terrace, pets allowed, car parking, traditional decor.
Address: Route Nationale 60, Villemandeur.
M. PASCAL CROUVISIER, tel 38.97.80.59.

SAINT MAURICE SUR FESSARD, Loiret 45700, Map 6 ⊗ ☿

CAFE DE LA GARE

Languages: English, Spanish
Restaurant: closed Saturday and Sunday afternoons.

Other points: bar.
Address: Route Nationale 60.
MME COLETTE JEHL, tel 38.97.81.00.

SAINT NICOLAS DE BOURGUEIL, Indre-et-Loire 37140, Map 6 ⊗ ☿

LE RELAIS, CD 035

Menu: 47 to 70 Frs
Restaurant: lunch 11.30–2pm, dinner
7.30–9pm. Closed Sundays, public holidays and
in August.
Hotel: 3 rooms: single 1, double 2. Showers.

Other points: bar, credit cards accepted, pets
allowed, car parking.
Address: place de l'Eglise.
M. JOEL JOULIN, tel 47.97.75.39.

SAINT PIERRE DES CORPS, Indre-et-Loire 37700, Map 6   ⊗ 🍸

LE GRILLON, RN 751

Restaurant: closed Saturdays, Sundays and in
July or August.
Other points: bar.

Address: 9 quai de la Loire.
MME LATOUR, tel 47.44.74.90.

SAINT SAVINIEN, Charente-Maritime 17350, Map 7   ⊗ 🍸 🏠

LE SAINT SAVINIEN, RD 18 between Saintes (12km) and Saint Jean d'Angely (10km)

Places of interest: Saintes (12km), Saint Jean
d'Angely (10km), port miniature, Saint
Savinien.
Menu: 60 Frs including wine and coffee
Accommodation: 120 to 210 Frs
Restaurant: lunch 12–2pm, dinner 7.30–10pm.
Closed Wednesday afternoons.

Hotel: 9 rooms: single 7, double 2.
Other points: bar, credit cards accepted,
children welcome, à la carte menu, pets
allowed, car parking, traditional decor.
Address: 27 rue de Champeroux.
MLLE ELISABETH DIEU, tel 46.90.20.33.

SAINT SORNIN, Charente 16220, Map 7   ⊗ 🍸

LES ROUTIERS, CD 6 between La Rochefoucaud and Montbron

Menu: 54 Frs
Restaurant: lunch 12–2pm, dinner 7–9pm.
Closed 15 days in August.
Other points: bar, garden terrace, pets allowed,

car parking, traditional decor.
Address: Le Bourg.
M. JEAN-MICHEL DUBOIS, tel 45.23.12.83.

SAINT SYMPHORIEN, Eure-et-Loir 28700, Map 6   ⊗ 🍸

LE RELAIS DES ESSARS, RN 10 between Rambouillet and Chartres

Places of interest: Château de Maintenon,
Rambouillet (18km).
Language: English
Menu: 51 Frs
Restaurant.

Other points: bar, credit cards accepted,
children welcome, garden terrace, car parking.
Address: Route Nationale 10, Essars.
M. ALAIN NAU, tel 37.31.18.30.

SAINT VICTOR DE BUTHON, Eure-et-Loir 28240, Map 6   ⊗ 🍸

CHEZ JOJO

Language: Italian
Menu: 51 Frs
Restaurant: closed from Saturday night to
Sunday lunch.

Other points: bar, car parking.
Address: La Hurie.
M. GEORGES MOCQUES, tel 37.81.13.38.

SAINTE MAURE DE TOURAINE, Indre-et-Loire 37800, Map 6 ⊗🍷🏠☆

L'ETOILE DU SUD, RN 10 between Tours and Poitiers

Places of interest: Chinon (30km), Loches, grottes Savonnières, Villandry.
Languages: English, Arabic
Menu: 50 to 80 Frs including wine
Accommodation: 80 to 250 Frs
Restaurant: lunch 12–2.30pm, dinner 7–10.30pm.
Specialities: orientales.

Hotel: 25 rooms: single 4, double 21. Showers, baths, private WCs.
Other points: bar, credit cards accepted, children welcome, à la carte menu, lounge area, garden terrace, pets allowed, car parking.
Address: Route Nationale 10.
M. KARIM MEDJAHED, tel 47.65.40.61.

SAINTES, Charente-Maritime 17100, Map 7 ⊗🍷

L'OASIS, RN 137, Saintes Centre

Places of interest: Ville gallo-romaine (arènes, thermes), châteaux, musées.
Menu: 45 to 93 Frs
Restaurant: lunch 12–2pm, dinner 7.15–9.15 pm. Closed Saturdays, Sundays, 3 to 25 August and 24 to 31 December.
Specialities: langoustine mayonnaise, goulasch de porc.

Other points: bar, à la carte menu, lounge area, garden terrace, pets allowed, car parking, traditional decor.
Address: route de Rochefort.
M. GUY FUMOLEAU, tel 46.93.07.20.

SANCERGUES, Cher 18140, Map 6 ⊗🍷🏠

LE BON LABOUREUR, RN 151 between la Charité sur Loire and Bourges

Places of interest: Sancerre (25km), cathédrale de Bourges (40km), abbaye de Noirlac (60km), parc d'Apremont.
Languages: German, Italian
Menu: 56,50 to 150 Frs
Accommodation: 90 to 100 Frs
Restaurant: lunch 11.45–1.45 pm, dinner 7–8.30pm. Closed Tuesday afternoons and from 5 July to 5 August.

Specialities: fruits de mer, poissons, choucroute.
Hotel: 4 rooms: single 3, double 1. Showers, private WCs, phone.
Other points: bar, children welcome, pets allowed, car parking, traditional decor.
Address: 54 Grande Rue.
MME MARTINE DUBOIS, tel 48.72.76.13.

SARGE SUR BRAYE, Loir-et-Cher 41170, Map 6 ⊗🍷

RELAIS DE MONPLAISIR, RN 157 Le Mans/Orléans/Mondoubleau Montoire

Place of interest: Vallée du Loir.
Languages: English, Spanish, Italian
Menu: 49 Frs
Restaurant: lunch 11.30–3.30pm, dinner 6.30–10pm. Closed Saturdays, Sundays and in August.

Other points: bar, credit cards accepted, garden terrace, pets allowed, car parking, traditional decor.
Address: Route Nationale 157.
M. MICHEL MOUJEARD, tel 54.72.72.21.

SAUJON, Charente-Maritime 17600, Map 7 ⊗🍷🏠☆

HOTEL DE LA GARE, RN 150 between Saintes and Royan

Places of interest: La mer et l'arrière pays.
Language: English.
Menu: 35 to 65 Frs
Accommodation: 140 to 200 Frs
Restaurant: lunch 12–2pm, dinner 7.30–9pm.
Closed Sundays and end of December.
Hotel: 12 rooms: single 6, double 6. Showers, private WCs, TV, phone.

Other points: bar, credit cards accepted, children welcome, self-service, lounge area, garden terrace, pets allowed, car parking, traditional decor.
Address: 2 rue Clémenceau.
M. MICHEL MELLOT, tel 46.02.80.33.

SAUZE VAUSSAIS, Deux-Sèvres 79190, Map 7 ⊗ ♉

LE RELAIS DES ROUTIERS, RD 948

Menu: 50 Frs
Restaurant: lunch 11.30–2.30pm, dinner 7–10pm. Closed Saturdays and in August.
Other points: bar, lounge area, car parking,

traditional decor.
Address: Chaignepain.
M. JOEL QUINTARD, tel 49.29.34.61.

SAZILLY, Indre-et-Loire 37220, Map 6 ⊗ ♉

RELAIS DE LA PROMENADE, RN 760, towards Chiron

Places of interest: Châteaux de la Loire.
Menu: 46 Frs
Restaurant: lunch 11.45–2pm, dinner 7–8.30pm. Closed Sundays.

Other points: bar, garden terrace, pets allowed, car parking, traditional decor.
Address: Le Bourg.
MME JOCELYNE BIGOT, tel 47.58.55.50.

SCOURY, Indre 36300, Map 6 ⊗ ♉ 🏠

LE RELAIS ROUTIERS, RN 151

Place of interest: La Brenne (20km).
Menu: 50 Frs
Accommodation: 70 to 120 Frs
Restaurant: lunch 11–3pm, dinner 7–10pm.
Closed Sundays and in December.
Hotel: 5 rooms: single 3, double 2. Showers,

baths, private WCs, phone.
Other points: bar, credit cards accepted, children welcome, garden terrace, pets allowed, car parking, traditional decor.
MME ROSELYNE PILET, tel 54.37.98.09.

SECONDIGNY, Deux-Sèvres 79130, Map 7 ⊗ ♉ 🏠 🍲

LES ROUTIERS, RD 949, exit Lusigny towards la Roche sur Yon

Places of interest: Eglises romanes, châteaux de Saint Loup (40km), Mervent (forêt) (25km), futuroscope à Poitiers (70km).
Language: English.
Menu: 50 to 120 Frs
Accommodation: 95 to 160 Frs
Restaurant: lunch 11.30–2.30pm, dinner 7–9pm. Closed Mondays, one week in February and one in September.

Specialities: escargots farcis, salade gourmande.
Hotel: 5 rooms: single 3, double 2. Showers, baths.
Other points: bar, credit cards accepted, children welcome, à la carte menu, car parking, traditional decor.
Address: 43 rue de la Vendée.
M. NOEL DURANCEAU, tel 49.95.61.35.

SERAZEREUX, Eure-et-Loir 28170, Map 6 ⊗ ♉

AU BON ACCEUIL, RN 154 between Dreux and Chartres

Place of interest: Cathédrale de Chartres.
Menu: 50 to 80 Frs
Restaurant: lunch 10.30–4pm, dinner 7–10pm.
Closed Saturday afternoons, Sundays and in
August.
Other points: bar, credit cards accepted,
children welcome, à la carte menu, pets
allowed, car parking.
Address: Route Nationale 154, known as Le
Péage.
MME ELIANE HERISSON, tel 37.65.22.49.

SERIGNY, Charente-Maritime 17230, Map 7 ⊗ ♎

CHEZ JOHAN, direction Nantes

Restaurant: closed Sundays.
Other points: bar.
Address: Route Nationale 137.
M. JOHAN MERCIER, tel 46.01.40.43.

SIDIAILLES, Cher 18270, Map 6 ⊗ ♎

CHEZ ROBERT, RD 977 between Culan and Boussac

Places of interest: Château de Culan, centre
nautique de Sidiailles.
Menu: 45 Frs including wine
Accommodation: 60 Frs
Restaurant: lunch 12–3pm, dinner 7–9pm.
Closed Wednesday afternoons.
Hotel: 3 single rooms.
Other points: bar, credit cards accepted,
children welcome, à la carte menu, garden
terrace, pets allowed, car parking, traditional
decor.
Address: Le Bouquet.
M. ROBERT MOREAU, tel 48.56.63.02.

SOLTERRE, Loiret 45700, Map 6 ⊗ ♎ ⌂

AUBERGE DE LA ROUTE BLEUE, RN 7

Places of interest: Nervers, les 7 écluses à
Rosny, Briare, Gien, arborétom de Barr.
Languages: German, English, Italian
Menu: 55 to 90 Frs
Restaurant: lunch 12–2pm, dinner 7–10pm.
Closed Tuesday afternoons, Wednesdays, and
mid-August.
Specialities: saumon à l'oselle, escargots
roquefort, ris de veau normand, escalope
cordon bleu.
Other points: bar, credit cards accepted, à la
carte menu, pets allowed, car parking,
traditional decor.
Address: 32 Route Nationale 7, La
Commodite.
ALBERT AND CHARLES ROCCO,
tel 38.94.90.04.

SOMMIERES DU CLAIN, Vienne 86160, Map 7 ⊗ ♎ ⌂

AUBERGE DES 3 PILLIERS

Menu: 45 to 120 Frs
Accommodation: 65 Frs
Restaurant: lunch 12–3pm, dinner 7–11pm.
Closed Mondays and 15 days in February.
Speciality: poitevines.
Hotel: 5 single rooms. Showers, baths.
Other points: bar, children welcome, à la carte
menu, garden terrace, pets allowed, car
parking, traditional decor.
Address: place de l'Eglise.
M. MARTIAL RICHARD, tel 49.87.70.09.

SUEVRES, Loir-et-Cher 41500, Map 6 ⊗ ♎ ⌂

LE RELAIS DE LA PROVIDENCE, RN 152 between Orléans and Tours

Places of interest: Les châteaux de la Loire, chocolaterie Poulain, centrale nucléaire de Saint Laurent, caves viticoles.
Languages: English, Spanish
Menu: 55 to 125 Frs
Accommodation: 100 to 180 Frs
Restaurant: lunch 12–3pm, dinner 7–10pm.

Closed Saturday nights and Sunday nights.
Hotel: 7 rooms: single 2, double 5. Showers.
Other points: bar, credit cards accepted, children welcome, à la carte menu, pets allowed, car parking, traditional decor.
Address: 1 place de la Mairie.
M. MICHEL GROSSE, tel 54.87.80.88.

SULLY SUR LOIRE, Loiret 45600, Map 6

CAFE DE LA GARE – Chez Lionel, RN 152

Restaurant: closed Saturday afternoons, Sundays, and from 8 to 23 August.
Hotel: 7 rooms.

Other points: bar.
Address: 47 avenue de la Gare.
M. LIONEL FUNTEN, tel 38.36.26.11.

SULLY SUR LOIRE, Loiret 45600, Map 6

LE SAINT GERMAIN – Le Cercle d'Or, RN 152, on leaving Sully, towards Orléans

Places of interest: Château de Sully sur Loire, basilique de Saint Benoît, faïencerie de Gien, musée de la chasse, la Vallée des Rois.
Menu: 47 to 98 Frs
Accommodation: 120 to 155 Frs
Restaurant: lunch 11.30–1.45pm, dinner 7–9pm. Closed Friday nights, Sunday nights, and second 2 weeks of December.
Specialities: andouillette de Jargeou, coq au vin maison.

Hotel: 6 double rooms. Showers.
Other points: bar, children welcome, à la carte menu, pets allowed, car parking, traditional decor.
Address: 2 place Saint Germain.
BERNARD AND PATRICIA SCHWARTZ, tel 38.36.27.02.

SURY AUX BOIS, Loiret 45530, Map 6

LE RELAIS DU PONT DES BEIGNERS, RN 60 between Orléans and Montargis

Places of interest: Sully sur Loire, Montargis.
Menu: 54 to 65 Frs
Restaurant: lunch 11.30–2.30pm, dinner 6.30–10pm. Closed Saturday afternoons, Sundays, and mid-August to mid-September.
Specialities: coq au vin de l'Orléanais, poulet sauté à la provençale.

Other points: bar, credit cards accepted, à la carte menu, garden terrace, pets allowed, car parking, traditional decor.
Address: Pont des Beigners.
M. JEAN-PIERRE GUERU, tel 38.59.47.72.

SURY ES BOIS, Cher 18260, Map 6

HOTEL DU LAURIER, RD 926 between Bourges and Vierzon

Places of interest: Château de la verrerie (15km), château de Blancafort (15km), les vignobles de Sancere.
Menu: 50 to 55 Frs including wine
Accommodation: 55 to 100 Frs
Restaurant: lunch 11.30–2.30pm, dinner 7–8.45pm. Closed Sundays, 1 week end August and 15 days for Christmas.

Hotel: 5 rooms.
Other points: bar, pets allowed, car parking, traditional decor.
Address: Le Bourg.
M. DOMINIQUE LE MERCIER, tel 48.73.74.62.

TAILLEBOURG, Charente-Maritime 17350, Map 7 ⊗ �

AUBERGE DU CHATEAU

Language: English
Menu: 50 to 120 Frs
Restaurant: lunch 11.30–2.30pm, dinner
7.30–10.30pm. Closed Saturdays.
Speciality: escargots à la charentaise.

Other points: bar, à la carte menu, self-
service, garden terrace, pets allowed, car
parking, traditional decor.
Address: 34 place du Château.
M. FRANCIS GARNIER, tel 46.91.70.23.

TAVERS, Loiret 45190, Map 6 ⊗ ♥

LA PIERRE TOURNANTE, RN 152

Restaurant: closed Sundays.
Other points: bar.

Address: 36 Route Nationale 152.
M. DANIEL LECOQ, tel 38.44.92.25.

TENDU, Indre 36200, Map 6 ⊗ ♥ ⌂

LE RELAIS, RN 20 between Paris and Limoges

Places of interest: Barrage d'Eguzon (25km),
Brenne (25km), vallée de la Creuse, Argenton.
Menu: 60 to 140 Frs
Accommodation: 120 to 180 Frs
Restaurant: closed Tuesday afternoons and
Wednesdays (out of season), 1 week end

September/beginning October and 1 in winter.
Hotel: 9 rooms: single 4, double 5. Showers.
Other points: bar, credit cards accepted, à la
carte menu, pets allowed, traditional decor.
Address: Route Nationale 20.
M. ANDRE LUNEAU, tel 54.24.14.10.

THIMERT, Eure-et-Loir 28170, Map 6 ⊗ ♥

LA CREMAILLERE, RN 839

Restaurant: closed Sunday afternoons and
third week of August.
Other points: bar.

Address: 1 rue de Chartres.
MME MADELEINE BRETON,
tel 37.51.60.90.

THIVARS, Eure-et-Loir 28630, Map 6 ⊗ ♥ ⌂

LE RESTAURANT DU STADE, RN 10, 5km from Chartres

Place of interest: Cathédrale de Chartres.
Menu: 50 to 68 Frs
Accommodation: 110 Frs (35 Frs per bed
supplement)
Restaurant: lunch 12–2.30pm, dinner
7–9.30pm. Closed Saturday nights and
Sundays.

Hotel: 8 rooms: single 4, double 4. Showers,
private WCs.
Other points: bar, credit cards accepted, à la
carte menu, pets allowed, car parking.
Address: 15 Route Nationale.
M. PATRICK PETIT, tel 37.26.40.05.

THOU, Loiret 45420, Map 6 ⊗

AU LIT ON DORT, RD 965

Restaurant: lunch 11.30–2.30pm. Closed
Monday afternoons and in August.
Specialities: vol au vent, filet de boeuf et
charlotte au chocolat.

Other points: pets allowed, car parking,
traditional decor.
M. SOLANGE BERTRAND, tel 38.31.62.07.

THOUARS, Deux-Sèvres 79100, Map 7 ⊗ ⅋

LE MILLE PATTES, RN 1

Languages: English, German.
Restaurant.
Other points: bar.

Address: 17 route de Launay.
MME MARTINE VALLEAU, tel 49.56.36.53.

TONNAY CHARENTE, Charente-Maritime 17430, Map 7 ⊗ ⅋

L'OASIS, RN 137, 300m from bridge

Restaurant: lunch 12–2pm. Closed Sundays.
Speciality: couscous.
Other points: bar, pets allowed, car parking.

Address: 27 rue de Lattre de Tassigny.
MME GENEVIEVE VACHON,
tel 46.88.70.84.

TONNAY CHARENTE, Charente-Maritime 17430, Map 7 ⊗ ⅋

LES FONTAINES, RN 137 between Nantes and Bordeaux, exit Rochefort

Places of interest: Cordeleries royales,
Rochefort, Maison de Pierre Loti.
Menu: 50 Frs
Restaurant: lunch 11.30–2.30pm, dinner
7–9pm. Closed Sundays.

Other points: bar, children welcome, garden
terrace, pets allowed, car parking, traditional
decor.
Address: 110 avenue d'Tonis.
M. JEAN-PAUL REVELAUD, tel 46.83.79.11.

TOURY, Eure-et-Loir 28390, Map 6 ⊗ ⅋

LE RELAIS DE LA CHAPELLE, RN 20

Menu: 59 Frs
Restaurant: lunch 12–2.30pm, dinner
7.30–11pm. Closed Saturdays, Sundays, first
week of May and 1 at Christmas.

Other points: bar, car parking, traditional decor.
Address: 60 avenue de la Chapelle.
MME CLAUDINE COMARLOT,
tel 37.90.64.96.

TREON, Eure-et-Loir 28500, Map 6 ⊗ ⅋ 🏠

LE RELAIS DE TREON, RN 928

Restaurant: closed Saturdays and Sundays.
Hotel: 7 rooms.
Other points: bar.

Address: 20 rue de Châteauneuf.
MME PAULETTE CUVELLIER,
tel 37.82.62.35.

TRIMOUILLE (LA), Vienne 86290, Map 7 ⊗ ⅋ 🏠 ☕

L'AUBERGE FLEURIE, RN 675 between Blois and Périgueux

Places of interest: Le Futuroscope (70km),
abbaye de Villesalem, église Saint Savin,
Château Bourg Archambault-Guillaume.
Menu: 50 Frs including wine
Accommodation: 70 to 140 Frs
Restaurant: lunch 12–2pm, dinner 6–9pm.
Closed Sundays and public holidays after
lunch.

Specialities: moules au vert, médaillon de ris
de veau à la Trimouillaise.
Hotel: 5 rooms: single 2, double 3. Showers,
private WCs.
Other points: bar, garden terrace, car parking,
traditional decor.
Address: rue Octave Bernard.
MME MONIQUE DUFOUR, tel 49.91.60.64.

VALENCAY, Indre 36600, Map 6   ⊗ ▼ ⌂

AUBERGE DU CHATEAU, RN 156

Place of interest: Château de Valençay.
Menu: 50 Frs
Accommodation: 60 to 110 Frs
Restaurant: lunch 11.30–2.30pm, dinner
7.30–10pm. Closed Sundays (from 1 October to
31 March), 15 days in September and 3 weeks
in February.

Hotel: 5 rooms: single 3, double 2.
Other points: bar, credit cards accepted, pets
allowed, car parking, traditional decor.
Address: 1 route de Blois.
M. VINCENT COULON, tel 54.00.02.94.

VARENNE CHANGY, Loiret 45290, Map 6   ⊗ ▼ ⌂

HOTEL DU CENTRE

Place of interest: Sully sur Loire (15km).
Menu: 50 Frs to 100 Frs including wine and
coffee
Accommodation: 130 to 160 Frs
Restaurant: lunch 12–2.30pm, dinner
7–8.30pm.

Hotel: 7 rooms.
Other points: bar, credit cards accepted, pets
allowed, traditional decor.
Address: 1 Grande Place.
MMES TRAMECON AND PENALVERT,
tel 38.94.50.14.

VATAN, Indre 36150, Map 6   ⊗ ▼ ⌂

HOTEL DU CHENE VERT, RN 20

Places of interest: Châteaux de Bouges,
Valensay.
Accommodation: 90 to 130 Frs
Restaurant: lunch 12–2pm, dinner
7.30–9.30pm. Closed Saturday nights, Sundays,
and in September .

Hotel: 7 rooms: single 4, double 3.
Other points: bar, credit cards accepted, pets
allowed, car parking.
Address: 13 avenue de Paris.
MME ANDREE LAHAYE, tel 54.49.76.56.

VENDOME, Loir-et-Cher 41100, Map 6   ⊗ ⌂

CHEZ MEMERE, RN 10 between Tours and Bordeaux

Menu: 60 to 120 Frs
Accommodation: 75 to 100 Frs
Restaurant: lunch 12–2.30pm, dinner
7.30–9.30pm. Closed Mondays (except
holidays) and from 20 February to 10 March.
Specialities: terrine de volaille, canard à
l'orange, fruits de mer.

Hotel: 14 rooms.
Other points: credit cards accepted, pets
allowed, car parking, traditional decor.
Address: 127 faubourg Chartrain.
MLLE ANDREE TOUCHARD,
tel 54.77.00.32.

VERRUE, Vienne 86420, Map 7   ⊗ ▼ ⌂

LA BALBINIERE – Chez Rémy et Paulette, RN 147 between Angers and Poitiers

Place of interest: Le Futuroscope.
Menu: 50 to 85 Frs
Accommodation: 110 to 200 Frs
Restaurant: lunch 12–2pm, dinner 7.30–10pm.
Closed Sunday nights, Mondays, in August,
first or second week of January and 1 in May.

Hotel: 8 rooms, showers, baths.
Other points: bar, credit cards accepted,
children welcome, pets allowed, car parking.
Address: La Balbinière.
MME PAULETTE NATIVELLE,
tel 49.22.84.01.

VIERZON, Cher 18100, Map 6   ⊗ ☺

MODERN'SPORT, RN 20

Restaurant: lunch 12–2pm, dinner 7–10pm.
Closed Saturdays and in August.
Other points: bar, car parking, traditional
decor.

Address: 141 avenue Edouard Vaillant.
MME JEANINE MADELEINE,
tel 48.75.13.63.

VIERZON, Cher 18100, Map 6   ⊗ ☺

AUX MILLE PATTES, RN 76 between Vierzon and Tours

Menu: 53 Frs
Restaurant: closed Sunday nights.
Other points: bar, pets allowed, traditional decor.

Address: 85 route de Tours.
M. LUDWIG JAKUBIK, tel 48.75.46.38.

VILLEDOMER, Indre-et-Loire 37110, Map 6   ⊗☺⌂🍲

LE RELAIS DES GRANDS VINS DE TOURAINE, RN 10 between Châteaurenault and Monnaie

Places of interest: Château d'Amboise (25km),
ville de Tours (23km), caves de Vouvray.
Menu: 55 to 120 Frs
Accommodation: 80 to 120 Frs
Restaurant: lunch 11.30–2pm, dinner 7–10pm.
Closed Wednesdays, and second 2 weeks of
July.

Specialities: coq au vin, andouillette et cuisse
de lapin au Vouvray, cuisses de grenouille.
Hotel: 4 rooms, showers.
Other points: bar, credit cards accepted, à la
carte menu, pets allowed, car parking.
Address: La Grand' Vallée.
M. CLAUDE ROMIAN, tel 47.55.01.05.

VILLEFRANCOEUR, Loir-et-Cher 41330, Map 6   ⊗ ☺

LE CONCORDE, RD 957

Speciality: Italian.
Restaurant: closed Saturdays and in August.
Other points: bar.

Address: Le Breuil.
MME ANDREE GEHANNO, tel 54.20.12.04.

VILLEROMAIN, Loir-et-Cher 41100, Map 6   ⊗ ☺

AU BON COIN, RD 957

Places of interest: Vendôme (son château et sa
cité).
Languages: English, Spanish
Menu: 55 Frs including coffee
Restaurant: lunch 11.30–3pm. Closed
Saturdays, Sundays, and end December/early
January.

Speciality: gibier (in season).
Other points: bar, credit cards accepted,
children welcome, à la carte menu, garden
terrace, pets allowed, car parking.
Address: 13 grande Rue.
MME ISABELLE RENOUF, tel 54.23.81.17.

VILLIERS AU BOUIN, Indre-et-Loire 37330, Map 6 ⊗ ☺

L'ETAPE, RD 959 between Château la Vallière and Laval

Places of interest: Châteaux de la Loire.
Menu: 45 Frs including coffee
Restaurant: lunch 11–4pm, dinner 7–10pm.

Closed Sundays (except with notice), 3 weeks
in August and 15 days in December.
Specialities: couscous, choucroute.

Other points: bar, credit cards accepted, pets allowed, car parking, traditional decor.

Address: 15 rue de la Libération.
MME CHANTAL HAIS, tel 47.24.03.76.

VIVONNE, Vienne 86370, Map 7   ⊗ ♀

LE ROUTIERS, RN 10 between Poitiers and Angoulême

Place of interest: Le Futuroscope (Poitiers).
Menu: 55 to 65 Frs
Restaurant: lunch 12–4pm, dinner 7–11pm.
Speciality: entrecôtes aux échalottes.

Other points: bar, credit cards accepted, children welcome, pets allowed, car parking.
M. SERGE JUDES, tel 49.43.41.03.

YMONVILLE, Eure-et-Loir 28150, Map 6   ⊗ ♀ ⌂ ☆

A L'ETOILE, RN 154

Places of interest: Moulin à vent, demeure beauceronne, cathédrale de Chartres (25km).
Menu: 90 to 150 Frs
Accommodation: 140 to 195 Frs
Restaurant: lunch 12–1.30pm, dinner 7.30–9pm. Closed Mondays, 2 weeks in February and 2 weeks in November.
Specialities: poulet de Beauce à la saveur de

truffe, tourte de petit gris.
Hotel: 10 double rooms. Showers, baths.
Other points: bar, credit cards accepted, children welcome, à la carte menu, lounge area, garden terrace, pets allowed, car parking.
Address: 31 rue du Haut Chemin.
MME THERESE BRULE, tel 37.32.25.67.

YMONVILLE, Eure-et-Loir 28150, Map 6   ⊗ ♀

LE RELAIS DE BEAUCE, RN 154 between Orléans and Chartres

Places of interest: Cathédrale de Chartres, Maison de Picassiette à Chartres, moulin à vent.
Menu: 58 Frs
Restaurant: lunch 11.30–2.30pm, dinner 7–10pm. Closed Saturdays, Sundays, public holidays and in August.

Other points: bar, credit cards accepted, pets allowed, car parking.
Address: known as La Michellerie, Route Nationale 154.
MME MARTINE MILLOCHAU, tel 37.32.26.34.

Central France

AIXE SUR VIENNE, Haute Vienne 87700, Map 11

LA CHAUMIERE, RN 21 between Limoges and Périgueux

Places of interest: Limoges (12km), Ouradour sur Glanes (20km), usine de porcelaine.
Menu: 50 to 120 Frs.
Accommodation: 90 to 120 Frs.
Restaurant: lunch 12–2pm, dinner 7–9pm. Closed Wednesday nights, Sunday nights and second 2 weeks in August.
Specialities: coq au vin, confit de canard, entrecôte bordelaise.
Hotel: 5 rooms: single 3, double 2. Showers.
Other points: bar, credit cards accepted, children welcome, pets allowed, car parking, traditional decor.
Address: 5 avenue de la Gare.
M. JEAN-LOUIS PECHALAT, tel 55.70.12.12.

ARFEUILLES, Allier 03640, Map 12

LE RELAIS DES CHEVREAUX

Restaurant: closed Saurday nights.
Place of interest: Château de Lapalisse, parc d'attractions.
Languages: English, Spanish
Other points: bar, children welcome, traditional decor, pets allowed, car parking, credit cards accepted.
Address: Route Nationale 7, Chatelus.
M. JOSEPH BERNARD, tel 70.55.03.80.

ARGENTAT, Corrèze 19400, Map 11

CHEZ RAYMOND

Place of interest: Tulle.
Menu: 60 Frs including wine
Accommodation: 100 to 150 Frs
Restaurant: lunch 12–2pm, dinner 7–9pm. Closed Sundays and in August.
Hotel: 7 rooms: single 4, double 3. Showers.
Other points: bar, credit cards accepted, children welcome, pets allowed, car parking.
Address: place du 14 juillet.
MME MONIQUE POUZAUD, tel 55.28.01.97.

AUBUSSON, Creuse 23200, Map 11

LE SPORTS BAR, RN 141 between Limoges and Clermont Ferrand

Places of interest: Lac de Vassivière, tapisserie d'Aubusson.
Language: English
Menu: 50 to 72 Frs
Restaurant: lunch 11–2pm, dinner 7–9pm. Closed Saturday afternoons, Sundays and second 2 weeks of February.
Specialities: pâté de pomme de terre, coq au vin, steak à l'échalotte.
Other points: bar, credit cards accepted, children welcome, à la carte menu, pets allowed, car parking.
Address: 15 avenue de la République.
M. CHRISTIAN GARNIER, tel 55.83.80.60.

AURILLAC, Cantal 15000, Map 12

BAR L'ESCUDILLIER, RN 120 between Tulle and Rodez

Places of interest: Saint Flour, Salers, Conques.
Menu: 50 Frs including wine and coffee.
Restaurant: lunch 11–2pm. Closed Sundays.
Speciality: coq au vin.
Other points: car parking.
Address: place du 8 Mai.
M. ROBERT MONTOURCY, tel 71.63.79.30.

AURILLAC, Cantal 15000, Map 12 ⊗ ♈

LA SABLIERE, RN 122 Toulouse

Languages: English, Spanish
Menu: 50 Frs
Restaurant: lunch 11–3pm, dinner 6.30–9pm. Closed Saturdays, Sundays and second and third weeks of August.

Other points: bar, garden terrace, pets allowed, car parking.
Address: Route Nationale 122, La Sablière. MME JEANINE DELORT, tel 71.63.53.88.

BEAULIEU SUR DORDOGNE, Corrèze 19120, Map 11 ⊗ ♈

CAFE DES VOYAGEURS, RD 926 and 951

Menu: 75 to 120 Frs
Restaurant: lunch 12–2pm.
Other points: bar, credit cards accepted, pets

allowed, car parking, traditional decor.
Address: place du Champ de Mars. M. DIDIER LE MAITOUR, tel 55.91.10.04.

BEAUNE LES MINES, Haute Vienne 87280, Map 11 ⊗ ♈ ⌂ ⌑

LA TERRASSE DE BEAUNE, RN 20 exit Limoges

Place of interest: Limoges.
Language: English
Menu: 50 to 110 Frs including wine and coffee.
Accommodation: 140 to 220 Frs
Restaurant.
Hotel: 9 double rooms. Baths, private WCs.

Other points: bar, credit cards accepted, children welcome, à la carte menu, garden terrace, pets allowed, car parking. SOCIETE HOTELIERE DE LA MAZELLE, tel 55.39.90.58.

BELLAC, Haute Vienne 87300, Map 11 ⊗ ♈

LE RELAIS, RN 147 between Poitiers and Limoges

Places of interest: Oradour sur Glane (20km), lac de Saint Pardoux (20km), Limoges (40km).
Menu: 50 Frs
Restaurant: lunch 12–2pm, dinner 7–9pm. Closed Sundays and in September.

Other points: bar, pets allowed, car parking.
Address: 3 rue Fernand Fourreau. M. HENRI COTTE, tel 55.68.00.22.

BELLERIVE SUR ALLIER, Allier 03700, Map 12 ⊗ ♈ ⌂

LE BOIS DE BOULOGNE

Places of interest: Cristallerie et les sources de Vichy.
Language: English
Menu: 50 to 100 Frs
Accommodation: 90 to 110 Frs
Restaurant.
Specialities: entrecôtes marchand de vin et escargots.

Hotel: 7 rooms: single 5, double 2. Showers, baths.
Other points: bar, credit cards accepted, children welcome, à la carte menu, garden terrace, pets allowed, car parking, traditional decor.
Address: 130 avenue de Vichy. MME EDITH MOLINER, tel 70.32.38.11.

BELLEVUE LA MONTAGNE, Haute-Loire 43350, Map 12 ⊗ ♈ ⌂

HOTEL DES VOYAGEURS, RD 906

Places of interest: Le Puy (25km), La Chaise Dieu (17km).
Menu: 42 Frs
Accommodation: 90 Frs
Restaurant.

Hotel: 7 rooms.
Other points: bar, lounge area, garden terrace, pets allowed, car parking.
MME ODETTE CHAPON, tel 77.00.60.15.

BESSAY SUR ALLIER, Allier 03340, Map 12

LE BAR DE LA ROUTE BLEUE, RN 7

Language: English
Restaurant: closed Saturday afternoons and Sundays.

Other points: bar.
Address: rue Charles Louis Philippe.
M. FRANCIS BLANCHE, tel 70.43.01.59.

BORT LES ORGUES, Corrèze 19110, Map 11

LE RELAIS DES ROUTIERS, RN 122

Restaurant.
Hotel: 5 rooms.
Other points: bar.

Address: 9 place du Champ de Foire.
MME ANTOINETTE CHEREIX,
tel 55.72.00.42.

BOURGANEUF, Creuse 23400, Map 11

LA BERGERIE, RN 141 between Limoges and Clermont Ferrand

Places of interest: Lac de Vassivière (25km), tapisserie d'Aubusson (30km), Oradour sur Glane, musée de Lévêché.
Menu: 40 to 220 Frs
Restaurant: lunch 11–3pm, dinner 6–11pm. Closed Monday nights (out of season).
Specialities: civet de gibier, poissons.

Other points: bar, credit cards accepted, children welcome, à la carte menu, garden terrace, pets allowed, car parking, traditional decor.
Address: La Gasne du Clos, Montboucher.
MME BRIGITTE BELZ, tel 55.64.20.18.

BRIOUDE, Haute-Loire 43100, Map 12

LES ROUTIERS, RN 102 Le Puy

Places of interest: basilique, la maison du saumon, vallée de l'Allier.
Menu: 50 to 65 Frs
Restaurant: lunch 12–2pm, dinner 7.30–9.30pm. Closed Sundays and 15 to 31 August.

Other points: bar, credit cards accepted, children welcome, pets allowed, car parking.
Address: route de Clermont.
M. ROGER DEVINS, tel 71.50.14.39.

BRIVE LA GAILLARDE, Corrèze 19100, Map 11

LE NOUVEL HOTEL, RN 89 autoroute between Paris and Toulouse, exit Brive East

Places of interest: Les Eyziers de Tayac (55km), grottes de Lascaux, Rocamadour (55km), Padirac (55km).
Restaurant: lunch 12–2pm, dinner 7–9.30pm. Closed Saturdays, Sundays and 15 days in August.

Specialities: quercynoises.
Hotel: 11 rooms: single 9, double 2. Showers, private WC.
Other points: bar, pets allowed, car parking.
Address: 2 rue Desgenettes.
M. PATRICK LOMEY, tel 55.86.01.66.

BRIVES CHARENSAC, Haute-Loire 43700, Map 12 ⊗ ♀ 🏠

LE RELAIS DU COMMERCE, RN 88 and 535 Valence

Places of interest: Le Puy (3km), châteaux de la Loire (25km), source de la Loire (45km).
Menu: 50 to 60 Frs
Accommodation: 80 to 130 Frs
Restaurant: lunch 11.30–2pm, dinner 7–9pm.
Hotel: 9 rooms: single 4, double 5. Showers.

Other points: bar, credit cards accepted, children welcome, pets allowed, car parking, traditional decor.
Address: 2 route de Lyon.
MME ELIE MASSON-FERRET, tel 71.09.16.16.

BROMONT LAMOTHE, Puy-de-Dôme 63230, Map 12 ⊗ ♀

RESTAURANT BOISSY, RD 941

Restaurant.
Other points: bar.

MME ANDREE BOISSY, tel 73.88.71.04.

BROUT VERNET, Allier 03110, Map 12 ⊗ ♀ 🏠

CENTRE ROUTIER, RN 9 between Gannat and Saint Pourcain sur Sioule.

Place of interest: La Sioule.
Menu: 55 to 60 Frs
Accommodation: 120 to 150 Frs
Restaurant: lunch 12–2.30pm, dinner 7–11.30pm. Closed Saturday afternoons and Sundays.

Hotel: 9 rooms: single 6, double 3.
Other points: bar, credit cards accepted, children welcome, garden terrace, pets allowed, car parking, traditional decor.
Address: Route Nationale 9.
MME GEORGETTE ROUX, tel 70.58.24.61.

CHAMALIERE SUR LOIRE, Haute-Loire 43800, Map 12 ⊗ ♀

LES ROUTIERS, RD 103 between Le Puy en Velay and Saint Etienne

Places of interest: Gorges de la Loire et ses châteaux.
Menu: 48 Frs
Restaurant: lunch 11.45–2.30pm, dinner 7–8.30pm. Closed Wednesdays.

Other points: bar, pets allowed, car parking.
Address: Rue Nationale.
MME MARIE-LINE ROURE, tel 71.03.42.10.

CHAMBERAUD, Creuse 23480, Map 11 ⊗ ♀

CHEZ CHANTAL, RD 55

Places of interest: Village de Masgot (pierres sculptées), Moutier d'Ahun.
Languages: English, German
Menu: 48 to 115 Frs
Restaurant.

Specialities: couscous, paëlla, cassoulet.
Other points: bar, credit cards accepted, garden terrace, pets allowed, car parking, traditional decor.
MME CHANTAL SCHIMPF, tel 55.62.51.15.

CHAMBORET, Haute Vienne 87140, Map 11 ⊗ ♀

LA BERGERIE, RN 147 between Limoges and Bellac

Places of interest: Oradour sur Glane, lac de Saint Pardoux, Mont de Blond.
Menu: 50 to 100 Frs
Restaurant: lunch 12–3pm, dinner 7–11pm.

Other points: bar, children welcome, à la carte menu, car parking, traditional decor.
ETABLISSEMENTS ALBENQUE, tel 55.53.44.16.

CHAPELAUDE (LA), Allier 03380, Map 12 ⊗♿🏠

LE RELAIS DES TARTASSES, RD 143 Châteauroux.

Menu: 55 to 100 Frs
Restaurant: lunch 12–2pm, dinner 7–10.30pm.
Speciality: pâté de pommes de terre.
Hotel: 4 rooms, showers.
Other points: bar, credit cards accepted, children welcome, pets allowed, car parking.
Address: Huriel.
MME COLETTE BOUTILLON,
tel 70.06.45.06.

CHAPELLE D'AUREC (LA), Haute-Loire 43120, Map 12 ⊗♿🏠

LE RELAIS DE LA CHAPELLE, RN 88 Le Puy.

Menu: 55 to 120 Frs
Accommodation: 120 to 180 Frs
Restaurant: lunch 12–2pm, dinner 7.30–9pm.
Hotel: 4 rooms, showers, baths, private WCs.
Other points: bar, credit cards accepted, children welcome, à la carte menu, self-service, lounge area, garden terrace, pets allowed, car parking.
Address: La Mioulaterre.
M. GABRIEL COLOMBET, tel 71.66.53.55.

CHATEAUNEUF LA FORET, Haute Vienne 87130, Map 11 ⊗♿🏠

AUX CEPS, RD 979 between Limoges and Tulle

Places of interest: Vassivière, Montgargon.
Language: English
Menu: 76 to 140 Frs
Restaurant: lunch 11–3pm, dinner 6.30–11pm.
Closed Tuesday afternoons out of season.
Specialities: ceps, potée limousine, poissons.
Hotel: 8 rooms: single 6, double 2. Showers.
Other points: bar, credit cards accepted, children welcome, à la carte menu, garden terrace, car parking.
Address: La Veytisou.
MME JOELLE FORESTIER, tel 55.69.33.38.

CLERMONT FERRAND, Puy-de-Dôme 63000, Map 12 ⊗♿🏠☆

AUVERGNE PYRENEES – Les Routiers, RN 9

Places of interest: Puy de Dôme (12km), Chamalières (4km), Royat (5km), Montferrand (2km), lacs, châteaux.
Language: English.
Menu: 54 to 90 Frs
Accommodation: 145 to 270 Frs
Restaurant: lunch 12–2pm, dinner 7.30–9pm.
Speciality: coq au vin.
Hotel: 15 rooms: single 13, double 2. Showers, baths, private WCs, phone.
Other points: bar, à la carte menu, lounge area, garden terrace, pets allowed, car parking.
Address: 12 bis place des Carmes.
MME MARIE-LOUISE LABORDE, tel 73.92.35.73.

CLERMONT FERRAND, Puy-de-Dôme 63000, Map 12 ⊗

RELAIS DES VOLCANS D'AUVERGNE, A 71, both directions

Restaurant.
Other points: children welcome, à la carte menu, self-service, garden terrace, pets allowed, car parking.
Address: Aire de Service des Volcans.

COSNE D'ALLIER, Allier 03430, Map 12 ⊗♿🏠

L'ESCALE, A 74 between Montluçon and Villefranche d'Allier

Places of interest: Châteaux.
Languages: English, Spanish
Menu: 50 Frs including wine and coffee
Accommodation: 95 Frs
Restaurant: lunch 11–3.30pm, dinner
4.30–10.30pm.
Hotel: 6 single rooms. Showers.

Other points: bar, credit cards accepted,
children welcome, à la carte menu, garden
terrace, pets allowed, car parking.
Address: 2 place de la Liberté.
MME MARIE-JOSEPH SAUVAT-
MAJDOUB, tel 70.07.21.10.

COSTAROS, Haute-Loire 43490, Map 12 ⊗♎⌂

LES ROUTIERS, RN 88 Le Puy and Marseille

Language: Spanish
Menu: 55 to 85 Frs
Accommodation: 90 Frs
Restaurant: lunch 12–2.30pm, dinner
7.30–9pm. Closed Saturdays out of season.
Hotel: 17 rooms: single 14, double 3. Showers.

Other points: bar, à la carte menu, garden
terrace, pets allowed, car parking, traditional
decor.
Address: rue Principale.
MME THERESE ROSSELLO, tel 71.57.16.04.

COUSSAC BONNEVAL, Haute Vienne 87500, Map 11 ⊗♎⌂

LE GAI COUSSAC, RD 901 between Pompadour and Lubensac

Menu: 50 Frs to 120 Frs including wine and
coffee
Restaurant: dinner 7–10.30pm.
Hotel: 6 rooms: single 2, double 4.
Other points: bar, credit cards accepted,

children welcome, à la carte menu, lounge area,
pets allowed, car parking, traditional decor.
Address: avenue du 11 Novembre.
M. CHRISTIAN RENAUDIN, tel 55.75.21.59.

CREUZIER LE VIEUX, Allier 03300, Map 12 ⊗♎⌂☆

CHEZ LA MERE RIBOULIN, Vichy industrial zone

Accommodation: 100 to 120 Frs
Restaurant.
Hotel: 13 rooms, showers, private WCs.
Other points: bar, credit cards accepted, à la

carte menu, garden terrace, pets allowed, car
parking.
Address: 10 rue des Ailes.
M. MARCEL JOLY, tel 70.98.44.88.

CUSSET, Allier 03300, Map 12 ⊗♎

HOTEL DE LA GARE

Menu: 50 Frs
Accommodation: 80 Frs
Restaurant: lunch 12–1.30pm. Closed Sundays
and in July.

Hotel: 3 rooms.
Other points: bar, car parking.
Address: 1 route de Paris.
M. JEAN LAROQUE, tel 70.98.26.10.

CUSSET, Allier 03300, Map 12 ⊗♎

LES MONTAGNARDS, exit Cusset towards Lapalisse

Places of interest: Montagne bourbonnaise
(20km), Vichy (3km).
Menu: 50 to 55 Frs
Restaurant: lunch 11.30–2pm. Closed Sundays
and in August.

Other points: bar, pets allowed, car parking,
traditional decor.
Address: 20 rue du Général Raynal.
M. ROGER POL, tel 70.98.38.60.

DEUX CHAISES, Allier 03240, Map 12 ⊗

LE RELAIS DE L'AMITIE, RN 145

Menu: 52 Frs
Restaurant: lunch 12–2pm, dinner 7.30–10pm.
Closed before 10am Saturdays and Sundays.

Address: Route Nationale 145, Le Montet.
M. LOUIS DOUGE, tel 70.47.15.64.

DOMPIERRE SUR BESBRE, Allier 03290, Map 12 ⊗🍷

LE RELAIS DE LA BRESBRE, RN 79 between Mâcon and Moulin.

Place of interest: Vallée de la Brebre.
Menu: 50 to 70 Frs
Restaurant: lunch 12–2pm, dinner 7–9pm.
Closed Saturday afternoons, Sundays and in
mid-September.

Other points: bar, credit cards accepted, pets
allowed, car parking, traditional decor.
Address: 207 avenue de la Gare.
M. JEAN-PIERRE MAROSSA,
tel 70.34.53.69.

DURDAT LAREQUILLE, Allier 03310, Map 12 ⊗🍷

RESTAURANT DES SPORTS, RN 144, 6km from Néris les Bains

Places of interest: Gorges de la Sioule (30km),
château de Chouvigny (35km).
Languages: English, Spanish, Italian
Menu: 50 Frs
Restaurant: lunch 11.30–2pm. Closed Sundays.

Other points: bar, children welcome, garden
terrace, car parking.
Address: Route Nationale 144.
GERARD AND NATALIE LOMBARDI,
tel 70.51.07.28.

EYMOUTIERS, Haute Vienne 87120, Map 11 ⊗🍷🏠☆☆

LE SAINT PSALMET, CD 940 and 941 between Limoges and Ussel or Gueret and Tulle

Place of interest: Lac de Vassivière.
Languages: English, Spanish
Menu: 45 to 120 Frs including wine
Accommodation: 125 to 180 Frs
Restaurant: lunch 12–3pm, dinner 7–10pm.
Speciality: gigot de lotte aux cèpes.
Hotel: 38 rooms: single 8, double 30. Showers,

baths, private WCs, phone.
Other points: bar, credit cards accepted,
children welcome, à la carte menu, lounge area,
garden terrace, pets allowed, car parking.
Address: place du Champ de Foire.
M. MICHEL LE PETIT, tel 55.69.10.06.

FRAISSE HAUT, Cantal 15300, Map 12 ⊗🍷🏠☆

HOTEL DES CIMES, RN 122, 6km from Murat

Places of interest: Parc des volcans
d'Auvergne, Salers (25km), station de Super
Lioran (4km), Garabit, Puy Mary.
Menu: 49 to 100 Frs
Accommodation: 74 to 210 Frs
Restaurant: lunch 12–1.30pm, dinner
7.30–8.30pm. Closed Saturdays, Sundays and
in October and November.

Specialities: gibiers.
Hotel: 20 rooms: single 10, double 10.
Showers.
Other points: bar, lounge area, garden terrace,
car parking, traditional decor.
Address: Laveissière.
M. CHRISTOPHE CROS, tel 71.20.07.42.

ISSOIRE, Puy-de-Dôme 63500, Map 12 ⊗ 🍸

AUBERGE DU CHAPEAU ROUGE, exit Chapeau Rouge

Place of interest: La chaîne des volcans.
Menu: 48 to 52 Frs
Restaurant: lunch 11.30–3pm, dinner 7–11pm.
Closed Saturday nights, Sundays and in August.

Other points: bar, credit cards accepted, pets allowed, car parking.
Address: route de Saint Germain.
M. MARC OLIVES, tel 73.89.14.74.

LAPALISSE, Allier 03120, Map 12 ⊗ 🍸 🏠 ☆

LE CHAPON DORE, RN 7 between Roanne and Moulin

Places of interest: Zoo, châteaux, centres d'attractions.
Menu: 55 Frs including wine and coffee
Accommodation: 65 to 130 Frs
Restaurant: lunch 11.30–2.30pm, dinner 7–10pm. Closed Sundays.

Hotel: 8 rooms: single 4, double 4. Showers, baths.
Other points: bar, garden terrace, pets allowed, car parking.
Address: 2 avenue du 8 Mai 1945.
M. JEAN-LUC LALAUZE, tel 70.99.09.51.

LIMOGES, Haute Vienne 87000, Map 11 ⊗ 🍸

CHEZ BICHON, RN 20 between Toulouse and Lyon

Places of interest: Cathédrale, usine et musée de porcelaine, Oradour sur Glane (20km).
Languages: English, Spanish
Menu: 55 Frs, children up to 10 half price
Restaurant: lunch 12–2pm, dinner 6–9pm.
Closed Saturdays.

Other points: bar, pets allowed, traditional decor.
Address: 68 avenue du Maréchal between Lattre and Tassigny.
M. ROLAND HOUARD, tel 55.30.68.83.

LIMOGES, Haute Vienne 87000, Map 11 ⊗ 🍸

LES LILAS, RN 21, enter Limoges at Périgueux

Place of interest: Limoges.
Menu: 50 to 68 Frs
Restaurant.
Specialities: lotte, beignet de gambas, potée limousine.
Other points: bar, credit cards accepted,

children welcome, à la carte menu, garden terrace, car parking, traditional decor.
Address: 233 avenue Baudin.
MME GILBERTE BROUSSAS,
tel 55.34.35.67.

MAGNAC BOURG, Haute Vienne 87380, Map 11 ⊗ 🍸

LE RELAIS PARIS/TOULOUSE, RN 20

Restaurant: closed Wednesdays (out of season).

Other points: bar.
M. MERIADEC, tel 55.00.81.53.

MALEMORT, Corrèze 19360, Map 11 ⊗ 🍸

CHEZ PAULETTE, RN 89 between Brive and Tulle

Places of interest: Collonge la Rouge, tour de Brénige Malemont.
Menu: 52 Frs
Restaurant: lunch 12–2.30pm, dinner 7–8pm.
Closed Sundays and in August.

Specialities: petit salé, choux farci, pâté de pomme de terre.
Other points: bar, pets allowed, car parking.
Address: 2 avenue Pierre et Marie Curie.
MME PAULETTE VERGNE, tel 55.92.28.14.

MARSAC EN LIVRADOIS, Puy-de-Dôme 63940, Map 12 ⊗ ♑ ⌂

LE KALLISTE, RD 906

Places of interest: Moulin Richard Le Bas, musée de la dentelle, musée de la fourrure.
Language: English
Menu: 50 to 160 Frs
Accommodation: 120 to 180 Frs
Restaurant: lunch 12–3.30pm, dinner 7–10.30pm.
Specialities: salade de gésiers, foie gras poëlé, coq en barboville.

Hotel: 20 rooms: single 18, double 2.
Other points: bar, credit cards accepted, children welcome, à la carte menu, garden terrace, pets allowed, car parking.
Address: Route Départementale 906.
M. DAVID BLANCHEFORT, tel 73.95.62.58.

MASSERET, Corrèze 19510, Map 11 ⊗ ♑ ⌂

HOTEL DES VOYAGEURS, RN 20 towards Brive, first right in Masseret

Places of interest: Limoges, Rocamadour, Pompadour, Oradour sur Glane, vallée de la Dordogne.
Menu: 50 to 180 Frs
Accommodation: 90 to 170 Frs
Restaurant: lunch 12–3pm, dinner 7–10pm. Closed Sunday nights.
Specialities: limousine et auvergnate, corrézienne.

Hotel: 6 rooms: single 2, double 4. Showers.
Other points: bar, credit cards accepted, children welcome, à la carte menu, showers, garden terrace, pets allowed, car parking, traditional decor.
Address: Route Nationale 20.
M. MICHEL PONS, tel 55.73.40.11.

MAURIAC, Cantal 15200, Map 12 ⊗ ♑ ⌂ ☆

LES ROUTIERS, RD 678 Ussel

Places of interest: Muy Mary, château de Val, Salers, vallée de la Dordogne.
Language: English
Menu: 50 to 90 Frs
Accommodation: 90 to 135 Frs
Restaurant: lunch 12–1.30pm, dinner 7–8.30pm. Closed Friday 3pm to Saturday 6pm.

Hotel: 10 rooms: single 7, double 3.
Other points: bar, credit cards accepted, children welcome, à la carte menu, pets allowed, car parking, traditional decor.
Address: 27 rue Saint Mary.
HOTELS LAROCHE-RONGIER, tel 71.68.00.79.

MERINCHAL, Creuse 23420, Map 11 ⊗ ♑ ⌂

HOTEL DU MIDI, RN 141

Places of interest: Lacs, châteaux.
Languages: English, Spanish, Portuguese
Menu: 50 to 146 Frs
Accommodation: 110 Frs
Restaurant: lunch 12–3pm, dinner 7–10pm.
Specialities: cassoulet au confit, feuilleté de fruits de mer.

Hotel: 10 rooms: single 8, double 2. Showers.
Other points: bar, children welcome, à la carte menu, garden terrace, pets allowed, car parking, traditional decor.
Address: Létrade.
M. JOSE BARTOLO, tel 55.67.23.63.

MONTLUCON, Allier 03100, Map 12 ⊗ ♑ ⌂

LE CADET ROUSSEL, RN 145 in industrial zone of Pasquis

Languages: Polish, Russian, Czech
Menu: 50 Frs including wine and coffee
Accommodation: 75 to 120 Frs
Restaurant: lunch 12–2pm, dinner 7–9.30pm.
Closed Sundays.

Hotel: 8 rooms: single 6, double 2. Showers, private WCs, phone.
Other points: bar, à la carte menu, car parking.
Address: 53 rue de Pasquis.
M. EDOUARD GAWRON, tel 70.29.32.27.

MONTMARAULT, Allier 03390, Map 12 ⊗ ♀

RELAIS DE L'ETAPE, RN 145, 100m from exit for A 71

Menu: 58 Frs to 75 Frs including coffee
Restaurant: closed Saturday nights and Sundays.
Other points: bar, credit cards accepted,

children welcome, à la carte menu, self-service, garden terrace, pets allowed, car parking.
Address: route de Moulins.
M. ROBERT LEGAL, tel 70.07.36.03.

MOULINS, Allier 03000, Map 12 ⊗ ♀

LES TROIS RUBANS, RN 7 Lyon

Restaurant: closed Saturdays, Sunday afternoons and in August.
Other points: bar.

Address: route de Paris.
M. PIERRE MOLINIE, tel 70.44.08.51.

NOAILLES, Corrèze 19600, Map 11 ⊗ ♀

RELAIS D'ANTAN, RN 20

Languages: Spanish, Italian, Portuguese
Restaurant.
Other points: bar.

Address: Fontrouvée.
MME JOSIANE BERTHELOT, tel 55.85.85.76

OBJAT, Corrèze 19130, Map 11 ⊗ ♀ 🏠

RELAIS DU PARC

Restaurant.
Hotel: 14 rooms.
Other points: bar.

Address: 1 avenue Poincaré.
MME MONIQUE RICHARD, tel 55.84.11.11.

PAULHAGUET, Haute-Loire 43230, Map 12 ⊗ ♀

LE COQ HARDI, RN 102 between Clermont-Ferrand and Le Puy

Places of interest: Le Puy, la vallée de l'Allier.
Menu: 60 to 80 Frs
Restaurant: lunch 12–2pm, dinner 8–10pm.
Closed Saturdays and in October.
Specialities: auvergnates: lentilles saucisses, poté choux salé.

Hotel: 2 rooms, baths, private WCs.
Other points: bar, lounge area.
Address: La Chomette.
MME MARIE-LOUISE MEYRONNEINE, tel 71.76.62.29.

PERIGNY, Allier 03120, Map 12 ⊗ ♀ 🏠 ☆

LE RELAIS DE PERIGNY, RN 7, 3km along RN 7 from Lapalisse

Places of interest: Vichy, Lapalisse.
Language: English
Menu: from 51 Frs

Accommodation: 100 to 150 Frs
Restaurant: closed Saturdays and Sundays.
Hotel: 6 rooms: single 2, double 4.

Other points: bar, credit cards accepted, lounge area, car parking, traditional decor.

Address: Le Bourg.
M. PATRICE CARDINAUD, tel 70.99.84.57.

PERTUIS (LE), Haute-Loire 43260, Map 12

LE RELAIS DU COL

Menu: 55 to 65 Frs
Accommodation: 100 to 200 Frs
Restaurant: lunch 12–2.30pm, dinner 7–10pm.
Closed Saturdays.

Hotel: 8 rooms.
Other points: bar, car parking.
Address: Route Nationale 88.
MME ODILE DIETRICH, tel 71.57.60.06.

PIERREFITTE, Allier 03470, Map 12

CAFE DE LA MAIRIE, between Moulins and Digoin

Menu: 75 Frs
Restaurant: lunch 11–2pm, dinner 7–9pm.
Closed Wednesday afternoons.
Other points: bar, credit cards accepted, children welcome, à la carte menu, garden

terrace, pets allowed, car parking, traditional decor.
Address: place de l'Eglise.
M. CHRISTIAN TEILLIER, tel 70.47.00.87.

PIERREFITTE SUR LOIRE, Allier 03470, Map 12

STATION TOTAL, RN 79 between Moulins (50km) and Mâcon (100km)

Languages: English, German, Italian
Restaurant.
Other points: credit cards accepted, à la carte menu, garden terrace, pets allowed, car parking,

traditional decor.
Address: Route Nationale 79.
M. MICHEL RAY, tel 70.42.91.91.

PINOLS, Haute-Loire 43300, Map 12

HOTEL DES VOYAGEURS, RN 590

Places of interest: Le Puy en Velay, Mont Mouchet.
Menu: 65 to 80 Frs
Accommodation: 60 to 75 Frs
Restaurant: dinner 7–9pm.
Specialities: potée auvergnate, ris de veau aux champignons.

Hotel: 6 rooms: single 5, double 1. Showers, baths.
Other points: bar, children welcome, pets allowed, traditional decor.
MME JACQUELINE CORNET,
tel 71.74.11.42.

PONT DE MENAT, Puy-de-Dôme 63560, Map 12

CHEZ ROGER, RN 144 between Clermont and Montluçon

Menu: 55 to 130 Frs
Accommodation: 100 to 150 Frs
Restaurant: lunch 12–2pm, dinner 7–9pm.
Closed Thursdays and in January.
Specialities: jambon d'Auvergne et sa garniture, potée auvergnate, truite.

Hotel: 8 rooms: single 6, double 2. Showers.
Other points: bar, à la carte menu, pets allowed, car parking.
Address: Menat.
MME MARIE PINEL, tel 73.85.50.17.

PONTAUMUR, Puy-de-Dôme 63380, Map 12 ⊗

CHEZ LUCETTE, RN 141 between Pontaumur and Aubusson

Places of interest: Puy de Dôme (50km),
viaduc des Fades, barrage de Sauret Besseve.
Menu: 50 Frs
Restaurant: lunch 12–2.30pm, dinner
7.30–9.30pm. Closed second 2 weeks of August.

Other points: garden terrace, car parking.
Address: Puy Maury.
MME LUCETTE CONDON, tel 73.79.00.40.

PORCHERIE (LA), Haute Vienne 87380, Map 11 ⊗ ⍋ ⌂

RELAIS DE LA BORNE 40, RN 20 between Limoges and Brive

Places of interest: Uzerche, Pompadour.
Menu: 50 Frs
Accommodation: 70 to 120 Frs
Restaurant: lunch 12–2pm, dinner 7–10pm.
Closed Saturday lunch and Sundays.

Hotel: 8 rooms: single 6, double 2.
Other points: bar, pets allowed, car parking.
Address: La Borne 40.
M. MICHEL REYROLLE, tel 55.71.90.30.

PUY EN VELAY (LE), Haute-Loire 43000, Map 12 ⊗ ⍋ ⌂

LA TAVERNE

Restaurant.
Hotel: 10 rooms.
Other points: bar.

Address: 50 Boulevard Carnot.
M. RENE ROLLAND, tel 71 09 35 16.

RAZES, Haute Vienne 87640, Map 11 ⊗ ⍋

RELAIS DU PECHER, RN 20 Châteauroux/Limoges

Places of interest: Limoges (20km), lac de
Saint Pardoux.
Menu: 55 Frs including wine and coffee
Restaurant: closed Saturday 4pm to Sunday 10pm.
Other points: bar, credit cards accepted,

children welcome, à la carte menu, garden
terrace, pets allowed, car parking, traditional
decor.
Address: Route Nationale 20.
M. ALAIN LAMOTTE, tel 55.71.00.89.

RIOM, Puy-de-Dôme 63200, Map 12 ⊗ ⍋

AU STAND, RN 9 Riom south

Places of interest: Volcans d'Auvergne,
musées et monuments de Riom.
Languages: English
Menu: 55 to 75 Frs
Restaurant: lunch 11.30–2pm. Closed
Sundays, public holidays and in August.

Other points: bar, credit cards accepted,
children welcome, pets allowed, traditional
decor.
Address: 24 avenue de Clermont.
MME JANINE DASSAUD, tel 73.38.04.06.

RIOM, Puy-de-Dôme 63200, Map 12 ⊗ ⍋

LE CANTALOU, RN 9

Menu: 50 Frs
Restaurant: lunch 11–3pm. Closed Sundays
and in August.
Other points: bar, pets allowed.

Address: 12 avenue de Clermont.
M. JEAN-LOUIS THOLONIAS,
tel 73.38.03.68.

RIOTORD, Haute-Loire 43220, Map 12 ⊗�

RESTAURANT DES CHASSEURS, RD 503

Restaurant: lunch 11.30–1.30pm, dinner 7–9pm. Closed Sundays and in August.
Other points: bar, credit cards accepted, children welcome, car parking, traditional decor.

Address: route de Dunières.
MME DOMINIQUE ARNAUD, tel 71.75.31.40.

ROFFIAC, Cantal 15100, Map 12 ⊗♟

AUBERGE DE LA VALLEE, RD 826 at St-Flour, towards Aurillac

Restaurant: closed Saturdays, Sundays and from 15 to 30 August.

Other points: bar.
M. PIERRE FARGES, tel 71.60.04.50.

SAINT AMAND LE PETIT, Haute Vienne 87120, Map 11 ⊗⌂

LA PROMENADE, RD 940 between Eymoutiers and Payrat le Château

Places of interest: Lac Vassivière (15km), les Monédières (30km).
Menu: 45 to 55 Frs
Accommodation: 60 to 90 Frs
Restaurant: lunch 11–2pm, dinner 6–8pm.

Hotel: 3 rooms.
Other points: garden terrace, pets allowed, car parking.
Address: Eymoutier.
MME ANNIE BOUBY, tel 55.69.15.38.

SAINT BONNET, Puy-de-Dôme 63200, Map 12 ⊗♟⌂

LE BON COIN, RN 143

Restaurant: closed 15 September to 10 October.
Hotel: 10 rooms.

Other points: bar.
Address: 2 rue de la République.
M. JEAN LEVADOUX, tel 73.63.31.14.

SAINT BONNET DE FOUR, Allier 03390, Map 12 ⊗♟

TRANS-EUROPEEN, RN 145

Languages: English, Italian
Restaurant.
Other points: bar, à la carte menu, lounge

area, garden terrace, pets allowed, car parking.
MME IVANA PIGNOT, tel 70.07.72.62.

SAINT FLOUR, Cantal 15100, Map 12 ⊗♟⌂🍽☆☆

HOTEL LE PROGRES, RN 9

Restaurant.
Hotel: 10 rooms.
Other points: bar.

Address: 61 rue des Lacs.
M. ALAIN MOURGUES, tel 71.60.03.06.

SAINT FLOUR, Cantal 15100, Map 12 ⊗♟⌂

LES ROUTIERS, RN 9

Places of interest: Garabit, cirque de Mallet, Chaudes Aigues, château d'Alleuze du Sailbant, Desierres, Mont Mouchet, cathédrale de Saint Flour.

Languages: English, Spanish
Menu: 60 to 100 Frs
Accommodation: from 100 Frs
Restaurant: lunch 12–4pm, dinner 7–10pm.

Closed Mondays (out of season), January and February.
Specialities: tripoux de Saint Flour.
Hotel: 7 rooms: single 4, double 3. Showers.

Other points: bar, credit cards accepted, à la carte menu, pets allowed, traditional decor.
Address: 49 place de la Liberté.
MME LILIANE TEISSEDRE, tel 71.60.23.00.

SAINT GENCE, Haute Vienne 87510, Map 11

LE CAMPANELLE, RD 20

Restaurant: closed Saturdays (except group dinners or weddings) and in August.
Other points: bar.

Address: route de Saint-Gence.
M. ALBERT DENARDOU, tel 55.48.02.83.

SAINT GEORGES D'AURAC, Haute-Loire 43230, Map 12

LES TILLEULS, RN 102

Restaurant: lunch 12–1.30pm, dinner 7–9pm. Closed Saturdays and Sundays.
Hotel: 9 rooms.

Other points: bar, garden terrace.
Address: Route Nationale 102.
MME BRIGITTE GUILLOT, tel 71.77.50.75.

SAINT JULIEN CHAPTEUIL, Haute-Loire 43260, Map 12

AUBERGE DU MEYCAL, RD 15 between Le Puy and Valence

Places of interest: Château, lacs (4 à 25km).
Menu: 50 to 90 Frs
Accommodation: 120 to 150 Frs
Restaurant: lunch 12–1.30pm, dinner 7.30–8.30pm.
Specialities: truites, grenouilles, omelette Norvégienne.

Hotel: 12 rooms, showers, private WCs, phone.
Other points: bar, lounge area, garden terrace, pets allowed, car parking, traditional decor.
Address: Boussoulet.
M. RENE CHAPUIS, tel 71.08.71.03.

SAINT JUNIEN, Haute Vienne 87200, Map 11

L'ETOILE, RN 141

Language: English
Menu: 55 to 160 Frs
Accommodation: 100 to 200 Frs
Restaurant: lunch 12–3pm, dinner 7.30–9.30pm. Closed 20 December to 6 January.
Hotel: 7 rooms: single 2, double 5. Showers, private WCs.

Other points: bar, credit cards accepted, à la carte menu, garden terrace, pets allowed, car parking, traditional decor.
Address: 8 avenue Henri Barbusse.
M. ALAIN NOBLE, tel 55.02.15.19.

SAINT JUST LE MARTEL, Haute Vienne 87590, Map 11

LE PETIT SALE, RN 141 between Limoges and Clermont Ferrand

Place of interest: Lac de Vassivière.
Menu: 56 to 150 Frs
Restaurant: lunch 12–3pm, dinner 7–10pm.
Hotel: 10 rooms: single 4, double 6. Showers, baths, private WCs.

Other points: bar, credit cards accepted, à la carte menu, garden terrace, pets allowed, car parking.
Address: Les Chabanes.
M. JEAN-PIERRE TEYTI, tel 55.09.21.14.

SAINT MATHIEU, Haute Vienne 87440, Map 11 ⊗ 🍷 🏠

LA GRANGE DU LAC, RN 699 to Limoges via Cussac

Places of interest: Château de Rochecouart, Monbrun, Oradour sur Glane, vallée Bandiat Tardoire, Tour de Chalus.
Language: English
Menu: 50 to 140 Frs
Accommodation: 110 to 200 Frs
Restaurant: lunch 11–3pm, dinner 7–12pm. Closed Tuesday evenings.
Specialities: cèpes, magrets, moules, gésiers, foie gras.
Hotel: 6 rooms, showers, baths.
Other points: bar, credit cards accepted, children welcome, à la carte menu, lounge area, garden terrace, pets allowed, car parking, traditional decor.
Address: known as Les Champs.
M. FRANCK VARACHAUT, tel 55.00.35.84.

SAINT POURCAIN, Allier 03500, Map 12 ⊗ 🍷

LE BELVEDERE, RN 9

Language: English
Menu: 55 to 145 Frs
Restaurant.
Specialities: coq au vin, pâté de pommes de terre.
Other points: bar, credit cards accepted, children welcome, à la carte menu, garden terrace, pets allowed, car parking.
Address: Les Plachis.
MME JEANNINE LACAUSSADE, tel 70.42.09.58

SAINT PRIEST DE GIMEL, Corrèze 19800, Map 11 ⊗ 🍷

LE RELAIS CHEZ MOUSTACHE, RN 89

Restaurant: closed Saturday nights, Sundays and in August.
Hotel: 3 rooms.
Other points: bar.
Address: Gare de Corrèze.
M. JEAN-CLAUDE LAVAL, tel 55.21.39.64.

SAINT SORNIN LEULAC, Haute Vienne 87290, Map 11 ⊗ 🍷

HOTEL DU CENTRE, RN 145 between La Croisière and Bellac

Places of interest: Lacs de Saint Pardoux, Le Dordat.
Language: English
Menu: 50 Frs including wine and coffee
Restaurant.
Other points: bar, credit cards accepted, children welcome, garden terrace, pets allowed, car parking, traditional decor.
M. PATRICK GAILLAC, tel 55.76.32.54.

SAUVIAT SUR VIGE, Haute Vienne 87400, Map 11 ⊗ 🍷 🏠 ☆

HOTEL DE LA POSTE, RN 141

Place of interest: Lac de Vassivière.
Accommodation: 120 to 160 Frs
Restaurant: closed Wednesdays and in September.
Hotel: 11 rooms: single 5, double 6. Showers, baths, private WCs, phone.
Other points: bar, credit cards accepted, pets allowed, car parking, traditional decor.
M. PIERRE CHASSAGNE, tel 55.75.30.12.

SEREILHAC, Haute Vienne 87620, Map 11 ⊗♈⌂

AUBERGE DES ROUTIERS

Language: English
Restaurant.
Hotel: 6 rooms.

Other points: bar.
Address: Route Nationale 21.
MME DENISE VIGNAUD, tel 55.39.10.46.

SOUTERRAINE (LA), Creuse 23300, Map 11 ⊗♈⌂

LES ROUTIERS, RN 145 near Limoges

Places of interest: Etangs de la Cazine et du Cheix.
Menu: 52 Frs
Accommodation: 70 to 120 Frs
Restaurant: lunch 12–3pm, dinner 7–11pm. Closed Sundays and from 24 December to 2 January.
Specialities: rognons au porto, coq au vin, potée auvergnate.

Hotel: 15 rooms: single 12, double 3. Showers.
Other points: bar, credit cards accepted, garden terrace, pets allowed, car parking, traditional decor.
Address: La Croisière Saint Maurice.
M. RAYMOND BOUTET, tel 55.63.77.55.

SOUVIGNY, Allier 03210, Map 12 ⊗♈

AUBERGE DE LA VALLE DE LA QUEUNE, RN 145 and A 71 between Montmaural and Maçon, exit Cressanges

Places of interest: Pagode de Noyant la Mine.
Languages: German, English
Menu: 47 Frs including wine and coffee
Restaurant: closed Wednesday afternoons and one weekend in April.
Other points: bar, children welcome, à la carte

menu, garden terrace, pets allowed, car parking, traditional decor.
Address: La Pierre Percée.
MME CATHERINE BUDTS, tel 70.47.29.49.

TENCE, Haute-Loire 43190, Map 12 ⊗♈

RESTAURANT DES CARS, RN 88, town centre

Menu: 42 to 70 Frs
Restaurant: lunch 11.30–3pm, dinner 7–9pm.
Other points: bar, children welcome, à la carte menu, pets allowed, car parking, traditional decor.

Address: 13 Grande Rue.
M. DAVID BONNET, tel 71.59.84.01.

TOULON SUR ALLIER, Allier 03400, Map 12 ⊗

LE FLAMBEAU, RN 7

Menu: 55 to 75 Frs
Restaurant: closed Sundays
Other points: children welcome, à la carte menu, car parking.

Address: Route Nationale 7.
HOTELS DES ILES, tel 70.20.90.28.

TOULON SUR ALLIER, Allier 03400, Map 12 ⊗♈

LE RELAIS FLEURI, RN 7

Restaurant: closed Sundays and in August.
Other points: bar.

Address: Route Nationale 7.
M. BELAIN, tel 70.44.47.16.

USSEL, Cantal 15300, Map 12   ⊗ ♀

LE RELAIS DE LA PLANEZE, RD 926 between Murat and Saint Flour

Places of interest: Salers, Garabit Murat, Saint Flour.
Menu: 50 to 65 Frs
Restaurant: lunch 12–2pm. Closed Sundays and last week of August, first week of September and 1 week at Christmas.

Other points: bar, credit cards accepted, garden terrace, pets allowed, car parking, traditional decor.
Address: Route Départementale 926.
MME GILBERTE ESBRAT, tel 71.73.20.52.

VARENNES SUR ALLIER, Allier 03150, Map 12   ⊗ ♀

LA RENAISSANCE, RN 7

Language: Portuguese
Restaurant.
Other points: bar.

Address: Bellevue.
MME ROSE GARDEL, tel 70.45.62.86.

VARENNES SUR ALLIER, Allier 03150, Map 12   ⊗ ♀ ⌂ ⊂

LE RELAIS DES TOURISTES, RN 7 near fire brigade barracks

Places of interest: Donjon gayette (3km), Vichy (5km), le centre omnisport (1km).
Menu: 45 to 90 Frs
Accommodation: 75 to 145 Frs
Restaurant: lunch 12–2pm, dinner 7.30–9pm. Closed Saturdays (from October to May).
Hotel: 9 rooms: single 4, double 5. Showers,

baths, phone.
Other points: bar, credit cards accepted, garden terrace, pets allowed, car parking, traditional decor.
Address: 1 rue des Halles.
M. ANDRE JUNIET, tel 70.45.00.51.

VERNET LA VARENNE (LE), Puy-de-Dôme 63580, Map 12   ⊗ ♀ ⌂

HOTEL DU CHATEAU, RD 999 Issoire

Places of interest: La Chaise Dieu, Ambert, mines d'Améthystes.
Language: English
Menu: 45 to 90 Frs
Accommodation: 70 to 115 Frs
Restaurant: lunch 12–2pm, dinner 7.30–9pm. Closed Mondays (after 3pm).

Specialities: pôtée auvergnate, terrines maison.
Hotel: 7 rooms: single 4, double 3. Showers.
Other points: bar, credit cards accepted, children welcome, garden terrace, pets allowed, car parking, traditional decor.
BERNARD AND DENIS CHARNAY-MAGAUD, tel 73.71.31.79

VICHY, Allier 03200, Map 12   ⊗ ♀ ⌂

RELAIS DE LA PASSERELLE, Le Puy

Places of interest: Vichy sous Sources, station thermale.
Menu: 50 Frs
Accommodation: 80 to 140 Frs
Restaurant: closed Sundays and in August (2 weeks).
Speciality: méridionales.

Hotel: 4 rooms: single 3, double 1. Showers, private WCs, TV, phone.
Other points: bar, lounge area, pets allowed, car parking.
Address: rue de Bordeaux.
M. JEAN-PIERRE PESCE, tel 70.98.57.70.

VIEILLE BRIOUDE, Haute-Loire 43100, Map 12   ⊗ ⍦ ⌂ ☆ ☆

LES GLYCINES, RN 102 between Clermont-Ferrand and Le Puy

Places of interest: Vallée de l'Allier, basilique, maison du saumon, musée de la dentelle.
Language: English
Menu: 59 to 220 Frs
Accommodation: 195 to 320 Frs
Restaurant: lunch 12–2pm, dinner 7.30–9pm. Closed Friday afternoon to Saturday afternoon and in January.

Speciality: saumon.
Hotel: 13 double rooms. Showers, baths, private WCs, TV, phone.
Other points: bar, credit cards accepted, garden terrace, pets allowed, car parking.
Address: avenue de Versailles.
MME VIVIANE CHARDONNAL,
tel 71.50.91.80.

VOREY SUR ARZON, Haute-Loire 43800, Map 12   ⊗ ⍦ ⌂

RESTAURANT DE LA BASCULE, RN 103 between Saint Etienne and Le Puy

Places of interest: Vallée de la Loire, Le Puy.
Language: Italian
Menu: 80 to 100 Frs
Restaurant: lunch 11.45–3pm, dinner 7–9.30pm.

Hotel: 5 rooms: single 4, double 1.
Other points: bar, children welcome, pets allowed, car parking.
Address: place des Moulettes.
M. SERGE HILAIRE, tel 71.03.41.67.

YSSINGEAUX, Haute-Loire 43200, Map 12   ⊗ ⍦ ⌂

LA PETITE AUBERGE, RN 88 between Saint Etienne and Le Puy

Places of interest: Barrage, châteaux, Mont du Velay, les rivières.
Language: English
Menu: 50 to 90 Frs
Accommodation: 70 to 100 Frs
Restaurant: lunch 12–2pm, dinner 8–10pm. Closed Sundays (out of season) and at end of July.

Hotel: 4 rooms: single 2, double 2.
Other points: bar, garden terrace, pets allowed, car parking.
Address: known as La Guide.
M. JOSETTE DELABRE, tel 71.59.05.32.